THE DOCTOR'S CASE

THE DOCTOR'S CASE

DR MAURICE GUERET

THE DOCTOR'S CASE

First Published in 2014 by IMD.

IMD
PO Box 5049
Terenure
Dublin 6w
Ireland

www.drmauricegueret.com

ISBN 978-0-9927312-0-5

**A CIP catalogue record for this book
is available from the British Library**

1 2 3 4 5 6 7 8 9 10

**Printed in County Kerry by
Walsh Colour Printing**
All Design by JohnBradyDesign.ie

For my parents
Paul & Bernice Guéret.
With love.

HOME DELIVERY
May 2004

A friend regaled us recently with a tale of how male obstetricians and gynaecologists are faring on the social scene. It would appear that they make very popular cocktail party guests. At one such event, the wife of an eminent obstetrician noticed that another guest, a large over-sexed blonde in her mind, was making overtures towards her husband. It was a big informal sort of gathering, so she tried to laugh it off. Until that is, she saw them disappear upstairs together. She rushed into the room, pulled the two of them apart and screamed, 'Look lady. My husband just delivers babies, he doesn't INSTALL them!'

SLOW K AND OTHER NICKNAMES
January 2006

Slow K is a popular version of a potassium chloride medicine that releases its dose gradually into the bloodstream. It is used to remedy potassium deficiency, principally in heart failure patients whose diuretics have depleted their supply of this major dietary element. For me, Slow K also stirs memories of bygone hospital days. As spotty interns, it was our job to act as clerks for the team who would write letters to specialists from other hospitals, requesting them to come and visit our patients. One Dublin consultant, whose surname began with K, was notorious for his tardiness in responding to requests. He became fondly known by all the medics, fellow consultants included, as *Slow K*. In truth, the man had an impossible workload. It wasn't that he was following the old medical dictum that the longer you make them wait, the fewer of them there are. He probably never even knew his pharmaceutical pet name. Medical nicknames are dying out, so I thought we would record some of the better ones here for posterity.

A colleague once told me that an extremely wealthy obstetrician was known to his colleagues as *Goldfinger*. A particularly flash gynaecologist whose first name was William was known behind his back as *Billy Bullshit*. A medical school in Ireland had a eminent teacher known as *Professor Coeliac Stools*. His colleagues christened him thus apparently because they considered him pale, bulky and offensive. A softly spoken physician called Victor was known as *Whispering Vic*. And a psychiatrist had the dubious honour of being named *Dr Bob*, in honour of the resident doctor on the Muppet Show.

A well respected army doctor from the Curragh Military Hospital was affectionately known to one and all as *The Badger*. 'The Badger' Burke died in the 1970s and the nickname was even recorded on his tombstone. I still don't know why.

A larger than life orthopaedic surgeon in Dublin was known secretly to his colleagues as *Yorkie*. The case for the prosecution was predicated on the fact that he was generally considered to be big, rich and thick.

In another part of the country there were five specialists who all had the same surname. Three of them had the first name Jack so the local family doctors had to resort to their specialties to sort them out. There was *Jackie Eyes* who was an ophthalmologist, *Jackie Gas* the anaesthetist and *Jackie Nuts*, not a urologist, but an eminent psychiatrist. There were also two Dinnys, one a urologist and the other a physician. One went by the nickname *Dinny Piss* and I believe the other may have been *Dinny Shite*.

Other nicknames include *Ted the Head*, a brain surgeon of some renown. *Stomachy Mick* was a gastroenterologist and there was a dermatologist (still alive I think) whose surname was always preceded by the name *Skinny*. Another informant tells me that a county surgeon was known as *Mac the Knife*, as his cutting skills were often called into question. A university lecturer whose specialty was osteology and anatomy was known as *Billy Bones*. And a Dublin physician who allegedly kidnapped a pig from the mart off the North Circular Road and took it back to the doctor's residence in the Mater Hospital was known for the rest of his days as *Rashers K.*

There was a mega-rich husky-voiced physician, a Rolls Royce driver who smoked foot long cigars during his ward rounds and according to his junior staff gave a very good impression of having something to do with Mario Puzo's Godfather. His moniker was *Big Gino*.

A doctor in Cork has written to tell me of his younger days in hospital medicine. He had a great surgical teacher, a part-time philosopher who used to be known locally as *Dongo*. Dongo's favourite saying to patients was 'Pain is a wonderful thing mister, it's mother nature's cry for help'. He also recalls two other doctors' nicknames - they were known as *Stripper* and *Slipper*. Sadly he didn't elaborate further. There was also a lecturer in pharmacy who rather laboriously used to spell out each word during his lectures. For example, he would say 'Bottle that's B O T T L E'. Whenever he came to the word Powders the class would roar the spelling back at him and he became known to a generation of students as *Powders*.

There was a dermatologist whose first name was affectionately replaced with *Spot*, though not on his referral letters. There was once a surgeon working in the north of Ireland whose first name was Colin. Junior staff knew him better as *Colon*. It had something to do with how slow he was at getting through his theatre list and nothing to do with the fact that he was full of something else. And I came across a lovely description of two Irish army doctors who were notorious for very different reasons on their frequent overseas duties with the United Nations. One played the guitar rather badly whilst the other excelled himself at breaking wind. When well out of earshot, not difficult – it's the Irish army after all, they were known as *Rattle and Hum*.

In a Dublin maternity hospital, two ancient obstetricians always sat in the front row of case conferences. When they weren't heckling the speakers they were mumbling to themselves all the time and they were affectionately known to all (but themselves) as *Waldorf and Statler*.

A lady doctor wrote to tell me of a now deceased obstetrician, a well-known professor in medical school, who was slim, elegant and always kind and gentle to his patients. He was known to one and all as *John the Divine*. He would always advise pregnant patients that horse riding was inadvisable but that 'a little golf' was permissible.

MEDICAL SAINTS

January 1999

A little delving can be a dangerous thing. Last week a patient initiated a chat about patron saints in medicine, and she spoke far more proficiently on the topic than her humbled doctor. Determined to improve my knowledge, I have been researching the subject in some depth. I am now much the wiser about all the saints my sick patients should be praying to, should their exemplary treatments fail to work. These patrons are either assigned by venerable tradition, or have been chosen by election to act as special intercessors with God. Sadly doctors, even believing ones, don't appear to have a vote.

No surprise perhaps that St. Patrick is the patron saint of snake bites, I didn't know that St. Hubert protects against dog bites or that St. John of God was the patron saint of cardiac problems. If your eyes are playing up, all diseases ophthalmological are in the queues of St. Clare and St. Lucy. I recall from my school days that we were all marched up to chapel to have our throats blessed with holy candles on the feast day of St. Blaise. Whether it did ward off sore throats is conjectural, but I see that Blaise is also patron saint of swollen thyroid glands (known to doctors as goitres) and whooping cough too. I never contracted either of those - perhaps there is something in this after all!

The dull social life of the pre-reformation Catholic world became animated with the idea of protecting groups of citizens. Each trade or guild had its respective patron that members could pray to for solace and comfort. St. Cosmas and St. Damian were chosen to protect doctors. Raymund Nonnatus looked after midwives. St. Dismas looked after those who were sentenced to death. Well until their executions anyhow. Finally, the patron saint of haemorrhoids is the seventh century Irish monk, St. Fiachrach. He also looks after gardeners and taxi drivers. Must be some connection there.

GOOD LOOKING SURGEONS
January 2007

Having qualified to eligible bachelor level in both disciplines, I have been examining a new study from Barcelona which suggests that surgeons are much better looking than physicians. The research methods are not pretty and the sample size was disappointingly small. Just twelve doctors from each grade had to submit photographs and measurements. The results show that surgeons are seven centimetres taller and somewhat less bald than physicians. External controls that were used to compare samples against were Dr Richard Kimble (Harrison Ford), Dr Doug Ross (George Clooney) Dr Derek Shepherd (Patrick Dempsey), Dr Gregory House (Hugh Laurie) and a certain Dr Maurice Gueret playing himself. (OK I made the last bit up). Eight female observers were used to judge the contest – three doctors and five nurses. They graded all entrants from 1 to 7 on a clinically approved scale where 1 is ugly and 7 is very good looking. At this stage I left the trial, arguing strongly that the upper parameters were too low. The surgeons scored an average of 4.39 as opposed to a very poor 3.65 for the physicians. But the film doctors scored considerably higher than real life medics in both groups. My new brass plate is ready. Dr Gueret – Physician, Surgeon, Film Star. Scored an 8 by his mother.

MEDICINE IN MADEIRA
November 1997

Madeira is the original holiday destination for old world Europeans. Winston Churchill liked to pack his brushes, canvas and favourite oil paints for jaunts around the island, whilst George Bernard Shaw preferred dancing lessons on the cliff of Reid's Palace Hotel at Funchal. The charm of this tiny isle's tourist brochures got the better of me when planning an autumn fortnight this year. In choosing this sub-tropical gardener's paradise, a doctor is directly trading lager lout surgery of other Mediterranean hot spots for medical care of the elderly by the swimming pool. For the first week of my break I disguised all medical credentials with great success. Not even my copy of Dr Noel Browne's *Against The Tide* on the sun bed aroused any interest. But the disguise fell off during Sunday afternoon's tea dance when a reverend gentleman from one of the posh shires took a major funny turn over his Darjeeling tea and crumpet. He went out like a light for two minutes and was just coming through as I got close enough to listen for the sounds of respiration. 'Are you an Irish doctor?' he asked. I had to think long and hard before answering that one. 'Yes' I answered, 'but the concierge has called the Portuguese one, he's got more equipment than I have'. I paid a house call to the reverend's room after my continental colleague had departed and was rewarded with a full medical history, a rummage through his bags of diabetes and blood pressure tablets and tales of his ancestors who hailed from Rathmines in Dublin. Yes, Madeira m'dears, can be very much a working holiday.

ROOSTER BOOSTER
March 2006

I received a lovely medical malapropism from County Cork this morning. A GP writes to tell me of a patient who attended surgery with her young son because he was overdue his *rooster* injection against meningitis The good doctor jests that this particular jab could be protective against Avian flu. And a GP in Waterford dropped me a line to say that some of these new private clinics springing up since Mary Harney came into office are really going overboard with their menu options. He had a lady in surgery who told him that her hiatus hernia was diagnosed in a clinic using a *bavarian meal*. Another doctor in Munster had trouble keeping a smile off his face when a lady told him that her elderly father had kidney problems and was attending hospital three times a week for *analysis*.

A Dublin consultant told me about a six year old boy who told his ear, nose and throat surgeon on a post-operative visit that the *Wallace and Gromits* inserted in his eardrums hadn't helped. And a chest doctor told me of a nice old lady who came back to outpatients after a trip to the pulmonary laboratory for a *breathalyser*. The same consultant also told me of an observation that more than one nurse has been overheard referring to the hospital's tobacco initiative as a *smoking sensation* service. Cessation it was. And a doctor wrote to tell me about a notice at an obstetrics meeting in England which read 'There will be an *internal* lasting ten to fifteen minutes, during which tea and coffee will be served'.

ROMANTIC HOSPITAL FICTION
October 2006

The name Lucilla Andrews didn't mean much to me until a number of newspapers carried prominent obituaries to her in recent weeks. Nurses all too rarely get recognition beyond the grave, but Ms Andrews bucked the trend, albeit for the unusual literary genre of 'romantic hospital fiction'. She championed this sort of book from the early 1950s. Lucy Andrews was born in the Suez, Egypt where her father worked for the Eastern Telegraphy Company. She began her Nightingale nurse training at St Thomas' Hospital in London just as Hitler's hostilities were breaking out in Europe. Following her own clinical romance, she married Dr James Crichton in 1947. To great dismay she discovered on the honeymoon that he loved another - prescription medication. Soon after their only daughter was born, Crichton was hospitalised for treatment. He died a young man in 1954. Left to fend for herself, Lucy Andrews took a job as night sister in a pie factory and began writing in her spare time. One of her books, *No Time for Romance*, later attracted the attention of Ian McEwan, who lists it in the credits of his famous novel, *Atonement*. Libraries often recorded Lucy Andrews at the top the their 'most borrowed' lists and her most popular work, *The Print Petticoat*, was reckoned to have been a very popular secret read amongst junior doctors.

By the way, one obituary for Lucy Andrews records that she had a fondness for both whisky and cigarettes and was encouraged to take up the latter by her aforementioned husband Dr Crichton. Her other bad habit was an very expensive taste in hats.

Post-Script: *I did ask around if any older doctors in Ireland had memories of her work - she also used the pseudonyms of Dianna Gordon and Joanna Marcus. But none volunteered any memories. Doctors are well known for reading the genre of romantic hospital fiction, but not so good at owning up to it. In 2007, Professor Brendan Kelly of the department of psychiatry at Dublin's Mater Hospital wrote a piece in The Lancet on the topic of medical romance. Such was the interest in his article, he was asked to read some purple prose on the hugely popular Today show on BBC Radio 4. For his research, the indefatigable Professor Kelly randomly selected twenty medical romance novels. His findings were most interesting. All had heterosexual plots involving medical protagonists. Most were set in general practice or emergency departments, though two involved airborne medical teams. The professor noted a marked preponderance of brilliant, tall, muscular male doctors with finely chiselled features. They were commonly of Mediterranean origin with personal tragedies in their past. Female doctors and nurses tended to be both skilled and beautiful, but they had to be compassionate too. The characters of both sexes had frequently neglected their personal lives to care better for their patients. Professor Kelly's main conclusion was that with the inevitability of such uncontrolled passions in these settings, medical and nursing students need urgent instruction in the arts of romance on their training programmes. And so say all of us!*

A POPULAR SHOWER
May 2011

It's official now. Doctors are the most trusted profession in the country. At least that's what the Medical Council tell us. They commissioned this ground-breaking research from a market research firm of the highest repute. Quite why this survey was ordered and paid for in times of unprecedented economic hardship, I cannot imagine. It's reassuring to know that 88% of the Irish public trust us to tell the truth. Doctors now float high and mighty above teachers, professors and judges, and a long mile clear of business leaders, pollsters and politicians who inhabit the other end of the spectrum. What should we do with the 12% of people who don't trust us. Well perhaps they don't visit us at all. They have acupuncturists to puncture them, homeopaths to sell water to them and reflexologists to diagnose emergencies from the odours and tickly soles of their feet. This business of doctors asking people what they really think of them can sometimes be a little fraught, and occasionally it can backfire. Back in 1996, the Irish Medical Organisation held a symposium at their annual general meeting entitled 'How Others See Us' and they invited leading lights of society down to Killarney to discuss their personal views of the curative profession. The wonderful Nell McCafferty was one of their guests. Nell didn't pulls a punch. Her apt and carefully-chosen literary description sent a shudder down the collective medical spine of Ireland. She called us a 'shower of bums'. And we can't argue with that.

FOG ON THE TYNE
February 2006

The Guardian had a fascinating piece last week about how health chiefs in the north of England, particularly Newcastle, are becoming worried that imported doctors and nurses may not understand the lingo of their patients. The county of Yorkshire already has its own medical glossary to assist foreign staff. It contains the famous 'Rotherham are playing at home' euphemism for 'I'm menstruating at present'. Now Newcastle's hospitals are helping to collate a phrase book to assist non-national NHS staff with their work. So when a grumpy Geordie marches his daughter off to the maternity unit shouting 'Wor Lass's Moongin She's Fallen Wrang', the staff will know that it's time to obtain a urine sample for a pregnancy test. Another Tyneside tongue-twister that might torment foreign born medics is 'The Gadgies Cakky's in the Gazunder', which in the Queen's English means Granddad's pee is in the pot.

BECKHAM OF THE BAIZE
October 2006

I was writing during the summer about the demise of former world snooker champion John Spencer who succumbed to stomach cancer, having already battled myasthenia gravis for many years. I didn't expect to be back to the health of potters so soon. The recent demise of young Paul Hunter, just a few days shy of his 28th birthday, has robbed darkened halls of one of their very finest and saddened hard hearts of those who follow the sport of bling. Some newspapers chose to ramp up the story with the casual disparaging headline 'Death of Beckham of the Baize'. Paul Hunter may have had a touch of the glamour-boy about him, but unlike the footballer, his celebrity never diluted, or outshone his sporting talent. At his best, Hunter was the most exciting, attack-minded and gung-ho snooker player the televised game has seen. Certainly since the hey-day of Higgins and White. He was also a modern day gentleman. He accepted the ills life threw at him, was respected for his sense of fair play and is reckoned to have been unique amongst his fellow professionals in that he never blamed an opponent, a referee or even bad luck for his failures.

Early in his career Paul Hunter tested positive for cannabis use. He apologised, pleaded guilty to the charge of 21 year-old stupidity, took his penalties and moved on. He won three Wembley Masters title in his short career, all from unfavourable scores at mid-session intervals. On each occasion the situation was remedied by what Hunter liked to describe as his 'Plan B'. An age-old relaxation technique that involved Hunter and his then girlfriend retiring briefly to their hotel room.

Judging from reaction today on the World Professional Billiards and Snooker Association website, fans of Hunter are having trouble believing that a young father with a world championship win around the next corner, should spend the final three days of his life receiving palliative care in a small hospice in Huddersfield.

All was well with Paul Hunter until early last year when he had reached number four in the world snooker rankings. He diverted to hospital one day with a sharp pain down the lower right side of his abdomen. According to his wife Lindsey, appendicitis was the chief suspect, but this was ruled out and a series of tests was booked to see if anything else was up. Despite the pain, Hunter travelled to Dublin's Citywest hotel to play in the Irish masters. After his first round victory, he was asked by journalists about his health. 'The doctor said I could come to Ireland and play, but if the pain is still there when I come back I'll need to have keyhole surgery'. said Hunter. With hindsight, it's eerie now to ponder what he said next. 'I didn't want to withdraw from the tournament. I'd play on my death bed'.

By March 2005, Hunter knew he had several strange tumours growing in his gut. A relatively rare series of tiny slow-growing cancers which nowadays are grouped under an umbrella term neuro-endocrine tumours or NETs. In my medical school days, patients with these miniature tumours (the best known is called carcinoid syndrome) were few and far between. But the condition merited much discussion. They were most interesting and unusual cancers because they didn't block up the ordinary workings of body organs. NETs caused problems with the chemicals they secreted.

Unexpected flushing of the head and neck, shortness of breath, intractable diarrhoea and tummy cramps are classically described in the textbooks. But because these are also symptoms of other maladies, delayed diagnosis and misdiagnosis is common. Few front-line medics would be willing to testify in court against a colleague who 'missed' such a diagnosis. They are rare, and the best doctor in a hospital could have trouble spotting a case quickly. Survival often depends on whether the condition has spread and how aggressive it is. If caught early on, well over 90% might survive the critical five year hurdle. However if the tumour has metastasised to other parts of the body, the percentage of patients who survive five years falls sharply.

Reading between the lines, it would appear that in Hunter's case, diagnosis was fairly swift. But the tumour had already spread to multiple sites, so surgery was not an option. Hunter faced into several gruelling four month regimes of aggressive chemotherapy.

With nappies not yet a feature of their home, Hunter and his wife arranged to have his sperm frozen in case chemotherapy damaged their prospects of starting a family. As luck would have it, just two days before his treatment began, his wife Lyndsey discovered she was pregnant. Four months of fairly extreme nausea later, Hunter's trademark mane of blonde hair had gone. More seriously, from a snooker viewpoint, he had developed a hand tremor. He also suffered numbness and a lack of sensation in both feet and hands. He bravely tried to continue with his snooker but his world ranking plummeted to 34. By November of last year, Hunter's oncologists at the famous 'Jimmy's Hospital' in Leeds, knew that the first line of chemo had not done the job they had hoped. This news was allayed somewhat by the birth of Hunter's daughter Evie the day after Christmas. At the Sheffield crucible in the world championship this year, Paul Hunter was a pale shadow of his former self. He lost in the first round to up and coming Australian Neil Robertson. After the match Hunter admitted he had pain 24 hours a day and was often stiff and light-headed.

In July he began a third course of chemotherapy. Snooker authorities, at the instigation of his fellow professionals, agreed to freeze his world ranking to allow Hunter concentrate fully on recovery. But there was no respite. Hunter and his wife spent many of their final months together raising funds for medical charities related to neuro-endocrine tumours. In September they organised a massive ball for sports celebrities. Hunter at this stage was himself too ill to attend. Another mortal engine has gone from the game. And a bloody good one too.

WORST FEARS
March 2000

It's not as common as scaremongers make out, but it's a fact of clinical life that the occasional patient does wake up under anaesthesia. Surgeons need to be on guard against saying things that might upset patients who wake unexpectedly. Somebody recently sent me a list of the top five things patients least want to hear when the anaesthetic stops working.

1. Someone call the janitor - we're going to need a mop.

2. Spot. Come back with that. Bad Dog!

3. Damn. Page 47 of the manual is missing.

4. He's gonna blow - Everyone take cover.

5. Please accept this sacrifice, O Great Lord of Darkness.

DEATH OF PARNELL
February 2012

One truth in medicine is incontrovertible. Doctors who ponder the deaths of historical figures are usually those without enough living patients to treat. The object of my recent research has been the demise of Charles Stewart Parnell. Depending on what source you believe, the man they call the greatest politician of 19th century Ireland, died of rheumatic fever, exhaustion, a passionate kiss, post-election fatigue, murder, heart attack or immorality.

Enigma is a recently published biography of Parnell by Professor Paul Bew. It adds to the mix of this differential diagnosis by quietly mentioning the possibility that the politician committed suicide. There are interesting passages in the book about mental illness and suicide in the Parnell family. There are details of an aborted plan to jump into the sea not long before his death. There is testimony of a society hostess who had no doubt about the cause, and said Parnell often spoke of suicide. It's unlikely after 120 years that much new light is there to be shone on the demise of this great parliamentarian. But rumours of self-harm were circulating, and within just a day or two of his death, the family had gone to the trouble of issuing a denial. Soon afterwards, there followed a public statement about the cause of death from Dr Jowers who had attended Parnell in Brighton. Jowers was categorical that rheumatic fever and high temperature led to 'failure of the heart's action' and went on to egg his case by saying that 'the case is one of the plainest I have ever attended' with 'not the slightest ground for doubts'. Now there's nothing I worry more about than doctors who don't doubt their own opinions. You could fill a medical textbook with what has been written about Parnell's health and quaint demeanours. He had an irrational fear of the number thirteen and detested the colour green. It apparently made him nauseous. He sought the attendance of many doctors for a multitude of ailments and worried obsessively about everything, especially money and the payment of bills. Just before his demise, his wife wanted to call an eminent specialist, Sir Henry Thompson, down from London to their house in Hove near Brighton. But Parnell forbade it, on the grounds of what the fee might be for a house call eighty miles from the capital.

Glasnevin Cemetery maintains the grave of Charles Stewart Parnell quite beautifully and it's well worth a visit. Alas I cannot say the same for Avondale, home and birthplace of the man. The house itself is only open from Easter through summer, but you can walk the forests and take picnics there all year around. The exterior of the house was quite shabby on my recent visit and somebody has built perhaps the ugliest edifice in Ireland within yards of the stately home. It's some sort of budget accommodation hostel and hideous in the extreme. It would be nice if somebody tidied up these things up for next year's Gathering event when the world and his mother are coming to Ireland. Alas there will be no Parnells. The man from the big house has no living descendants.

SPANISH FLU - A FORGOTTEN FOOTNOTE
January 2003

Next time you stroll through an old graveyard, keep an eye out for headstones that record deaths from late 1918 on into early 1919. You won't be long finding them. This was the era of the most lethal influenza pandemic the world has witnessed. Five hundred million people caught the virus during that fateful winter and twenty one million of them didn't live to tell the tale. This was the legacy of Spanish flu. As the first world war armies disbanded, a mutant strain of swine influenza spread throughout the world. Soldiers inadvertently carried the virus back to their communities, families and loved ones.

Whilst much is written about the Great War, Spanish influenza has been relegated to the status of historical footnote. Yet this pandemic claimed twice as many lives as all the gruesome battles and disease-ridden trenches put together. Contrary to popular notion, the virus did not originate in the Iberian peninsula. In fact epidemiologists suggest that the first cases may have surfaced in Tibet a year before, in 1917. France was the first affected European country, but war time censorship ensured that news of the disease did not become widely dispersed until neutral Spain began documenting calamitous effects on its own population. Soon doctors across the globe were struggling to cope with the virulent outbreak. Frantic but fruitless efforts were made to ascertain the cause and to devise treatments. It was to take another fifteen years before influenza viruses were first identified. The particular strain hit patients with a very rapid onset of symptoms - raging fevers of 105 degrees, wild delirium and muscle weakness so severe that victims often couldn't drink or feed themselves. A medical student in Pennsylvania aptly summed up the helplessness of those drafted in to assist the very sickest patients.

'As their lungs filled, the patients became short of breath and increasingly cyanotic (blue). After gasping for several hours they became delirious and incontinent, and many died struggling to clear their airways of a blood-tinged froth that sometimes gushed from their nose and mouth. It was a dreadful business'.

In Ireland, heroic work was performed by nursing and medical staff who struggled to cope with the volume of patients presenting at their doors. Following a long tradition, the Royal City of Dublin Hospital on Baggot Street refused to turn away a single patient. For many months they treated anyone sick enough for admission on temporary mattress beds. The hospital paid a price for its efficiency. It was forced to close beds for many years after the outbreak in order to survive. The books had to be balanced so the hospital remained a going concern.

The Spanish flu struck with impunity and without respect for youth, status or previous good health. More than half of those who perished during that long winter were not in the traditional 'at risk' groups. In the United States, more than half a million citizens perished. The 33,000 who died in New York alone puts an interesting perspective on the terrible losses of the recent twin towers terrorist disaster. In San Diego, California the civil authorities were desperate enough to threaten a thirty day jail term for any citizen who ventured outdoors without a surgical mask. Celebrity victims included silent screen star Harold Lockwood, actress Mary Pickford, champion swimmer Harry Elionsky and Irmy Cody, the daughter of Buffalo Bill.

The politicians Franklin Roosevelt and Woodrow Wilson were forced to their beds. Spanish flu offers one further interesting anecdote to world history. Some historians have claimed that President Wilson's bout of flu in Paris led directly to the harsh terms of the Versaille treaty. Some revisionists even suggest that had he escaped the dose, the second world war might have been averted. Josef Stalin always claimed there was no such thing as invincible armies. Spanish influenza was his proof.

PRIVILEGED LIVES
March 2012

This week's book at bedtime is *Privileged Lives - a Social History of Middle-Class Ireland 1882-1989*. I agree. It sounds like a dull academic textbook. But it certainly doesn't read like one. This new title is wonderfully researched and keenly observed by Tony Farmar who has that rare gift in all his historical works of transporting the reader right back in time. He describes how the people of Dublin behaved themselves during royal visits a hundred years ago. How the 1907 Great Exhibition in Dublin's Herbert Park was the place to be seen. There is gossip about who had the very first telephone, who had the most servants and who was wearing the best bustles, corsets and hats. I learned that one hundred years ago a general practitioner or dispensary doctor, earned between £100 and £200 per annum. This was the exact same salary as a national school teacher, half the salary of a manager at an Eason bookshop and twice the wages of a skilled worker. I did not know that the top specialist, master of the Rotunda Hospital, had an annual salary of between £3,000 and £5,000 in the same year. Had one known these sort of details at the time, a medical student might have assisted a little bit more at childbirths. There is a wonderful chapter dealing with the Irish hospital sweepstake, dreamed up in the late 1920s to fund health facilities. It also made multimillionaires of its instigators. They in turn became major funders of Irish politics. No change there then. Memorably described as 'the greatest bleeding heart racket in the world', blind boys were used to pick winning tickets from the sweepstake drums. Later they were replaced by nurses in uniform. Such lotteries had been banned by the British government in 1826, in favour of income tax. So a lot of the money gambled on the Irish sweepstakes actually came from the United Kingdom. On one memorable occasion, sweepstake tickets were smuggled over to England in a coffin. Tony Farmar describes the ludicrous pageants held three times a year in the 1930s, as millions of ticket stubs were ushered into town. In 1932 they used two hundred jockeys. Later that decade, in homage to the emerging superpower of Germany, the organisers engaged two hundred Brünnhildes to lead the sweepstakes parade. Trojan slaves pulling a wooden horse full of tickets was another gimmick. Less than 5% of the prizes were claimed in the Free State but the revenue to the Irish government in one year was often greater than the total take in income tax. Between 1940 and 1965 two hundred hospitals were built according to the whim of politicians, far more perhaps than it was prudent to construct. And therein lies the real reason we have so many out-of date and inadequately sized competing hospital facilities scattered throughout the country. And we also have the reason that Ireland has probably the worst development of community based services in the entire western world.

SPAGHETTI SAUCE
March 2000

Murphy the obstetrician was having a torrid affair with the theatre nursing superintendent. One evening when the labour ward was empty, she told him that she was pregnant. Not wanting his wife to know, he offered her a sum of money and asked her to go to Italy and have the baby there. 'But how will I let you know when our baby is born?' she asked.

'Just send me a postcard and write 'spaghetti' on the back. I'll take care of expenses' he replied. Not knowing what else to do, the nurse took the money and flew to Italy. Six months went by, and then one day Dr Murphy's wife called him at the office.

'Dear, you received a very strange postcard in the mail today from Sorrento, and I don't understand what it means'.

The obstetrician said, 'Just wait until I get home and I will explain it to you'.

Later that evening Murphy came home, read the postcard, and fell to the floor clutching his chest. The ambulance rushed him to the emergency department but he was dead on arrival. The casualty doctor stayed back to comfort Murphy's wife. He asked what particular trauma had precipitated her husband's cardiac arrest. Mrs Murphy told him about the strange postcard from Italy. She took it from her bag and read it out. 'Spaghetti, Spaghetti, Spaghetti, Spaghetti - two with sausage and meatballs and two without'.

DOCTOR IN THE HOUSE
February 2003

I have been asking medical colleagues to help me compile a list of famous children of doctors. There might be a research paper or coffee-table book in it someday, but I haven't yet had the time to do it. The long, winding and alphabetical list we came up with is as follows:

Aristotle (philosopher). Jane Asher (actress). Chip Beck (golfer). Hector Berlioz (composer). Sandra Bernhard (actress). Jacqueline Bisset (actress). Tony Blackburn (disc jockey). Humphrey Bogart (actor). St Boniface IV (pope). Kate Bush (singer). Miguel de Cervantes (writer). Salil Chowdhury (composer). Glenn Close (actress). Eric Coates (composer). Samuel Coleridge-Taylor (composer). Robbie Coltrane (comedian). Pierre Curie (physicist). Jeffrey Dahmer (serial killer). Charles Darwin (naturalist). Dame Judi Dench (actress). Fyodor Dostoevsky (novelist). Jean Claude Duvalier (politician). Rainer Werner Fassbinder (film director). Paul-Michel Foucault (philosopher). Jean-Luc Godard (film director). Jeff Goldblum (actor). Dexter Gordon (saxophonist).

Marius Goring (actor). Martha Graham (dancer). Stephen Hawking (physicist). George Frideric Handel (composer). Ernest Hemingway (writer). Katharine Hepburn (actress). Sir Ian Holm (actor). Robert E. Howard (pulp fiction author). Mila Jovovich (supermodel). Sir Ben Kingsley (actor). Stanley Kubrick (film director). Lisa Kudrow (actress). Monica Lewinski (intern). John Lovitz (comedian). Archer Martin (chemist). Jonathan Miller (artistic director and doctor). Brian Moore (novelist). Edward Munch (painter). Cardinal Murphy-O'Connor (churchman). Olivia Newton-John (singer). Randy Newman (musician). Conan O'Brien (television presenter). Brian O'Driscoll (rugby player). Ardal O'Hanlon (comedian). Mike Oldfield (musician). Frédéric Ozaman (writer). Brian de Palma (film director). Nicholas Parsons (television presenter). Edgar Allan Poe (author). O. Henry (writer). Natalie Portman (actress). Arthur N. Prior (philosopher). Marcel Proust (novelist). Bill Pullman (actor). Rania of Jordan (queen). Nancy Reagan (first lady). Mary Renault (writer). Joan Rivers (comedian). William Roache (actor). Mary Robinson (politician). Richard Rodgers (composer). St Elizabeth Seton (educator). Jane Seymour (actress). Ravi Shastri (cricketer). Jean Sibelius (composer). Clyde Snow (forensic anthropologist). Tom Stoppard (playwright). John Suchet (broadcaster) and his brother David (actor). James Taylor (musician). Pierre Trudeau (politician). Beate Uhse (pilot and entrepreneur). Wendy Beckett (art historian). Maurice White (musician). Captain Matthew Webb (swimmer). Andreas Vesalius (anatomist). Fay Weldon (writer). Oscar Wilde (playwright). Reese Witherspoon (actress). And finally Lee Kuan Yew (politician).

So what conclusions, if any, can we draw from this eclectic list? Not a lot, I'd say. Men are over-represented. And I was surprised at how few were involved in the upper echelons of sport. There does seem to be a large number who are on some sort of stage or other. Confirming perhaps that old adage that the top doctors are those who best entertain the patient, whilst the disease gets better on its own.

Post-script: *More than a decade on, I am sure this list can be added to again. The doctor who tipped me off about the medical parenthood of Olivia*

Newton-John told me that her father was a retired surgeon who basked happily in the glory of his daughter's fame. The Newton-John family used to rent out their beach-house on the New South Wales coast, mainly to other medical families and I'm told by my informant the opportunity to sleep in Olivia's old bed was always a major attraction.

A name I had missed on my original list was Graeme Garden, who with Bill Oddie and Tim Brooke Taylor, made up that mad 1970s comedy trio called the Goodies. His father, Mr Robert Symon Garden, was a very famous bone surgeon who has an orthopaedic classification of hip fractures named after him. Mr Garden also invented a piece of surgical kit for fixing hip fractures known as the Garden screw! Somebody was not too happy about serial killer Jeffrey Dahmer appearing on my original list and pointed out that his father was a Ph.D. doctor and not a real one. Medical doctors do get rather exercised about this sort of thing.

VISITING VIENNA
May 2000

Much has been written of Vienna and its ageing inhabitants. Not all if it is complimentary. Whilst recent electoral successes of Jörg Haider and his far right Freedom Party doesn't cover modern Austria with glory, there were no signs of rampant neo-fascism on my recent trip to its beautiful capital. How might one describe Vienna to the uninitiated? Well if the city was a doctor, one might describe him as formal, a little distant and organised to the point of obsessional. He would vote true-blue conservative every time. His opening hours would be very much restricted His fees are no more than they are at home and he would definitely never strike. Austria has less industrial unrest than any country in the western world. His hobbies might include stamp-collecting, reading newspapers and walking in the Vienna woods at weekends.

Having scoured the guide-books for medical attractions, we set off on Sunday morning for Apartment no 5 in Number 19 Berggasse. This is the former home of Sigmund Freud, the world's most famous psychiatrist. Not only did he live there, he had surgery too, between the hours of 3 and 4pm each day.

Although born at Freiburg, Moravia and buried in London, Freud spent most of his productive working life in Vienna. His former apartment and consulting rooms have been turned into a rather unassuming but compelling museum. There were about twenty five visitors there when we arrived. Most were studious-looking and were buried in books in the reading room. The furnishings were rather Spartan, but there was a terrific collection of photographs that tell the story of Freud family. When he wasn't writing about every topic under the sun from penis envy to death wishes, Sigmund Freud's hobbies included a famous old card game called Tarock, visiting the elegant Café Landtmann on the Ringstrasse, and taking his family for weekend walks in the Wienerwald. Participants on these walks would deck themselves out in traditional peasant gear right down to the leather shorts. The Nazis put paid to Freud's Bohemian lifestyle in Vienna and he died within a year of beginning his exile in London. An old medical friend kept his promise and administered a lethal dose of morphine when Freud's jaw cancer showed signs of impending victory. It was the end of a brave sixteen year battle with a terrible disease.

The other medical must-see for visitors to Vienna is the Fool's Tower or Narrenturm, which is located in a courtyard of the old General Hospital, not far from Freud's rooms. It's an eighteenth century circular building with five floors that was built as living quarters for the mentally ill. Each level had 28 centrally heated cells and when it ceased functioning in 1866, the hospital administrators in their infinite kindness allowed it be used as a residence for junior hospital doctors. Today it's a museum of pathological anatomy. Amongst its gruesome collection of pathological abnormalities, the Narrenturm holds the world's largest kidney and gallstone collection. Approximately 50,000 items are presently in exhibit, divided into four categories. These include macerated preparations (soft tissues are removed from solid elements of the body with the aid of bacteria or chemicals), wet preparations (body parts preserved in formaldehyde), moulages (castings in wax), and medical devices. It's a real-life chamber of horrors. In true Austrian style, the tower only opens on Wednesday afternoons and Thursday mornings. The

Viennese have their own title for the building which they regard as being shaped like a local cake. They call it the Gugelhupf. Politicians who fall out of favour are said to 'belong to the Gugelhupf'. I'd like to see Jörg Haider in there.

VIRTUOSO OF VAGINAS
January 2007

Professor James Steel Scott, an obstetrician par excellence and former dean of the University of Leeds medical school, has died. He passed away to a celestial womb over the winter and his obituary in the *Guardian* caught my eye by describing him as a 'virtuoso vaginal surgeon'. Now I've heard obstetricians and gynaecologists being described as many things - mean fiddlers, strummers and even pluckers - but this wonderful description of a man who sought to minimise the use of large incisions was a first for me. A native of Glasgow, Professor Scott trained in our own Rotunda hospital in the grim post-war period and retained links here for many years as a visiting clinical examiner for student exams in gynaecology. His obituary writer said that examiners and speakers who visited him in his own Yorkshire home were always treated to roast pheasant on a glittering Georgian table, washed down with the finest Bordeaux. A virtuoso performer indeed.

THOUSANDS OF QUESTIONS
September 1997

Murphy, the village vet was feeling wretched and went down to see O'Reilly the local doctor. Doc O'Reilly sat Murphy down and started to reel off reams of questions. He asked him to describe all his symptoms, how long he had them, his family history, social history, whether he had travelled recently, whether he kept pigeons and how much he smoked and drank. Half an hour later an irritated Murphy stood up and shouted 'Hey look O'Reilly, I'm a vet. I don't need to ask my patients thousands of questions. I can tell what's wrong just by looking at my patients. Why can't you doctors use your eyes and forget all your bloody questions'. Doc O'Reilly nodded sagely. He looked Murphy up and down and then pulled a dirty old bottle out of his bottom drawer. 'Take that Murphy' he said, 'and if it doesn't work by tomorrow, I'm putting you down'.

BOTANICAL PRESCRIPTION
October 1998

Somebody left a magnet on my surgery fridge last week which read as follows: Never trust a doctor whose office plants are dead. The culprit has yet to be identified, but a clever decision by the practice manager many years ago to use only the finest artificial flowers meant that the magnet's message inflicted little damage on the Guéret practice. Thinking of waiting room plants reminded me of the story a medical rep once told me about an old Dublin GP who was famous for his vigorous campaigning along family solidarity lines. He fought long and hard against each and every item on the liberal shopping list. Yet whenever drug reps visited the doctor, he always insisted on getting more than his fair share of contraceptive samples. It took some time for his guilty secret to emerge, but the vibrant growth of his wife's hanging baskets and award-winning houseplants were hiding the truth. The good doctor was using hormonal contraceptives to oestrogenise his domestic flora. It was only his fauna that were denied the prescription on moral grounds.

GRANDFATHER'S VEINS
October 2014

All families have their own peculiar anatomical quirks and medical ailments that rear heads from generation to generation. In my own relatives, varicose veins are a weakness. I have escaped, but these tortuous vessels have troubled members of at least three consecutive generations of the Guéret family. This historical propensity for weak venous valves and prominent blood vessels came to light when I applied to the National Archives at Kew in England for some military records. They belonged to a grandfather of mine, who never knew any of his thirteen grandchildren. It transpired from study of these detailed records, that grandfather Guéret's varicose veins may even have preserved his life during the Great War.

The Guérets had moved to Ireland *en famille* from Paris on September 4th, 1870. The date is important, because it was the very same day that the Third Republic was declared in France. Emperor Napoleon III had surrendered at the battle of Sedan and the Franco-Prussian War was getting bloody. The whole future of France was uncertain. Indeed the city of Paris was to remain under siege from that fateful day until it finally fell to the Prussian army many months later. Motives can be lost or blurred in sands of time, but it's likely that the Guérets made a commercial decision, probably a wise one, to leave town. In Paris, they had a successful church art and religious furnishing business on the Rue Duguay-Trouin. Orders from new churches in Catholic Ireland, then in holy resurgence, were flourishing. The family, Jean Léonce Guéret, his wife Estelle, their teenage children Paul and Mathilde, and his mother-in-law Marie Victoire Guillet, arrived in Dublin and within months were trading from Number 7 Wellington Quay under the style of *La Maison Française*. Business was good. My great grandfather, Paul Léonce, one of the teenage emigrés in 1870, was a supporter of Charles Stewart Parnell. In 1890, he stood as the nationalist candidate in a Dublin election, but the local unionist narrowly beat him by seventeen votes. The election was unpleasant. Paris-born Paul Léonce was continually referred to by his opponent as an 'alien'. This despite the fact that the family had received their naturalisation papers some years before. Parnell died in 1891 and my great-grandfather grew disillusioned with politics. He continued the family business and spent his leisure time as an opera and music hall impresario around Dublin. The family lived at Belvedere House on Strand Road in Sandymount.

My grandfather, Paul Joseph Guéret, was born a Dubliner in 1892. He was sent to boarding school at Castleknock College in 1903 where he was remembered as a 'quiet, unassuming student, with a sense of humour all his own'. Cricket and rowing were his twin passions, and on leaving school, he continued both at Railway Union in Sandymount and the Commercial Rowing Club near Islandbridge.

My grandfather's education continued at Skerry's College on St. Stephen's Green. This was the Dublin branch of a popular Scottish service that prepared school leavers for careers in the civil service. His first job was at the Custom House. War was declared in 1914, and later that year he applied to join the Officer Training Corps at Trinity College. His application was turned down, as all places had been taken. At about this time, Paul met my grandmother, Julia Fitzharris. She was working as a secretarial for Lady Aberdeen, who lived at the Vice-Regal Lodge, now Áras an Uachtarán in the Phoenix Park. Julia was the eldest daughter of Laurence Fitzharris, a Ringsend publican who had hailed from Carlow. After some years in America, he returned with his wife Mary to set up the Fitzharris public house at Number 4 Bridge Street in Ringsend. They lived above it with their eight children. Laurence Fitzharris was an active member of the Irish National Foresters and his politics were of the left wing.

Paul Guéret moved to the Post Office engineering department at Aldborough House in Dublin and persuaded a professor of engineering at Trinity to second a further application to the Officer Training Corps. This time he was successful, and he began his army training at the University early in 1916. Our family has a fine picture of all members of the Officer Training Corps, well over one hundred of them in uniform, outside the dining hall in Trinity's front square.

My grandfather's military medical was performed on the 15th of April 1916 at the recruiting office at 24 Great Brunswick Street (later to be Pearse Street):

Occupation: Clerk
Date of Birth: 14th October, 1891. (24 years old)
Height: 5 foot 11¼ inches.
Chest: 35 inch chest which expands 2½ inches on inspiration
Appearance: Group of scars on left side of face.
Vision: 6 out of 6 both eyes. (perfect vision)
Other findings: Slight varix on right leg.
Smart, intelligent and respectable lad of good appearance and suitable for Officer Corps.
Result: Passed fit for general service home and abroad.

Nine days later, the Easter rising began in Dublin. A later note on my grandfather's file, signed by a major at Officer Training Corps in early July, commented that he had 'a good bearing and word of command'. It also noted that he 'took an active part in the suppression of the Sinn Féin rebellion. Should make a good officer'.

Now this was a piece of family history that had not reached younger generations. Cadets had to defend the university during the uprising and used its many vantage points to fire on the rebels. As soon as firing started in the rising, the heavy gates of Trinity were closed. Armed members of the Officer Training Corps were given orders to deploy on the roof and shoot any armed men who were not wearing uniforms.

It was recorded that their actions saved lives and property, not just at the college, but on nearby Grafton Street, Nassau Street and Westmoreland Street. They also protected the Bank of Ireland at College Green. There were Canadian, South African, New Zealand and Australian cadets at the Officer Training Corps, and they also acted to protect the university and its environs, some as snipers on the roof.

By January 1917, Paul Guéret was in France, defending the country of his father and grandfather against the Germans. He arrived in Bologne, as a second lieutenant in the 8th Battalion of the Royal Dublin Fusiliers.

By March 1917, the Germans had retreated to the Hindenburg Line, a huge series of fortified defences that allowed them to hold position and regroup. In April, the Dublin Fusiliers took part in battles associated with what became known as the Arras offensive. In August 1917, the 8th and 9th Battalions of the RDF were involved in the infamous 3rd Battle of Ypres which took place around the village of Paschendale. But grandfather wasn't there. All the marching had worsened his varicose veins and he was confined to hospital in April with thrombophlebitis, inflammation and clots in his varicose veins. A decision was made to ship him home through England for rest. A surgical opinion was also sought to ascertain whether an operation was advisable. The surgeon noted that the great saphenous vein in his thigh and many of its tributaries were extensively dilated in his right leg. He declared him unsuitable for surgery and unfit for active duty. His file was marked P.B. which meant Permanent Base. He could return to France after some rest and treatment, but for base duties only, not front line action. Many of his comrades died in that summer of 1917. So many lives were lost from the 8th and 9th battalions, that the two had to be merged to keep going. Even the chaplain of my grandfather's battalion, Father William Doyle of Dalkey, was killed by a shell during that terrible summer.

My grandfather had troubles of his own at home. As he recuperated with his parents in Sandymount, his twenty one year old brother Joseph was away, whereabouts unknown. On the third day after my grandfather returned from the front, the house on Stand Road was visited early in the morning by a squadron of Black and Tans. Despite pleading that he was a British Army soldier home on sick leave, my grandfather was taken into custody and brought to Beggars Bush barracks under suspicion of being an active member of the Irish Republican Brotherhood. Two days later, he was released, and was driven home to Sandymount in a Rolls Royce. That night, he was disturbed and woken from his sleep by his sister, who brought him to the back garden. Later that night he met his brother Joseph who was a 'runner' for the IRB and was trying to avoid captivity. It was Joseph Guéret that the Black & Tans were after.

In happier news, Paul asked Julia Fitzharris to marry him on that trip home, just as soon as the war was over.

Grandfather Guéret rejoined his comrades in late 1917. He saw action during the German spring offensive of May 1918 at Vieux Berquin. Enemy artillery was particularly heavy here and hundreds of men were gassed, burned and blistered by the thousands of gas shells fired over their heads. Many billets suffered direct hits with heavy casualties. My grandfather survived. He was assigned to a German prisoner of war camp and promoted to Lieutenant. We have a wonderful photograph of him with a football at his feet, captaining the camp's soccer team. He was always referred to in our family as Captain Paul Guéret, but as far as we can ascertain now from his military records at Kew, his final rank was Lieutenant.

He remained in the army, and in France, after the Armistice. He got on well with many of his German prisoners. On learning of his impending marriage, the prisoners made several gifts for him, wonderful examples of trench art, which are still treasured by his family. These include vases, ornaments, cigarette boxes, carvings made from shell casings, bullets and wood. Several are now housed in the Royal Dublin Fusiliers archive at Pearse Street Library in Dublin. My grandfather returned on leave in April 1919 and he and Julia Fitzharris were married in St Andrew's Church in Westland Row. He married in full military uniform and surviving colleagues in Dublin used their rifles to form a guard of honour.

My grandfather returned to civilian life as an official in the high court. He continued rowing, and family lore has it that a family friend, the actor Noel Purcell, once saved his life on the Liffey. My grandfather's boat capsized and Noel was the only person present who spotted that my grandfather was in trouble under the water. With all his love of rivers and rowing, he had never learned how to swim.

Like many who were gassed and fought in the trenches, his health in later life was not as good as it might have been. He and Julia raised four children at Sandymount. My father recalls that our grandfather found wintry and stormy nights very difficult. The wind would howl and screech through the house and remind him of his time at the front. If there was advance warning of a storm, my grandmother would collect newspapers to stuff every crevice in windows and doorways in their exposed house on the Strand Road.

Paul Guéret died in a nursing home on Mount Street Crescent in February 1940. He was 48 years old. The certified cause of death was pulmonary tuberculosis of one year duration with exhaustion. Amongst the small collection of war time memorabilia, the family had a collection of six uniform buttons, that they assumed were part of his regimental dress. Recent examination however revealed that they were not Royal Dublin Fusiliers buttons as the family had always believed, but buttons from the Irish Volunteers. Clearly they belonged not to Paul, but to his brother Joseph.

A QUICK PEE
April 2007

I have been wondering how many doctors get caught short at their clinics and have to ponder a quick pee in the surgery sink. Always better to think the wiser of it, particularly if the practice nurse is in the vicinity. A dentist from Batley in West Yorkshire, whose further blushes I will spare by not mentioning his name, has been found guilty of professional misconduct by the United Kingdom's Dental Council. His troubles began when he refused to wear gloves for a molar removal. A hygiene-conscious patient made a complaint about him and it was then that his personal hygiene practices were examined in clinical detail. His nurse of sixteen years standing was called to give evidence. She alleged that he had urinate in the sink of his surgery on at least one occasion. She also claimed that he was partial to using dental instruments to clean not just nails, but his ears too. His personal hygiene practices were discussed for three full days by the council before they decided whether to floss him. In mitigation, the tooth-puller claimed a latex allergy as the reason why he couldn't wear gloves. He denied that the urination incident ever happened and said it was his habit only to clean his teeth in the sink between patients. The council could not reconcile this statement with his nurse's claim that she saw him tucking something into his trousers before she got the whiff of urine. His punishment was extraction from the dental register. Wee justice.

Post-Script: *I mentioned this case to a dentist who is longer in the clinical business than I am. He told me that peeing in the sink of consulting rooms was once a well recognised practice amongst eminent medical and dental specialists on Dublin's Fitzwilliam Square. Long before the fancy clinics of Blackrock, and Charlemont came into being, Fitzwilliam Square and surrounding streets housed the very best of the city's clinical talent. But the buildings were notoriously short of ensuite facilities. Eight flights of stairs can be hard on specialists caught short, particularly those whose prostate glands have started to rumble. The dentist told me that doctors and dentists were known to boast to each other about their lavatorial exploits. And furthermore, those with tendencies to hypochondriasis, would always keep a jar of urine test sticks close to hand.*

LICKING YOUR WOUNDS
November 2010

The cultural diversity amongst our traveller population is fascinating. Just before Christmas, doctors from Crumlin and Tallaght Hospitals reported cases in the international journal *Burns*, where two patients from the travelling community were sent to a 'licker' to have their burns coated with saliva before accessing mainstream medical care. The licker, usually an older member of the community, would sometimes be paid for the service. A figure of forty euro was mentioned. On another occasion, a treatment in the hospital was attempted during visiting hours. The appropriateness of adults licking the burns of children has been queried and it was also pointed out that one traveller girl contracted a herpes zoster (chicken pox) infection from her therapist. In the *Irish Medical News*, the traveller support organisation Pavee Point, suggested that the practice is no longer common and that only much older members of the community recall its use. Licking of wounds and burns is very common in the animal world, and there have been scientific studies showing that licking of burns can accelerate healing. A hormone in saliva known as epithelial growth factor (or EGF) is believed to me the mediator of faster recovery. Which all goes to prove that settled and travelling communities have a lot they can learn from one another. The authors of this article in the *Burns* journal believe the practice is an isolated cultural phenomenon that is unique to Ireland, and say that it has been recorded in every burns unit in the country.

INVESTMENT ADVICE
August 2007

I am no Eddie Hobbs, and certainly not in the habit of giving out investment advice with my prescriptions. But as an amateur collector of first editions, children's books especially, you might allow me tip Emily Gravett, an extraordinarily gifted illustrator and writer in this genre, for very great things. Two years ago Ms Gravett won the Kate Greenaway medal for her first children's book *Wolves*. This is a feat few manage so early in a career. She followed it up with four other illustrated books, each of which is a gem. In time, her first editions may well command the same sort of values that Beatrix Potter attracts today. That's if anyone remembers what a book is. Today, a first print of *Peter Rabbit* could fetch you £65,000 sterling at an auction. Gravett's latest offering, *Little Mouse's Big Book of Fears* ventures into the world of phobias. It's a wonderful refresher course for any doctor or nurse whose psychiatric knowledge is a bit rusty. It covers all the common childhood fears like clinophobia (fear of going to bed), ablutophobia (fear of bathing) and the very rare one rupophobia (fear of dirt). Remember that name. Emily Gravett.

BLOOPERS
March 2007

Readers have been sending me some more medical malapropisms. A secretary on a cancer day ward told me about a dear old lady who arrived at check-in one morning saying '*I'm here for my Lambretta'*. She was due to receive a chemotherapy treatment called Zometa. An employee of an urban district council told me about a man who tripped up in a pothole and subsequently said he was going to sue by hiring the best *banister* in the country. A country lady was overheard sympathising with the daughter of a deceased neighbour. 'She was grand until she had that *P&T* on her womb'. It was a D&C or Dilatation & Curettage. The same lady was later overheard in prayer at a wake saying 'Blessed is the fluid of thy wound Jesus'. A retired nurse in Cork wrote to tell me about an elderly lady who was knocked down on her way to church by a *sensation*. During her hospital admission it was clarified that it was a dog, an alsatian. She also looked after a gentleman who was glad to be transferred back to her hospital as in the previous one he was *prostituted* by the nurses. Persecuted was the word that escaped him. Other recent arrivals include the child who recovered from a bout of *melongitis*, and the man with a heart attack who was rushed to the *extensive care unit* to be placed on an *incubator*.

An eagle-eyed specialist received the following e mail from a hapless hospital administrator. 'Subject: Power Outage. Dear Colleague. Normal phone and email Services have been resumed. Apologies for any *incontinence* caused'.

A retired medical secretary wrote to me about sharing an office with another secretary who 'to be kind to her, was in the wrong job'. This lady showed a lot of religious fervour in her work as she once typed a letter to a family doctor about a female maternity patient stating that 'she had a normal *virginal* delivery'. (As opposed to the traditional vaginal one.) Doctors don't always get things the right way around either. A patient emailed to tell me how his topsy-turvy GP once told him he had found urine in his blood.

JOHNNY SIXPENCE
December 1998

Johnny Sixpence was a Dublin man who used to attend every casualty department in the city having deliberately swallowed loose change. I remember him well, for the poor unfortunate was opened up more often than a bishop's poor box. In later years, with the advent of endoscopy, it was no longer necessary to open Johnny up. You could hunt for his coins by inserting top and bottom tubes instead. Until that is, one brave surgeon made the decision that enough was enough. Resources were scarce, and he issued instructions to the doctors residence that Johnny was only to be admitted if he presented with an acute abdomen, by which I mean it was a life threatening emergency. We never did see Johnny Sixpence again. We used to wonder if he graduated to five pound notes or swallowing holy medals in heaven. But he came to mind when I read a piece recently about the accidental swallowing of American cents that are dated after 1981. Paediatricians and vets have been warned that children or pets who swallow a penny minted after 1981 should be monitored closely to see if they pass the coin. A paediatric radiologist from North Carolina reported the case of one toddler who swallowed a penny that caused a nasty stomach ulcer within a matter of days. It would appear that newer pennies made after 1981 are predominantly made from zinc, which isn't so good for stomach lining. Maybe Johnny Sixpence went to America.

DR RUTTYS' SPA
May 2000

This month's *Journal of the Irish Colleges of Physicians and Surgeons* carries a wonderful article about Dr John Rutty who lived from 1698 to 1775. Rutty was a native of Wiltshire who came to Ireland two years after qualifying in medicine from the University of Leiden, south of Amsterdam. He arrived in Dublin, armed only with an introductory letter from his local Society of Friends. A committed Quaker, Dr Rutty spent a lifetime studying the diseases of Dubliners and the effects upon them of such things as the weather, the seasons and natural history. This article about John Rutty revived a memory for me of a picturesque spot up in the Rathfarnham hills called Kelly's Glen. It's many years since I walked the valley, but I recall the presence of an old well there, known for over two hundred years as Dr Rutty's Spa. A quick check of an old volume of Joyce's *Neighbourhood of Dublin* confirmed that Rutty was one and the same doctor. I have a vague memory of trespassing up there late one evening in a vain search for the spring. Rutty consumed the water himself on a regular basis, and beat Ballygowan and Tipperary to the market by bottling it for the general consumption of Dublin's citizens. Whether my thirst was quenched that night, I cannot recall, but a trip to Kelly's Glen on a sunny evening is a magical journey to be recommended. A precise description of its location is contained in the above mentioned book by Weston St. John Joyce, but be careful. Not everybody up the Dublin mountains likes you tramping on their land. In his article, Professor Breathnach of University College Dublin points out that Rutty's writings 'somewhat naively betrayed an excessive enthusiasm for mineral waters'. He did live to a grand old age for his era. He was 76 when he succumbed to a paralytic stroke in his consulting rooms. Dr Rutty was buried in the Friends' burial ground on York Street near St. Stephens Green, on the very spot where the Royal College of Surgeons now stands.

BELLA ITALIA
October 1998

This week I am on a medicinal trip to Florence, Tuscan capital of art, architecture and nuclear power. My arrival coincided with the 650th anniversary of the black death which once wiped out more than half of the city's population. It has recovered well now, but painful memories of 1348 perhaps explains why Italy is the only country in the world to have more doctors than taxi drivers. Between epidemics, when clinics are quiet, many of their less popular doctors moonlight as taxi drivers to put Chianti and bread on the family table. Those same tables that margarine companies spoof on about no-one growing old at. But the truth is that Italian men live just a few weeks longer than their Irish counterparts.

My guide book tells me that if urgent medical attention is required, the pronto soccorso (outpatients) of the Florence Hospital is the place to go. No confusing health board messages here about visiting your off call family doctor first. Patients expecting to stay overnight in Tuscan hospitals should bring their own cutlery, crockery, towels and toilet paper. As my base was the very fine Excelsior hotel where such consumables were of the highest quality, I chose to self-medicate all holiday ailments. Nurses in Italy are so busy with important ward tasks that they expect the families of patients to wash and feed their loved ones on the wards.

Florence is noteworthy for a rather strange ambulance service. You may recall it from the Merchant Ivory movie *Room With a View*. In one early scene, two young Italian men start a brawl in the beautiful Piazza della Signoria, yards from the renowned Uffizi art gallery. One of them is mortally wounded following a fall. Enter these strange looking stretcher bearers dressed head to toe like grim reapers in black Ku Klux Klan type cassocks. These are the famous volunteers of the Misericordia, one of the oldest charitable lay bodies in the western world. The scary sight of them surely tipped many patients from the serious list onto the critical one and beyond. The Misericordia are still around, but the traditional garb is only worn now on ceremonial days.

A satirical guide called *All you need to know about Europe* once depicted the typical Italian as a cowardly baritone who consumes 78.3 kilograms of carbohydrates a month, drives a car slightly smaller than he is and is always looking for a divorce. Crude stereotyping perhaps, but Italy's department of health has just drafted a three year plan to improve the mental and corporal conditioning of its citizens. Health minister, Ms Rosy Bindi has specified targets that must be achieved by the year 2000. Amongst other things, the plan covers obesity, smoking and alcohol consumption. Judging by cafe life in Florence, in the supposedly healthier northern part of the country, she has her work cut out. It's said that very little counts for less in Italy than the state. Plans for a 40% reduction in the number of smokers and a similar decrease in the number of cigarettes smoked are very optimistic. All the more so as the recent European ban on cigarettes containing more than 12 mg of tar will not be enforced in Italy. This strange decision reflects an extremely lax attitude of consecutive Italian governments towards smoking. Mortality for lung cancer among young men is higher in Italy than in neighbouring countries.

Smoking is still permitted on Alitalia's international routes and on Italian trains. Few restaurants and bars have separate areas for non-smokers and smoking rates among 15 to 24 year olds are on the increase.

Some Irish politicians can thank their lucky benefactors and house builders that they don't live in Italy. An Italian judge has just convicted Italy's former prime minister, Silvio Berlusconi of illegal party financing and has meted out two and a half years in prison to him. The guilty ruling was the billionaire's third prison sentence in nine months. Last month he was sentenced to almost three years in jail for bribing tax inspectors and in December 1997, he received a sixteen month sentence for false accounting. But the 61 year old opposition leader remains at his sumptuous villa just outside Milan as his legal advocates initiate a lengthy appeals process. Italian punishments that are not set aside end up outliving their wealthy recipients.

It's not so 'Bella' after all for the self-proclaimed miracle cancer treatment that hit the headlines earlier this year when thousands of Italians took to the streets demanding that the government finance their treatment. Backed by populist political parties and the Italian rotary club, the protagonists succeeded in forcing an easily-led government to issue the treatment free of charge. An international body of experts is now completing its initial study into Dr Luigi di Bella's potions and have uncovered no evidence of its potential to cure cancer. They have also pronounced that it may be toxic. Dr di Bella whipped up mob enthusiasm by claiming over 10,000 cancer cures, but researchers have decreed that thousands of his patients never had cancer in the first place. The Italian health ministry, under pressure from cancer patients, ignored warnings from oncologists and pharmacologists and agreed in June to allow Luigi di Bella's treatment to be given free to all terminally ill patients while official testing on 397 patients was underway. No patients reviewed so far have shown any improvement and many have died. Wholesale insanity is how one clinical pharmacologist in Milan has described the fiasco. Must be time to go home soon for some insanity of our own.

FINE SPECIMENS
February 1999

Scruffy Murphy goes to the doctor feeling a little unwell. He's a bit taken aback when Doc hands him four little jars and asks for samples of his stools, urine, blood, and semen. Murphy takes the jars home and asks his wife how in God's name he's is going to collect them all. 'No problem,' she says. 'Just give him the bottom of your pyjamas.'

MASONIC POWERS
January 2000

Little surprises me anymore when it comes to our health service but I still raise the odd chuckle at the ingenuity shown by patients who are able to access hospital services more readily than others. Just recently I had an older gentleman in the surgery whom I referred on for a non-urgent, but quite necessary x-ray. Forty eight hours later, six weeks earlier than I expected, the result popped up on my desk. When the man returned for his result, I asked him how his stroke of good fortune with the notoriously poor appointments system came about. 'It's not who you know, it's how you know them' he answered somewhat cryptically. He wasn't giving any more away and this made me all the more inquisitive. Information later came to hand that the gentleman was quite an active mason, more of the free type than stone. It transpires that at least one eminent diagnostic radiologist in the city is also a member. Indeed I have also become aware that there is quite a long list of medical men on Masonic books, who can be handy to know when there's a orderly queue to jump. You never quite know who you're shaking hands with.

SCRIBBLED NOTES
April 2006

Most practices have a small sub-group of patients that rarely grace the waiting room. Family doctors get to know them from their handwriting. Communications are scribbled on pages torn from children's copybooks or on the back of supermarket receipts. These are what I call correspondence patients. And here is one such classic request, minus the punctuation:

'Hello Doctor, Would you ever give me some tablets to keep me off the bread. I am 11 stone and I can't do much about it with the baby and something for Sean's cold. Thank you'.

In many ways, these patients are easy to manage. Their ailments and needs can be met with quick prescriptions and advice between consultations. Sometimes they use relatives or neighbours to drop in the requests and to collect the prescriptions and advice. Some patients feel they are better at writing down their ailments than describing them in person. Some have social phobias. Others are simply unable to get to the surgery - perhaps because they are carers or have a disability themselves. These consultations can pose dangers and the quality of care given to them might not always stand up well in a court of wigs. An long-standing trust is needed between doctor and patient. Another note in the genre that doctors would regularly come across is the prescription shopping list. This would be a fairly typical one here:

100 Disposable Sheets
Radiomulsion
Calpol
2 Baby Powders
2 Shampoos
2 Savlons
Pink Tablets
Malt and Vitamins for Water.
Please give those things as I could not do down to you.

I have been collecting such anonymous communications from colleagues over the years. I sometimes feel that they comprise a whole new realm of literature, worthy of a prize perhaps. They are usually polite and respectful in the extreme. Sometimes the clinical descriptions are very apt. Symptoms are rarely classical and you will not find them in any medical textbook. Here is another of my favourites that demonstrates their beauty.

'Doctor, I am sorry to trouble you but I have terrible pain in my eye since yesterday, now this is my bad eye that snow or sunshine always causes trouble in it. Last night beat all pains and my head is bursting with pain and I feel like a staggering sheep. I am sorry to be such a bother all the same but if you could give me something I would be very grateful thanking you Doctor'.

SIR ALAN'S HERNIA
November 2010

I don't usually follow the machinations in Sir Alan Sugar's board room for his BBC programme *The Apprentice*, but he does appear to have a very buccaneering East Ender style that he carries into his daily life and business. I was interested to read recently of his experience with hernia surgery. When an inguinal hernia in his groin re-appeared very soon after undergoing an operation, he decided to write a deliberately incorrect cheque to the surgeon who carried out the procedure. He did this by filling in two different monetary amounts on the cheque. When the professor phoned to tell him that 'the cheque had come back' Sir Alan was lying in wait and was able to bellow down the phone 'So has my f****ng hernia!'

MAGNETS FOR
THE MENOPAUSE
August 2011

On a trip to Wexford last month, I spotted a pharmacy urging menopausal women in the town to discreetly place magnets in their knickers. I'm not sure if the idea attracts or repels the good sunny ladies of the south east, but I was so intrigued that I took photographs of the advertising material for later study. 'Possibly the most exciting discovery for the menopause' it said. 'May completely eliminate symptoms as diverse as vaginal dryness, bloating, weight gain, irritability and sleeplessness'. Not to mention flushes, sweats and irritability. Alas I am unaware of a single item of reputable scientific research in any international journal showing that ladies of any vintage might benefit from placing thirty euro worth of magnets in their underwear. If this pharmacist, or indeed any other chemist shop in the country who stocks menopausal knickers magnets has the evidence I am lacking, please do feel free to enlighten me.

THE THIN MAN
July 2004

Nobody knows for sure where our growing fanaticism with body shape is taking us. But one thing is certain. Making weight such a huge public health issue will create misery for another generation of folk on the other end of the scales. There are many myths and misapprehensions about anorexia nervosa, loosely termed as the slimming disorder or self-starving disease. Whilst primarily a condition that affects younger women, the number of men seeking help for the condition is climbing. A recent study of teenagers in the United States revealed that 3% of young males diet obsessively and that an even higher number deliberately vomit after eating. Eating disorders in men were first described in medical journals one hundred and thirty years ago. The vomitorium of ancient Rome provides proof that males in distant times practiced bulimic activities by purging their stomachs so that they could eat more.

It may once have been a condition found in gladiator schools, but male anorexia today particularly affects joggers, long distance athletes, jockeys, male dancers, models, wrestlers and boxers. Young men with anorexia tend to present slightly later than their female counterparts, with the average age between 17 and 24 years. It's slightly more common amongst homosexual males and research suggests that men with slimming disorders tend to have more sexual anxieties than females. There are all sorts of theories and hypotheses about what drives men into obsessive slimming. Experts suggest that men in close-knit sporting, gay and other communities experience the same cultural pressures to be thin as adolescent girls. Psychological profiling of male patients in eating disorder clinics shows higher than average levels of obsessional traits and a tendency towards perfectionism.

Much of the interesting work in this field has contrasted the personality traits of anorexic men with anorexic women. Personal characteristics such as social immaturity, anti-social behaviour and a tendency to hysteria or hypochondriasis are more common in male patients than in female. But to avoid misconceptions, it should be stated that most men with anorexia are quite well adjusted in other aspects of their lives. Indeed family members and doctors have traditionally been slow to spot the condition in male patients. Under-diagnosis may mean that the true prevalence of the disease in males has been underestimated. In contrast with most female patients (who tend to be of normal weight before submitting to the rituals of anorexia), men who develop the condition are likely to have been overweight before it took hold. Ministers who carp on about how fat we are getting as a nation, might do well to consider the collateral damage that high profile anti-obesity campaigns can generate. If they are serious about tackling eating disorders, let them provide adequate services for patients at both ends of the eating disorder spectrum. The compulsive eater and the obsessive slimmer have one thing in common in Ireland. State facilities for both disorders are quite appalling, if they exist at all.

HOSPITAL DINNERS
October 2012

A friend used Twitter recently to post a picture of a meal that was offered to her mother in hospital. I say offered, because it certainly wasn't consumed. A debate ensued as to whether it looked more like a cat's feed or a dog's dinner. My own feeling was that it looked more like something that would exit the other end of a domestic pet, on a bad tummy day. To be perfectly frank, today's ward food can be pretty disgusting. In my training days, hospitals served freshly purchased food that was plainly cooked on the day. Some of my favourite restaurants in Dublin were the canteens at the old Adelaide and the children's hospital on

Harcourt Street. Sir Patrick Dun's was best of all. Baggot Street hospital was pretty good too. Portions there for male doctors and students were particularly generous if Nellie the cook was on duty. By and large, patients enjoyed the same grub. A good appetite provided evidence for clinical staff of a patient recovering and getting well enough for discharge. The only complaint, if there was one, was an occasional problem with food temperature. Delivery of a few hundred hot meals from basement to distant floors and wings had to be a military style operation, and wasn't always easy in a world as eventful as a hospital. I left the hospital service in the early 1990s. Soon afterwards, two dreaded words entered the lexicon of Irish healthcare, cook and chill. Most hospital food is now cooked months in advance, stored for lengthy periods and reconstituted just prior to serving. It's food designed for institutional convenience rather than human taste. Satisfied patients are as thin on the ground as Michelin stars. That's why hospitals rarely ask them to rate their own food.

Things aren't any better on wards for kids. A young lad had to get up at four in the morning recently to get to his local regional hospital for an elective operation. It was a day case. His Mum was very impressed with the level of care received from the nurses, doctors and all others involved in his surgery, but was a little taken aback by the nourishment provided after his operation. It consisted of coco pops and ribena, followed a bit later by toast and ribena. He was then handed a further carton of ribena for the long journey home. It does seem odd that the same health authority which cuts essential dietary items like coeliac foods from the medical card scheme has no problem handing out large numbers of expensive sugar-laden food and drinks on the wards. Ministers commission reports on obesity and wag fingers at the general public, yet their own hospital services are often the very worst offenders.

Another mother wrote to me recently about an experience in a Dublin hospital some years ago. Her son was admitted with bacterial meningitis. He was isolated and drip fed antibiotics and fluid for a week before he recovered. Medical permission was then granted for the starving teenager to have some solid food. He and his Mum whiled away the afternoon fantasising. Maybe an egg

- lightly boiled, poached or even scrambled? Maybe hot toast or even ice cold milk? Would ice cream be possible? At 'tea time', a large beaming Dub trundled her trolley into the room and made an announcement. 'Now der's a choice. Yeh can have a burger n' chips or a lumpa chicken n' chips'. Mistaking their stunned silence for indecision she reconsidered and added - 'Ah shure yir after being that sick son, shure have the both'. She then presented him with an enormous grease laden plate of burger n' lumpa chicken n' chips and said 'Now son, eat that fir yir Mammy'. She then gave the mother a great big warm hug and said 'Now Missus, don't you be worrying. Shure he won't know hisself after he eats dat!' The mother tells me that she wept with relief at both the kindness and prognosis. She has long felt there are two constants in the health service. A complete lack of joined up thinking between hospital dieticians and catering staff, and secondly, an incredible kindness and empathy of hospital staff at the coal face. A diagnosis that's spot on.

THE HARDEST TEST
March 2005

Doctor Murphy was beginning to regret asking Paddy about his medical and life history. 'First, I got angina pectoris, atherosclerosis, hypercholesterolaemia and myocardial infarction. Just as I was recovering from these, I got tuberculosis, psittacosis, double pneumonia, and bilateral pneumothorax. Then they gave me hypodermics, oral pharmacotherapy and Sulphonamide suppositories. Appendicitis was followed by tonsillectomy, cholecystectomy, pancreatoduodenectomy and a Nissen's fundiplication. These gave way to aphasia, fulminant hepatitis and hypertrophic cardiomyopathy. Then I completely lost my memory for a while. I know I had diabetes mellitus and acute porphyria, followed by peri-oesophagitis, rheumatism, epididymitis, lumbago, polyneuritis and pneumonosis cystoides intestinales. To be honest doc, I don't know how I pulled through it'. 'And what hospital was all this in' asked Dr Murphy. 'Oh, I wasn't in hospital, ' exclaimed Paddy, 'I was still in school. It was the hardest spelling test they ever set me'.

ENDA'S SURGICAL FLUID
April 2007

Will somebody please tell me what are the exact contents of Enda Kenny's bottle of 'surgical fluid'? The leader of the opposition appears almost every night on RTE news dowsing himself and all others in his immediate vicinity with a spray on liquid. Mr Kenny is a politicians of some gravitas. Two years ago he rocked the state's foundations by promising to ban the sale of spray paint to young people. Then we had his speech worthy of the United Nations when he said that white powder was 'dusting every town, village and suburb in the state' and 'vanishing up the noses of professional and respectable Ireland with alacrity'.

He was interviewed about his own spray can recently. This is what he said to the *Irish Medical Times*. 'I carry a bottle of surgical fluid with me in the car, when I go into hospitals and wards, to demonstrate that everybody can participate in this'. When asked what exactly he was talking about he said 'everyone can play a part in fighting MRSA infections'. Will somebody please tell this gormless man that surgical fluid is the last thing you should be spraying around the place if you are concerned about hospital acquired infection. Surgical fluid is bloody body water that leaks out of patients that have undergone recent surgery. It's the reason a drain is sometimes put into a wound after major surgery and a collection bottle sited under the bed for fluid to ooze into. Somebody needs to tell him urgently of this fine distinction between surgical fluid and what I assume is some sort of antiseptic that he is spraying around the place. So much bloody nonsense oozes from Mr Kenny these days, I'm surprised one of his many medical candidates hasn't suggested inserting a drain in him.

DOCTOR LELIA
April 2012

The death of any lady at the grand age of 114 is a newsworthy event in itself. But Lelia Denmark, who passed away this month, was special. She was reckoned by the gerontology research group in the United States to be the fourth oldest person in the world at the time. What made her life even more extraordinary, is that she worked right up to the age of 103. After Benjamin Spock, Dr Lelia Denmark was perhaps the best known paediatrician in America. I remember reading about her over a decade ago, when it was reported that failing eyesight was preventing her from continuing to practice. She hailed from a well-off farming family in the southern state of Georgia, and was the only lady in her medical school class. Soon after qualifying in 1928, she opened a surgery at her home and raised her baby daughter as she worked. She never had a receptionist, or a nurse, and no appointments were ever required. You just called in with your children when you needed her advice. And in time, the children she tended to, took their own children, and these children then took theirs. Dr Denmark had bees in her bonnet, or as one obituary writer put it, pet peeves. She disapproved of day care for children This was an easier stance to take when you had just one daughter as she did, and a job that allowed her to work from home. She also recommended to parents that children should not drink cow's milk after weaning. She liked to point out the window to healthy cows in the fields and tell mothers that the cows themselves never touch a drop of milk after weaning. She also disliked sugar. She refused to eat cake on her 100th birthday and always advised parents to give their children water instead of juice drinks. Away from practice, she became quite an authority on vaccination. Her research on combining immunisations in the 1930s and 1940s was widely praised. Dr Denmark's 1970s book on rearing children *Every Child should have a Chance* is still available. It never had the same exposure or big publishing business behind it that Dr Spock's books did, so her theories of child rearing weren't as widely dispensed. By the time Lelia Denmark retired in 2001, her consultation fee was just ten dollars. A very great lady doctor indeed.

DR ASHER'S SEVEN SINS OF MEDICINE
February 2003

The father of actress Jane Asher was a well known figure in London medicine. Dr Richard Asher was a somewhat eccentric fellow of the Royal College of Physicians and he was appointed a medical consultant at the Central Middlesex Hospital during the blitz. He was keen on teaching good habits to students. For their benefit, he once wrote an immodestly titled tome called *Richard Asher Talking Sense*. He encouraged critical thinking, something that doesn't always come naturally to medical students who have so much to learn in a handful of years. Asher catalogued what he called the Seven Sins of Medicine that were (in no particular order) Obscurity, Cruelty, Bad Manners, Over-Specialisation, Spanophilia (loving the rare), Stupidity and Sloth.

Obscurity might be categorised as a venial medical sin. Asher believed it to be a common enough failing, particularly in lecturers and that strange breed of doctors who prefer research to real patients. A patient arrived in the emergency room and told the medical student that 'Half-way up a hill and I feel I'm done for'. When the student wrote up the case, Dr Asher was less than pleased to read in the notes that 'the patient complains that during ambulation up a moderate incline he suffers a feeling of impending dissolution'. Asher warned the profession against turning the simple English of their patients into the jargon of medical textbooks. Obscurity is bad, not only because it is difficult to understand, but because it is easily confused with profundity. Asher observed wryly that muddy pools may look very deep, but most of them are quite shallow.

The second sin is Cruelty, described by Dr Asher as the most important and probably the most prevalent. He divided medical cruelty into mental and physical. Mental cruelty arises in three ways. Saying too much. Saying too little. And saying nothing at all. Dr Asher deplored the age-old hospital practice of bedside teaching where the patient was treated as if they were deaf, dumb and might as well have been dead on a necropsy slab. I have a personal memory of this practice from a morning round in the old Sir Patrick Dun's Hospital many years ago. A popular physician gathered twenty students around the bedside of an old merchant seaman and proceeded to ask them for their everyday observations of this patient, who it could not be denied, was far from handsome. A dozen students gave what pertinent clinical observations there were to be made, but the remaining stragglers were cajoled by the consultant into making observations that grew more offensive by the minute. They mentioned the dirt of the man's nails. The large tufts of hair that flowed from his ears. And so on. That was my first lesson in mental cruelty of the medical kind. The fact that the poor man did not subject his tormentors to physical cruelty was testament to his extreme patience.

Bad Manners is the third sin of medicine. Dr Asher once asked a student to examine the abdomen of lady in an outpatient cubicle. The impatient youngster dashed in, flung back the blanket, plumped his hand on her abdomen and shouted 'Gosh, what a beauty!' Asher was not best pleased although he did clarify that the student was referring to the patient's enlarged spleen and not to her overall appearance. He gave three further examples of bad manners towards patients. Impatient history-taking from slow-witted informants. Making jokes at the expense of patients. And most seriously of all, reading the patient's newspaper from the head of the bed when their life history gets boring. Dr Asher insisted that his medical students would address ward sisters and their nurses with a courteous good morning, conveniently noting that this makes access to patients and ward equipment much easier. Asher advised students to aim for reasonable respect towards their clinical seniors, but to avoid oily deference. He encouraged juniors to write to their seniors to congratulate them on all their publications and appointments!

Overspecialisation was Dr Asher's fourth sin. He was very much in favour of doctors having a special interest or extra knowledge of one subject, but he castigated fellow medics who showed special indifference to and ignorance about all other subjects. He spoke of an eye surgeon who diagnosed a case of retinitis pigmentosa, and then referred the patient to another specialist enquiring as to whether there was any evidence of polydactyly. In plain English, the eye specialist was asking another specialist to count the number of fingers and toes on the patient rather than do it himself. As Asher put it 'For an ophthalmologist to feel himself incapable of counting fingers is surely the limit of overspecialisation!' He went on to describe another complication of overspecialisation, namely that 'it allows bees to remain undisturbed within their master's bonnets. An allergist looks at the world through allergic-coloured glasses and beams myopically at a world where everything is allergic'.

Richard Asher's fifth sin of modern practice was Spanophilia. Now this is a word that has yet to reach my largest dictionary. I could find neither sight nor sound of it in Webster's. It refers to a forbidden kind of love that sadly is all too prevalent amongst medical students and their tutors. That unbridled love of the rare. Dr Asher claimed it was the main reason for bookworms failing clinical exams. He pointed out in no uncertain terms that nose-bleeds are more likely to be due to picking the nose than multiple hereditary haemorrhagic telangiectasia. He suggests that wasting of the small muscles of the hand is more likely to be a consequence of old age than motor neurone disease or a cervical rib. I remember another bed-side lecture of ours in Sir Patrick Dun's when a fellow student was first in line to interrogate a patient with a chronic cough. His opening gambit 'Do you keep pigeons?' didn't go down too well with the professor. Ringing in our ears as medical students was the line, that common things are common.

Asher's final two sins claim a hefty stain on all of our medical souls. They are Common Stupidity and Sloth. The former takes many forms but Asher put special emphasis on those who treat by rote and role, without recognising that special circumstances attenuate in every case. *Therapeutic Automatism* is the wonderful term he coins and he describes the case of a woman who fell whilst skating on a local squire's pond. She fractured her tibia. First aiders in attendance were of the opinion that she shouldn't be moved under any circumstances until a doctor arrived. Were it not for the intervention of a non first-aider who ignored their protestations and dragged her off the ice, their dogmatism would have claimed the life of the lady, and her valuable furs.

Sloth is a sin of omission that's indelibly marked on many

medical consciences. Omitting to conduct a blood pressure check, disregarding an examination of the back of the eye or being too lazy to do a rectal examination are particular examples quoted by Asher. Another is the pretence that the tip of the lumbar puncture needle did not actually touch the bed clothes before insertion. Nurses come in for special mention, particularly those who tire of counting the breaths of patients and just add another twenty to a huge row of twenties already on the chart. Mental sloth regularly comes to the surface in history-taking. Hot day, rushed doctor, patient has twin horrors of poor hearing and loquaciousness. We all know the picture. Accepting a patient's diagnosis without elaborating on history is a form of unconscious sloth. Asher mentions the patient who claimed rheumatic fever at the age of ten. What he meant was that he was a single day in bed with a sore ankle and his auntie made an amateur diagnosis. Finally, there is sloth in thinking. Dr Asher berated doctors who are too lazy to think. They are easy prey to poor scientific papers and blindly accepting myths. Asher advises medics to cultivate a healthy doubt without being unduly sceptical. This he says may reap the reward of the Queen of the Fairies in *Iolanthe*:

> *On fire that glows*
> *with heat intense*
> *I turn the hose*
> *Of common sense*
> *And out it goes*
> *at small expense*

CONCIERGE MEDICINE
March 2013

Concierge medicine is all the rage in the United States where money talks, and doctors are keener than anywhere else to listen. This new craze has nothing to do with hotel lobbies.

Concierge medicine is a new sub-speciality of family practice where an individual doctor (as opposed to a group of them) takes on only a very small number of patients, and treats them to a 24/7 personalised medical service. Just as the concierge at a swanky hotel might look after V.I.P. guests. Your concierge medic will make all your test and hospital bookings for you. Your illnesses will be followed up with regular phone calls. Taxis and ambulances will be arranged. The concierge doctor will pop around to your house as often as you need, and perhaps even visit you whilst you are under the care of specialists in hospital. Patients will be welcome at the doctor's home. You will have the doctor's mobile phone number and e mail address for all your medical queries. Hell, he might even become your friend on facebook. There must be many patients who would really love this sort of service. When it began nearly twenty years ago, the fees were set at about $10,000 a year. But with more competition in the concierge market, the price has dropped down to less than $2,000 a year. Doubtless there are doctors in Ireland who feel like they have been offering concierge medicine to patients for decades, at no extra charge. If you have one of these guys, count your blessings!

ROALD DAHL
August 2005

I was in Hodges Figgis the other day and grabbed *Boy – Tales of Childhood*, an early autobiography from Roald Dahl. It's a great little read and took just an hour and a half to finish in the garden. Amateur psychologists would have great fun combing the fine details of Dahl's family life and schooldays, but the two stories he tells of Norwegian doctors fascinated me. His father Harald fell from the roof of his home whilst doing some slate repair work. He was just 14 at the time. Help was summoned and half an hour later a medical gentleman made a majestic and drunken arrival in a horse drawn buggy. He was so drunk that he mistook a simple elbow fracture for a dislocated shoulder. The resulting efforts of burly men to put the undamaged shoulder back into place (by pulling on the fractured elbow) left the young Harald Dahl facing a needless amputation of his arm.

Roald Dahl had his own rather brutal childhood encounter with the medical profession which may have contributed to his well-documented loathing of adults and authority. The family usually left Britain to spend their summers with grandparents in Oslo and Roald recalls one such visit when his mother took him to a doctor 'to examine your nose and mouth'. His mother had suspected adenoid trouble but the word meant nothing to an inquisitive Roald who was told not to worry about them. Taking his mother at her word he happily opened wide for the doctor as a long thin shiny steel instrument was being boiled in a pot of water front of him. 'This won't take two seconds' said the doctor. A nurse held a bowl under his chin and a tiny blade flashed before him before being plunged high into the roof of his mouth twisting and turning as it ascended. Out of his mouth tumbled a mass of flesh and blood. In a vivid portent to the imagination the world would come to know and love, Dahl imagined that the doctor had 'cut out the whole middle of his head'. 'The roof of my mouth was on fire. I couldn't believe that anyone would do this to me'. This was ear, nose and throat surgery 1924 style. His mother took him by the hand and they walked the half hour journey home. The same barbaric-sounding procedure must have happened here in Ireland but I'll say no more. Norwegians write about their experiences. Our saints and scholars hire tribunal lawyers.

Post-Script: *I had a very nice letter from a cardiologist who by chance had just finished the same book. He recalled an experience of his mother from the 1920s. She was taken as a ten year old to see the rather eminent figure of Dr Oliver St John Gogarty in his Dublin rooms. The same anaesthetic-free adenoidectomy was performed and she was left with the lifelong opinion that he was a vicious and brutal man who performed an operation in a manner that suggested he was in a terrible hurry. His subsequent literary efforts cut little mustard with her, but as her medical son now points out, it may simply have been the safest method at the time.*

WILDE'S RUSTY INSTRUMENTS
March 2013

I have been doing a bit of study on the life and career of Sir William Wilde, father of Oscar and a noteworthy eye and ear specialist of 19th Century Dublin. He left a wonderful literary contribution in the form of books on an array of subjects. His clinical legacy was pretty impressive too. He left doctors an ear operation called Wilde's incision and also invented some medical instruments like Wilde's aural forceps. His reputation with the ladies was not quite so saintly. Let's just say that legacies from this side of his character trailed him through much of his life. There is a lovely story in Professor Barry O'Donnell's *Irish Surgeons and Surgery in the 20th Century* about what happened to Sir William Wilde's own surgical instruments long after he died. Apparently they were proudly owned by the late ophthalmic surgeon Mr Beecher Somerville-Large (1901-1966) of Fitzwilliam Place in Dublin. On enlisting for the second world war, Mr Somerville-Large entrusted the valuable instruments to the care of a theatre sister in his hospital. He failed however, to enlighten her as to their provenance. On his return from the field hospitals of Burma, he was informed by the senior nurse that 'them rusty instruments has been binned'.

COMPETENCE ASSURANCE
February 2008

A wag at the Society of Medical Writers shares some of our scepticism about this so-called 'competence assurance' that is soon to be foisted on a reluctant profession of doctoring. He has unearthed some confidential reports on underperforming doctors that were recently discovered in a rubbish heap across the water. A certain Dr A. Fleming was described as a sloppy worker whose laboratory was a disgrace. He was overly fond of holidays and never tidied up before he went. His sink was piled high with agar plates, so old that some even had mildew growing on them. Dr R. Bannister was red-flagged for long absences from his practice.

Patients reported that he would regularly go running just for the fun of it. Dr A. Conan-Doyle was accused of artificially keeping the size of his practice very small so that he could write trashy thrillers. Dr A. Comfort was referred urgently to the GMC professional practice committee as vile publications were found on his bookshelves. Dr W.G. Grace was cited for being overweight, a poor sporting role model and for facial hair that bordered on the unhygienic.

A Dublin consultant took the time to write to me with a few more competence assurance reports. Dr S. Maugham, resident on the French Riviera, was hauled up for a reprimand for not publishing any of his work in peer-reviewed journals. The rather indignant graduate of King's College London responded to his accusers by stating that *Cakes and Ale* was not a scientific study of nutrition, nor indeed was *Of Human Bondage* a psychiatric study of sexual deviants.

When the patients of Dr J.H. Watson of 221B Baker Street, London were questioned about his activities, he was ordered to re-train. A common thread running through his competence reports led the Medical Council to believe that he spent much of his time not practising, but playing buffoon to a lodger called Holmes, his lodger. Most of his journal club activities and investigations were wholly unconnected with medicine. The only mitigation in Watson's defence was that he had been injured in an explosion whilst serving with the British army in Afghanistan. However lawyers for the Medical Council pointed out evidence from the *Sign of Four* in which Watson boasted an experience of women extending over many nations and no less than three continents. Not something you would ordinarily associate with post-traumatic stress.

The final competence report alleges that a Dr H. Jekyll of London used his own laboratory to manufacture potions but failed to seek approval from the ethics committee or to register any of his subsequent trials. The Medical Council took a dim view of the fact that Jekyll failed to apply for product authorisation in the usual way and tended to play down side effects of his compound, namely its propensity to split the personality. The council was alarmed that that an unqualified and querulous gentleman known as Mr Edward Hyde was frequently allowed access to Dr Jekyll's rooms and laboratory after hours, and could have had access to privileged and highly confidential information. Dr Jekyll was ordered to retrain, but turned down this particular transformation in favour of another. His name was struck from the register.

JUDGING DEV
January 2008

The Christmas book that made a lasting impression into the new year was *Judging Dev*, Diarmaid Ferriter's reappraisal of former Taoiseach and President, Eamon de Valera. Some biographers have been rather harsh on the tall fellow, and I carry baggage here. Not a single ancestor of mine ever seemed to have a good word to say for him. Dr Ferriter implies that Dev has borne more than his fair share of blame for the poor economic performance of Ireland prior to the Lemass years. There is ample coverage of how he escaped a death sentence, his erratic behaviour after the death of Herr Hitler and a wonderful tale about how a Dutch businessman secured his agreement to have the de Valera brand on packets of cigars all around the world.

There was little mention of health matters. I would have been interested in Ferriter's explanation of de Valera's 'Catholic doctors for Catholic patients' policy which forced many fine young Protestant and Jewish graduates across the Irish sea, simply because hospitals and dispensaries here didn't entertain them. De Valera's own health does get an airing. There is some brief mention of a series of eye operations for which he travelled to Utrecht in 1952. Dev spent four months under the care of the renowned retinal surgeon Professor Weve. He was not the last Irish politician to seek personal health services abroad.

There is also some private correspondence in Ferriter's book penned by de Valera's personal physician, the late Dr Bryan Alton. The letter was written to Taoiseach Jack Lynch from Dr Alton's rooms in early 1973 suggesting that President de Valera 'is tending to develop a depression'. The next line states 'The main basis for the matter appears to be financial'. Dr Alton suggests that 'his fears may be totally unfounded but he speaks of them very rationally and convincingly'. Dr Alton then writes coyly to Mr Lynch, 'If he is right, I felt you should know the problem exists'. His presidential salary and pension was increased immediately, and doubtless the anxiety subsided.

Cold water pours from Diarmaid Ferriter's biography on suggestions that de Valera had Asperger syndrome. About four years ago, Trinity College's professor of child psychiatry, Michael Fitzgerald published a book on autism and creativity in which he laid out supportive evidence for de Valera to be some sort of autistic genius. Ferriter points out with some force, that the list of symptoms attributed to de Valera could be applied to many electorally successful politicians. Nor is he convinced by other 'evidence' such as flashing eyes, a lurching gait or a preoccupation with mathematics and detective novels. Whether he had or hadn't true autistic symptoms in early childhood, is probably something only a mother, or in de Valera's case the grandmother who reared him, could answer.

MORE RUDE CONSULTANTS
September 2006

I have written previously about our dying breed of rude hospital consultants and I continue to pester colleagues with requests for distant memories of atrocious medical behaviour. An old classmate, well not that old - she's the same age as I am, texted me during the week with a reminiscence of her time working as a junior doctor in a Cork hospital. A well-upholstered lady was in outpatients one day with a working diagnosis of gallstones, occasionally a consequence of obesity. The investigating surgeon grabbed hold of her rather ample spare tyre and said 'Tis not here you should be dear, tis Clonakilty Mart'.

Another colleague told me about an orthopaedic man, now deceased, who once told a lady with widespread spinal osteoarthritis 'Madam, if you were a horse I would have you put down'. Charming. I was also told a story about a very suave dermatologist who was consulted by a scruffy-looking young man with acne vulgaris who said 'I've tried all sorts of lotions but nothing seems to work, doctor'. 'Did you ever consider washing?' was the consultant's reply.

The same contributor also tells me of an exasperated eye specialist who advised a patient he wasn't getting on with to 'Stand up, put one foot in front of the other and before you know it you'll be right outside the hospital!'

A colleague also sent me what he terms the 'ultimate in arrogant consultant' stories. It involved an ear, nose and throat specialist, long deceased now, who had conducted a singularly unsuccessful procedure on a lady patient. She attended his outpatients department umpteen times, but on each occasion he steadfastly refused to see her. Finally she accosted him on a hospital corridor and demanded that he explain himself. The following conversation ensued:

'Madam, have you an appointment?'

'No'.

'Madam, I see patients only by appointment. Please go away'.

'Mister, you're a disgrace. I've a good mind to report you to your superior'.

'Madam, I have no superior. In fact, Madam, I have no equal'.

Another patient complained to his consultant that 'I've been to three other doctors and none of them agree with your diagnosis'. The consultant replied calmly 'Just wait until the post mortem. Then they'll see that I was right after all'.

Institutional racism was once widely tolerated in the Irish hospital scene. In his autobiographical book *Against the Tide*, Dr Noel Browne described one appalling comment by a lung specialist in the 1970s. He had a retinue of staff from what he called 'the commonwealth' and one day when a radiographer refused to use a certain x-ray machine as it was faulty and possibly dangerous, he said, 'never mind I'll get one of my black boys to push the button'. Such bigotry has now gone underground if it exists at all. Hospitals are now places where a line has being drawn between acceptable clinical humour and unjustifiable racist prejudice.

KNOCKDOWN PRICE AT BELFIELD
September 2007

A carriage driver was on the radio last week discussing a savage attack on his horse by a loose Staffordshire pit bull terrier. This horrendous episode on St Stephen's Green left his nag bleeding profusely and in need of fifteen stitches. What particularly amused me was when the driver told listeners that his horse had to be taken to the 'College of Surgeons' for suturing at a cost of €100. It transpired that what he meant to say was the new University College Dublin veterinary hospital in Belfield. I don't think his four legged beast would have got any change from a thousand euro at the College of Surgeons!

BILLY'S ASTHMA
June 1998

Billy Joel and Elton John played a joint concert at Croke Park the other week. There were no illicit drugs, no riots and surprisingly little alcohol consumed. The handful of doctors with the St John's Ambulance brigade were able to enjoy themselves no end. I watched the whole event with binoculars from the top of a new stand, and was amazed to see the amount of inhaled medication Mr Joel was taking during his sets. Billy didn't look a well man at all. His voice was weak and the uptown girls of his backing group had to carry him through the night. In between each song, Billy could be seen puffing frantically from one of his inhalers. It came as little surprise to me when I heard that many of the subsequent tour dates in the United Kingdom were cancelled, initially because of an asthmatic attack that was then followed by a throat infection. In Manchester, Billy Joel apologised to over 30,000 fans who had tickets for the show as Elton John did not wish to appear alone. Unlike Michael Jackson, Billy doesn't bring a personal physician with him as part of the entourage. I wonder if an insurance company might insist on such an arrangement for future tours.

DANGEROUS DISCIPLINES
January 2013

There is a worry that the malpractice sword hanging over the delivery of babies as a medical career choice, is now beginning to swing on other disciplines. Take psychiatry for instance. Just before Christmas, an extraordinary verdict was reached in a Marseille courthouse, when a 58 year old French psychiatrist was found guilty of manslaughter following an axe murder. She was sentenced to one year in prison, suspended on certain conditions. Yet Dr Danielle Canarelli hadn't touched a single hair on anyone's head. One of her patients, who had a severe paranoid illness, killed his grandmother's partner, with the axe. Dr Canarelli was charged with improperly evaluating the risk. Psychiatrists protested outside the courthouse. One carried a placard saying 'dark day for psychiatry'. Murders by patients with severe mental illness are still a rarity compared with those committed by mentally well populations. Nor is there any good evidence that such murders are becoming more common. What has changed is the public and media outcry every time a known mentally ill patient takes a life. Any honest psychiatrist will admit that the prediction of such risk is more art form, than precise science. A mature society has to decide whether it wants to go back to the days where patients are locked up in their thousands just in case they do something. It's not a scenario that psychiatrists want to go back to, but it may be forced on them if there are more verdicts like the one handed to Dr Canarelli. For one small mercy we can be thankful, her one year prison term has been suspended.

THE SILVER SWAN
November 2007

He's back this Christmas and should fill many a stocking. Benjamin Black has penned a folly-upper to *Christine Falls*, last year's inaugural story of Dr Quirke, the troubled hospital pathologist who pounds the streets and mortuaries of dark 1950s Dublin. *The Silver Swan* is another tour-de-force thriller from the *nom de plume* of John Banville who paints his prose an ecclesiastical shade of purple. We have a chemist who is a bit touchy-feely with his young counter assistants. There's a 'quack' doctor who takes lewd photographs of his patients. And a pharmaceutical salesman who doesn't want a post mortem conducted on his wife's body. Not forgetting the boozy midwife, Nurse Haddon, who can afford a flashy sports car on the earnings of her busy back-street abortion practice. Banville's realistic ingredients don't materialize out of thin air, but he does stir a very fine soup indeed. Do try and get the hardback first edition with the dust-jacket because Banville's publishers are set to abandon hard cover titles in the new year and mark these words, first editions of Benjamin Black thrillers will have a market all their very own in the dark 2050s.

THE QUEEN'S BED PAN
February 2001

Sometimes I close my eyes at health board meetings and just listen. It's easy to imagine that one was in the Dáil, Senate or county council chambers. Indeed for some of our local politicians, the monthly health board meeting is their Leinster House. Their faces light up like the red light on their live microphones as they get dug into the concerns of the day. But most of the issues they do discuss have nothing whatsoever to do with health. Political animals prefer to talk about matters of procedure and protocol than matters pertaining to healthcare. Reports on weighty clinical subjects can be passed in seconds whilst wrangling about who goes on what new committee or who is entitled to attend a conference in Ballydehob and what the attendant fee is can go on for an age. I suspect there is some secret code for the Queen's bed pan attendant that forbids disclosure of precisely what they might witness. If the same rule applies to health board members, I could be in trouble ahead.

MULTIPLE BIRTHS
October 1998

Paddy Englishman, Paddy Scotsman and Paddy Irishman were sitting in the waiting room as their wives all went into labour. The nurse walked in and said to Paddy Englishman 'Congratulations sir, you're the new father of twins!' 'How about that?', said Paddy, 'and there's me working for the Doublemint chewing gum company in London'. About an hour later, the same nurse entered the waiting room and announced that Paddy Scotsman's wife has just had triplets. Paddy stood up and said 'Och, how do ye like that, and there's me working for the 3M company in Glasgow'. Paddy Irishman started sweating and turned a deathly shade of pale. 'Are you alright sir, your wife won't be long'. said the nurse. 'I'd be feelin' a good deal better' said Paddy 'if I didn't work for Seven Up in Dublin'.

STRONG WRISTS
May 2007

Talented folk in various fields of endeavour are sometimes asked what anatomical part of the body they believe that their power comes from. Irish tenor John McNally recently told an interviewer that the power in his voice comes from his belly button. The golfer Jack Nicklaus has a different take. His self-help books firmly attribute most of his power to strong hips and thighs. I've always been more of a wrist man myself. I was saddened the other day to read of the death of Australian golfer Norman Von Nida at the age of 93. He almost pipped Irishman Fred Daly to the British open title in 1947. In his heyday, Von Nida was a somewhat belligerent and testy individual who weighed just 9 stone and stood small for a golfer at just five a half feet tall. Strong hands and strong wrists were his thing, and thrown putters and snapped clubs sometimes followed on a bad day. Before he turned professional, he had worked in an abattoir cracking open the skulls of sheep after they had been sliced by a machine. A legend grew up about Von Nida on the golf tour that he was invincible in an arm wrestle. The sheep would nod in agreement.

DIVERSITY
November 2003

My local hospital could solve the world's unemployment difficulties if given half a chance. They have a big advertisement in today's newspaper telling the country that they have €49,000 a year in their coffers to give to a diversity officer. I like the sound of that job and wonder if they might give it to a doctor in need. I could inject piles on Mondays and Fridays, freeze warts on Tuesdays and Thursdays and pull a few rotten teeth in between. Nothing like a bit of diversity. But wait. What's this? 'An ability to produce written reports and policy documents a distinct advantage'. That puts a quick end to my dream. It must be a health board type employee they are after. A paper chasing, pen-pushing, conference-attending type. I cannot think why the layers of administrators we have already cannot do a bit of officering in diversity themselves? Perhaps they are too focused on curing unemployment.

Health provider BUPA has instituted a new code of conduct for its UK staff engaged in putting up Christmas trees at their offices, clinics and nursing homes. The *BUPA Care Services Health & Safety Manual* calls for a full risk assessment to be performed before the erection or removal of Christmas trees and decorations. If it's a large tree, a separate second assessment is needed. This weighs up the manual handling risk. Staff who double up as Christmas tree installers must wear appropriate eye protection and protective gloves. If it's a tall tree, then staff must carry out a further risk assessment, the working at height one, and refer to the BUPA policy on heights for guidance. They should talk to my local hospital. Sounds like they need a Christmas tree diversity officer.

SOUND OF SILENCE
December 1997

Patients who have noticed that medical waiting rooms are lacking a bit of musical sustenance recently, might like to know the real reason behind the withdrawal of doctors' radios, CD and tape players. Physicians and surgeons the length and breadth of the country have been targeted by an outfit called the Irish Music Rights Organisation (IMRO). They collect royalties on behalf of songwriters from anybody who wants to play music in public places. The waiting rooms of family doctors and specialists have been designated by IMRO as chargeable areas, and they have written to doctors in recent weeks asking them to declare surgery sizes and wireless specifications. The organisation has already taken 900 cases against members of the vintner's federation, an organisation who are in turn taking their own case against IMRO. The music rights people are a persistent lot and last year they took in a revenue of £13 million. One wonders if a few thousand doctors will be reaching deep into the back pockets to help them up their income. I suspect many will be putting the transistor in the bin, and switching the goldfish back on.

MOLES ON THE BUS
January 1999

A group of doctors were asked what they would do if they boarded a bus and saw a likely case of melanoma on the face of a fifty year old lady who was a fellow passenger. Would you believe that three quarters of them said they would do nothing at all? Surgeons and family doctors were less likely to intervene than cancer specialists or laboratory pathologists. The same study was done on lay people and just one third of them said they would act on their suspicion. Better than the doctors, but not by much. I find this study a bit disturbing and I would hope it's one of these cases where interviewees answer a survey one way, when they know in their hearts they would actually do the other.

CONFERENCE SEASON
January 2004

With abolition now in sight, 250 health board members have secured a final hurrah. They have all been invited to three fascinating conferences that will be of untold benefit to patients. First up is the spring seminar of the Association of Municipal Authorities. It's a two day event in February at the appropriately named Holiday Inn in Letterkenny. Always a delightful location for mileage claims. There is not a single health related item on the agenda but entertainment will be laid on thick. Two weeks later, patients with urgent problems will be able to contact their local health board appointees as they listen to a *Seisiún Ceol Gaelach* or participate in a *Guided Scenic Walk* at the 15th Colmcille Winter School. Surprise, surprise, it too is in Donegal. And two weeks after that, in mid-March is the annual conference of the Association of County Councils – a three day Kilkenny festival that once again contains not a single health related issue on the agenda. That won't stop health boards footing the entire bills from their health budgets for those who attend. After the Irish breakfasts, the carvery lunches, and the back-slapping banquets at that one, there is a good dose of healthy entertainment will be provided by TR Dallas and his legendary band. Let's hope he plays *The Last Waltz* for the whole lot of them.

HAUGHEY'S HORSE
February 1998

> *Charles J. Haughey rode his fine horse*
> *Charles J. Haughey fell with great force*
> *All the states' ambulances came charging in fleet*
> *and bypassed Beaumont*
> *for dear Eccles Street.*

Some weeks ago I was commenting about the unusual fact that the twelve year old child of the President of Ireland was treated in the Mater Misericordiae Hospital, rather than the more appropriate paediatric casualty service at Temple Street, following an injury sustained in the Áras an Uachtaráin. Shortly afterwards, a second episode struck me as equally odd. Our onetime Taoiseach Charles J. Haughey was taken to the Mater Hospital's emergency department when his horse threw him

69

off at Portmarnock. The appropriate hospital for a casualty in Portmarnock is always Beaumont. Doctors and their patients are led to believe that Dublin ambulances operate strict catchment areas to the letter. Patients whose life histories are documented in one hospital are frequently refused transport to it, and whisked off to another one. I think ambulance control on the eastern seaboard should explain why Mr Haughey was taken the extra miles to the Mater Hospital when he lives and indeed had his accident in the Beaumont catchment area. There is nothing very egalitarian about access in Irish healthcare. It seems to have more inside tracks than a greyhound stadium.

HEFTY SENTENCE
January 2006

The wife of a well known Dublin specialist was arrested for shop lifting in Brown Thomas. When she went before the judge he asked her, 'What did you steal?' 'A packet of tights' she replied. The judge asked her why she had stolen them and she answered that her legs were cold and that she had forgotten her purse. The judge asked her how many tights were in the packet. 'Six' she replied. The judge then said, 'Very good. I will give you six days in jail'. But before the court rose, the woman's husband stood up and asked the judge if he could say something. ' What is it?' asked the judge. 'Your honour, she also stole a giant sack of coffee beans from Bewley's'.

BRIAN LENIHAN SENIOR
February 1999

I've recently finished an excellent biography of the late Brian Lenihan senior, one of the most theatrical and popular men ever to grace Irish politics. Some legendary performances are related in the book, ranging from the comical, to the farcical, to the tragic. But an overall decency and a fine intellect of the man shines through. I was struck by the similarity between Lenihan's early constituency life and that of a rural doctor. With his catchphrase 'no problem', he hated to say no to anybody. He was regularly besieged by petitioners who would congregate inside the family home seven days a week. This could make life quite intolerable for any young family rearing children, so Lenihan built an office on to the house with a separate entrance. Some of his constituents then complained that 'we're not good enough to go into the house, are we?' The author, distinguished political commentator James Downey, recalls the impossible life of a man at the permanent beck and call of his people, the same folk who were quick to denigrate and complain about him when their impossible favours were not possible. In many ways, Lenihan was ahead of his time. He had a profound contempt for local government as practised in Ireland and once described it as no more than an 'endemic nursery of corruption'. It was. And it's a very great pity is that his own party did so much to encourage it, and so very little to stamp it out.

HEALTH SPEAK
September 2004

I think it's only fair to give our new fangled monster, the Health Service Executive, time to bed down. But I am not encouraged by the newspaper advertisements looking for a gaggle of executives and national directors. Looks like the same sort of managerial guff we had from top-heavy health boards. The verbose job descriptions are classic turkey-gobbling. Both the national director of primary care and the national director of the national hospitals office may need gardening skills as they are expected to *'ensure the achievement of optimum client pathways'*. The national director of information technology is expected to *'establish strategic alliances . . . in order that a world class health system can be developed and supported by the most appropriate technologies both internally and externally'*. The rest of the advertisement is littered with the sort of meaningless flannel that marks health minister Martin out as the Government's waffler-in-chief. Phrases like 'priority initiatives proceeding apace' and 'migrating to new arrangements' with staff 'ensuring effective interface arrangements' and 'building capacity to enable the system to respond to change'. Confucius says that a minister who cannot utter a single sentence without saying 'going forward' is usually going nowhere.

VIAGRA'S BIRTHDAY
April 2000

I've greatly enjoyed my first year of Viagra prescribing. Though it has created some pretty awful jokes, the humour and bonhomie associated with this new medicine is welcome in otherwise staid consultations. It has created a new era of openness amongst men visiting surgery. One gentleman likes to tell me a different Viagra joke every time he visits. Though humour sorely lacks from most, we still manage a grin or chuckle. Contrary to much of the hype, take-up of the drug has been steady if unremarkable. It does seem to be a little more popular with medical card patients that private ones, but no gentlemen have looked to exceed the government quota. Most are happy to indulge themselves with the four a month stipulated by the minister for sex. Just a few have graduated to the higher 100mg dose. But I have heard tales of some patients on the 100mg dose asking for eight 50mg tablets rather than four 100mg ones. That is what is called manipulation. I've had no reports yet of any side effects, although I do continue to counsel gents about the tiny possibility of sudden death, from over-exertion. A not uncommon reply is 'way to go, doc'.

GREAT GRAPES
March 2005

Medical wine lovers will be delighted to know that Californian vintners in Napa Valley, who up to now were primarily producers of fine wines, have developed a new hybrid grape. It acts as an anti-diuretic and prevents frequent trips to the lavatory. It's expected to have a dramatic effect on Irish nocturia rates by reducing the number of bathroom trips the older generation have to make during the night. The new wine follows in the wake of its successful siblings Pinot Blanc, Pinot Noir and Pinot Grigio, and will be marketed as Pinot More.

ACUTE POLITICITIS
August 2006

As lethal diseases go, politics may be one of the very worst you can catch. There is rarely such a thing as a short bout or a bad dose of it. Political involvement tends to terminal, a serious and unremitting condition, which never has a happy end. Victims rarely present for medical attention, and if they do, it's invariably too late. Jeremy Paxman, the BBC's inquisitor general, wrote a defining book about politicians some time ago and it regularly gets taken down from my shelves and dusted.

The Political Animal - An Anatomy succeeds in getting under the skin of the modern politico as no other textbook has done. Paxman compares all the assets of a typical member of parliament to those of a compulsive gambler. The outward self-confidence. The incurable optimism. The manic persistence. The unbridled reserves of energy. And the possession of a spouse dutifully resigned to a second best role in life. He decrees that politicians are not without insight, as the most damning critics are usually their very own kind. Paxman says he has lost count of the number of parliamentarians described by party comrades as 'corrupt', 'bonkers' or simply 'off their trolley'.

He looked for common early factors that might help define a political future and found plenty of fodder. Lonely childhoods, unhappy schooldays, dynastic parental ambition, simple vanity, a desire to be noticed, a quest for celebrity or a belief that one can change the world simply by speaking in council chambers or parliament were just a few. The warning signs can be there from early days. Barbara Castle, a one-time minister in Harold Wilson's cabinet, wrote her first election address at the age of six. It read 'Dear Citizuns (her spelling). Vote for me and I will give you houses'. John Prescott was even less fortunate. Paxman records that Prescott once sent a love letter to a girl in his class. She had just passed her eleven-plus exam to get into grammar school, something the deputy prime minister Prescott had failed to do himself. What did she do? She sent it back to him with all the spelling mistakes corrected. Ouch.

MADRILENOS
July 2002

I have just returned from a brief tour of art galleries in Madrid. If you have any dark, dusky or broody paintings hidden in your attics, I'm in the market. There are lost works of Goya still to be found, the blacker the better. Madrid is a wonderful city, understated and surprisingly under visited too. There are daily flights from Dublin airport and it's not in the least bit pricey. Hard to find a cappuccino that costs more than a euro. My only minor criticism might be of its inhabitants. The madrilenos can be a trifle rude about the efforts tourists make (well me, anyway) to speak Spanish. They also eat extremely late in the evening which cannot be good for you. No point looking for early birds as creatures, whether feathered or furred, aren't roasted on spits until well after dark. You will be laughed at if you try to book a table before ten in the evening. If I could get used to the late nights I'd say viva España, Madrid especialmente.

THE LATE MR NELIGAN
October 2010

The passing of Maurice Neligan has left a hole in the heart of Irish medicine. One that will not easily be filled. Estimates vary on the number of cardiac operations he carried out in a long career. The guess is somewhere between 15,000 and 18,000. In 1975 he carried out Ireland's first coronary artery bypass graft. This operation became very useful, indeed fashionable before the arrival of stent technology. The coronary artery bypass graft was abbreviated in medical vernacular to CABG, pronounced cabbage. Maurice's humour was never far from the surface, reflected in the fact that his e mail address for many years was headcabg@indigo.ie

I only met surgeon Neligan once. It was in a radio studio and we had been invited in at an ungodly hour of the morning by Eamon Dunphy to discuss Mary Harney's appointment as minister for health. Maurice was a lot more cynical about her abilities and prospects than I was. History has proven his judgement to be more accurate than mine. I recall introducing myself to him and he looked me in the eye and said 'I think your brother sold me a pup once'. Not sure whether this was banter or a barb, I had to ring around after the programme and was happy to confirm that one of my brother's golden retriever puppies had indeed found a good home with the Neligans.

Though involved in bypass surgery, and the first heart transplant here in Ireland, most colleagues would agree that Maurice's finest legacy was in children's heart surgery where he was a true Irish pioneer at Our Lady's Hospital for Sick Children. When one of Mr Neligan's own children was murdered just a few years ago he wrote a very public and poignant tribute to his lost daughter. His description of going through his late daughter's belongings still brings a tear to the driest eye.

'Sara, love, when I went through your papers and saw your miserable pay cheques as a fully qualified intensive care nurse, I made a promise to you that your old dad would fight this cynical inequality developing in our society. So I shall'.

And he did, and we thank Maurice for being the dad, the doctor, the surgeon and the writer, for he did that splendidly too, that the rest of us can only aspire to be.

KIDNEY SUPPORT
August 2007

A lady judge in Carlow's district court has hit upon a novel idea for townsfolk who are 'caught short' on its Tullow Street thoroughfare. Late night urination in doorways has been declared a public menace by shop-owners. The judge is now fining those defilers and ordering that their penalties should flow into the coffers of the Irish Kidney Association. You could argue that the money might better be spent on providing public conveniences in the town, but top marks for the judge for making a worthy association with a deserving charity. Tullow Street residents and shopkeepers must hope that the nation's bowel support groups don't similarly profit from her wisdom.

WATCHING THE GAIT
March 2013

There is much that a doctor can tell from somebody's gait. A good psychiatrist will try and observe how a patient walks into the clinic. It helps make judgements not just about a state of mind, but also about how a patient is being affected by medication. A GP can also learn a lot from patients by watching their journey from waiting room to surgery chair. Parkinson's disease is one condition where the way a person walks can be key to diagnosis. The classic parkinsonian or 'festinant' gait comprises rapid shuffling little steps with the body bowed forward and difficulty stopping at the end of the propulsion. Patients with a 'reeling' type uncoordinated gait may appear to be drunk, whereas the real reason may be a problem with the inner ear or perhaps the cerebellar part of the hindbrain. Others may have a waddling gait like a duck, with the body tilted backwards as they plant feet wide apart and sway from side to side. This may indicate particular muscle diseases or a degeneration in the hip joints. If your doctor is one of those who shouts 'Next' from his surgery and has his head buried in a card or computer when you grace his door, he might well be missing out on a vital sign. So let him come for you in the waiting room. In that way, you can observe his gait and he can observe yours. Observation and plenty of time are two of the two best tools in a doctor's bag. A shame we don't always get to employ them to full effect.

THE NATION'S DOCTOR
August 2007

A former surgeon general in the United States gave evidence to a congressional committee this summer about the limitations on his office. It might give food for thought to some politicians like Gay Mitchell who are always calling for such an office in Ireland. Not only was Dr Richard Carmona forced to give positive praise to the American president at least three times in every page of every speech, he was absolutely forbidden by the current White House administration from speaking about any of the following - stem cell research, sex education, emergency contraception, prisoner health, mental health, passive smoking or global health. It's hard to know how a 'nation's doctor' can be charged with giving truthful information to the great American public when these are the no-go areas.

The surgeon general was free to warn the most free nation on earth about the dangers of choking on pretzels. To be fair to team Bush, Carmona wasn't exactly a shrinking violet of tolerance and reason. He has often stated that he wants a total prohibition on both tobacco sale and consumption. He once urged all Americans to stay away from smokers. 'Even a few minutes around drifting smoke is enough to spark an asthma attack, make blood more prone to clot, damage heart arteries and begin the kind of cell damage that over time can lead to cancer'. With extreme views like that, maybe it's just as well they kept him quiet.

BRAGGING IN THE YARD
March 2011

Three boys were in the school yard, bragging about their fathers, as little men do. First lad, son of a general practitioner, says his Dad puts on a tweed jacket, scribbles a few words on a piece of paper and gets fifty euro for every prescription he writes. Second boy, son of a hospital consultant, says his Dad puts on a pin-stripe suit every day, scribbles a few words on a piece of paper and gets 200 euro for every prescription he writes. Third boy says his Dad works one day a week, puts on a big robe, scribbles a few words on a piece of paper and reads them out on Sundays. He says they need eight people to collect all the cash that his Dad collects. 'What does he do?' asked the boys rather jealously. 'Oh nothing much. Just a parish priest'.

ENOCH
February 1998

The death of Enoch Powell is all over in the newspapers, with most emphasis on his infamous 'rivers of blood' speech (incidentally, a term he never mentioned at all) and on his latter-day flirtation with Ulster unionists. They adopted this Birmingham man as one of their own. But there has been very little said about his cabinet career, where he distinguished himself as one of the most interesting health ministers his country has ever seen, or is ever likely to see again. Powell was deeply touched by the plight of the mentally ill. He spoke of those who inhabited the many 'asylums our forefathers built with such immense solidity to express the notions of the day'. He was the first post-war politician to recognise the importance of care in the community and insisted that the medical profession would have to be assisted by a whole new development of local services if they were to accomplish this task. One characteristic which is often lacking in modern holders of this important ministry, is an ability to rationalise and avoid over-reactions to health scares that arise from time to time. Robert Shepherd, who penned the definitive biography of Powell, describes how he could not understand the attitude of fellow countrymen who continued smoking in their millions, yet were reduced to absolute panic and trepidation after a single incident of a young Pakistani girl entering the UK with smallpox.

SCALPED
November 2002

Total scalp avulsion is one of those catastrophic industrial injuries that's thankfully quite rare. But it can also be a major cause of sleep-disturbance amongst casualty staff who witness its horrific result as close quarters. Young women with long hair are most commonly affected. The usual cause of this catastrophic separation of scalp and skull is when long hair becomes entangled in moving machinery. The current edition of the *Journal of the Irish Colleges of Physicians and Surgeons* details the treatment of a young male factory worker, who had the misfortune of having his ponytail snared in an overhead spinning shaft. This moving paper also carries before and after photographs. The avulsion included the entire scalp, forehead, both eyebrows, the upper half of both ears and part of one cheek. An extraordinary re-attachment operation by the plastic surgery team of St James's Hospital, followed by some grafting of areas with dead skin and treatment with leeches is detailed in the article. What amazed me most was that full hair growth had resumed one year after the operation. I hope, and rather suspect, that the brave man gave up on the ponytail.

THE ETERNAL COUCH
September 1997

I was saddened today to hear of the death of Viktor Frankle, the renowned Viennese neurologist, psychiatrist and psychotherapist. He has gone to lie on his eternal couch at the age of 92. Author of *Man's Search for Meaning*, Frankl developed the theory of logotherapy, which aimed to help his patients find more meaning in life. A survivor of Auschwitz, he published his theories widely and received countless honorary doctorates from universities around the world. Frankl died of heart failure and his explicit wish was that he would be buried in a quiet setting, with only close family attending. Frankl's advice on happiness always rings true. 'Don't aim at success - the more you aim at it and make it a target, the more you are going to miss it. For success, like happiness, cannot be pursued; it must ensue, and it only does so as the unintended side effect of one's personal dedication to a cause greater than oneself or as the by-product of one's surrender to a person other than oneself'. Wise man.

READ AND WRITE
April 2000

The illegible handwriting of doctors is back in the headlines. I read that as many as one in twenty of our prescriptions has been deemed completely indecipherable by experts in such matters, chemists probably. The *British Medical Journal* had a case report recently on the legal difficulties faced by a Texan cardiologist who wrote what he thought was a reasonable squiggle for an angina medication. He wrote Isordil 20mg qds (four doses a day). Sadly the pharmacist dispensed the same dose of Plendil, a very different drug, for which the maximum daily dose is 10mg. The unfortunate mistake caused the death of a 42 year old man and the journal printed a copy of the offending prescription which to my semi-trained eye looked for all the world like a third drug, Zestril 20mg every six hours. Both pharmacist and cardiologist had to cough up £140,000 each to the bereaved family. Doctors with poor handwriting are now being advised to issue computerised or typed scripts. But how many doctors would actually pass their medical exams if their writing was actually legible?

IRELAND'S FIRST VASECTOMY
February 2003

Following a shout-out in the medical newspapers, I have now received details of the very first vasectomy operation to take place in Ireland. Accidental or violent ones may have taken place before, but the first planned operative procedure took place in March 1974 at the headquarters of the Irish Family Planning Association. Extraordinarily, the operation was performed, not by an Irish surgeon, but by a lady eye specialist who was flown in to Dublin for the big snip. The only pity was that she was not asked to appear on the *Late Late Show*. Such an operation being performed by a lady surgeon would have given the Irish viewing public a tremendous shock thirty something years ago. Who was the first patient? Well he was a healthy member of the Garda Síochána from a Kingdom in the south west of the country. And a very satisfied customer, I am reliably told.

ABERDEEN ENGLISH
September 2006

I was doing a spot of research recently into the correct spelling of the word *auxters*, when my interest was diverted to some medical terms that are peculiar to the city of Aberdeen in Scotland. Apparently the colloquial term used if a bone breaks is that it is *gassed*. And if it is badly broken, then it is *hosed*. A plaster cast is a *stoockie* and if this stoockie is left on too long on a patient, the body part underneath can get *minky* (a bit smelly) or *fusty* (starts smelling of mould). If a patient starts to *gie it laldy* or appears *blutered* with his *erse oot the windae*, it might be time for a doctor to defend himself. Either with an electric plaster sawing machine, or by calling in some nursing reinforcements.

ECSTASY TABLETS
September 1998

Mrs Buttle is a big powerful woman, a virtual stranger to the surgery. She's far too busy minding her single brothers, her married sons, her many grandchildren and her elderly neighbours than to bother me with her own minor health matters. She turned up recently and looked worried. Her problem was the 'ecstasy' tablets she'd found in her friend's garden. The chemist had been unable to positively identify the tablets and advised Mrs Buttle to see me for advice. When I frowned, she quoted the chemist verbatim. She said 'He's got a big chart showing the names of all the tablets and what they look like'. Mrs Buttle could see I hadn't a clue what the tablet was, nor had the means within my surgery walls to find out. I promised to investigate for Mrs Buttle. Later in the day I phoned the National Medicines Information Centre for advice and gave them a description of the triangular shaped white tablet with the capital letter S stamped on each side. The Centre were eager to help, quick-witted and assisted as always. Within seconds they had a suggested name for the offending medication and by my arrival home in the evening they had faxed me through photographs and manufacturers details on the offending tablet. It turned out to be a combination of Xylitol, Peppermint Oil and Aspartame - sold in every corner shops as *S Mint Mini Mints*! I rang Mrs Buttle with the good news. She was pleased but did ask how we live in a country where sweets are manufactured to look just like drugs. And I have been wondering the very same myself.

AN ASIDE TO A HUSBAND
July 2004

I am not responsible for the jokes that colleagues send me. I merely pass them on to you in case I am caught in possession. A doctor examined a woman and then took her husband aside. He said rather dolefully, 'I don't like the look of your wife at all,' 'Me neither doc,' replied the husband. 'But she's a great cook and really good with the kids'.

DEAF TO THE WORLD
February 2006

A colleague told me a nice story about his time as a locum for a rather shy and retiring GP many years ago. The doctor had actually gone to the trouble of placing a big printed sign on the wall, directly opposite the patient's chair and in their eye line. It read PLEASE DO NOT TALK TO THE DOCTOR WHEN HE HAS THE STETHOSCOPE IN HIS EARS. Funny enough, this sort of surgery signage has never really caught on. But I think we all understand how he felt.

THE LATE ANTHONY CLARE
October 2007

The untimely death of Professor Anthony Clare diminishes us all. Just a month before he passed away, I had a nice letter from him adjusting his current details in the *Irish Medical Directory*. he wished to include a new clinic he was working in and to add occupational stress to his broad list of clinical interests. Just a few months before, he had been in touch asking us to assist him with charitable work for children in East Africa. He was looking for a list of all his fellow psychiatrists in Ireland. I first met Professor Clare well over a decade ago in Luttrellstown when he joined the early editorial board of another medical publication, *Modern Medicine*. The honour was very much mine. His series of lucid books based on his *In the Psychiatrist's Chair* radio series were great favourites of mine, and remain to this day a very trusted source of information on maladies of the mind. Professor Clare was a stalwart and expert practitioner of both print and broadcasting in the 1980s, and was the outstanding medical communicator of his generation. He was noted in one obituary as having 'turned his back' on the media in later years. I suspect he simply had the good sense to sit comfortably with the beast for mutual advantage, and then walk away when his job was done. A full life in the glare of publicity is not good for anybody. May he rest in peace.

A YANKING OF DENTISTS
March 2001

Well known Dublin GP, Dr John Fleetwood senior, has been amassing collective nouns for some time. A yowling of cats, a piddling of puppies, a sleuth of bears - that sort of thing. At a recent clinical dinner he decided with some colleagues to come up with the best pack names for groups of medical specialists. He has been writing recently about the results. Favourites include a yanking of dentists, a rotundity of midwives and a harpooning of acupuncturists. There have been some taxonomies of medics compiled before with such gems as a murmur of cardiologists a stain of histopathologists, a speck of forensic pathologists, a rash of dermatologists, a poke of gynaecologists, and a stream of urologists. I invited colleagues to send in some more for Dr Fleetwood and we received a ray of radiologists, a complex of psychiatrists and a clot of haematologists. Others include a tangle of old age psychiatrists (insider clinic knowledge require for that one) a colony of microbiologists, a monocle of ophthalmologists, a swallow of laryngologists, a school of paediatricians, a richter of neurologists, a projection of researchers and an opinion of consultants.

MEDICAL FOR THE PRESIDENT
November 2011

Personal physician to the American President, Dr Jeffrey Kuhlman, chose Halloween last month to release details of Barack Obama's most recent check-up. The first thing I noted on the report was that it was late. President Obama's previous physical was performed in February 2010 and it stated clearly then that the next one would be in August of 2011. The delay of almost three months has not been explained, but could have something to do with the fact that President Obama has now been deemed a smoke-free zone. Maybe such a claim could not have been made during the summer. Anyhow, all seems well at the clinic. When the only medical items of note are skin tags, a spot of physiotherapy on the lower back and a healed lip laceration, Mr Obama must be fit as a fiddle in his oval office. Perhaps that single pint of black stuff poured in Moneygall has kept him well oiled. Interesting to note that President Obama opted to have the PSA (prostate) blood test as part of his medical. There is growing controversy at home and abroad about the use of this test to diagnose prostate cancer in men who have no worrying symptoms. An influential group of American family doctors, known as the U.S. preventive services task force, recently caused a storm when they downgraded the status of the test from one which had insufficient evidence to support its routine use, to one where there is real evidence that it is of no benefit, in the absence of symptoms. Though the President's medical does not allude to it, it is of course possible that Obama may have urinary tract symptoms, perhaps getting up during the night to urinate, slow flow or more frequent voiding of the bladder. His doctor would also be aware that the incidence of prostate cancer is higher in American men of African heritage.

FINAL JAB
January 2006

The United States gave the world a lesson last week in the modern management of diabetes. Clarence Ray Allen, a 76 year old native American who is legally blind, severely diabetic and survived a heart attack five months ago, was helped into a chair by four orderlies and given an injection that he never had before. Fifty witnesses, including members of his family crowded around his chamber. Just before the needle was produced he reportedly mouthed the words 'I love you' to them. The injection was so powerful that Clarence Ray Allen would not need another one. It was given in the death chamber of California's San Quentin prison on the instructions of the state's Austrian-born governor. Doubtless the twenty-something year old crimes of Clarence Ray Allen were pretty heinous. But crimes conducted on behalf of the masses very rarely atone for the crimes of the few.

SCRAPING THE BISCUIT BARREL
April 1999

There are enough diseases to go around already without making up new ones every week. A north American professor of psychiatry, has coined a new one that he calls night eating syndrome. He claims that one and a half per cent of the population suffers from it. Symptoms include waking anything up to four times during night, creeping downstairs, and raiding the pantry for high carbohydrate foods like biscuits and crisps. The learned professor says patients with night eating syndrome eat five hundred more calories a day than non-sufferers. You'll be bowled over to hear that the principal cause is stressful living. By next week, we could well have another new condition from the professor called stressful living syndrome.

A STUDY OF STALKERS
June 2011

A junior doctor working in our mental health services has conducted an interesting survey to see how many psychiatrists have been stalked by their patients. The results were fascinating, not least because they threw up some doubt in my own mind about the precise definition of stalking. The doctors seemed to suggest that unwanted phone calls were the most common form of stalking. My assumption was that stalking involved somebody physically following you or constantly watching what you do. But the dictionary definition is a broader, namely any harassment or persecution with unwanted attention. According to this study, one in four Irish psychiatrists have been stalked at some stage in their careers. Fifteen of those questioned were being actively stalked at the time of the survey. Two thirds of stalkers were male, one third female. Some doctors had been stalked by both sexes. The majority of events took place at work, but one quarter involved patients stalking psychiatrists at their family homes. Doctors were asked what diagnoses had been attributed to patients that stalked them. Just 3% had anxiety, 6% had a mood disorder like depression or mania, and 11% had a problem with addiction. The bulk of patients who stalked them were labelled as having either a major psychosis or a personality disorder. It's a subject that's attracting more and more interest from psychiatrists. Perhaps because they belong to a sector that knows more than most about the harrowing consequences.

THE DOCTOR'S CASE
May 2007

I returned this week from a fascinating new exhibition at the science museum in London. Entitled 'Penicillin - a story of triumph and tragedy', it tracks the use and abuse of antibiotics over the last century. As well as samples of various mouldy materials and ubiquitous phlegm, part of the display includes the fully equipped Gladstone bag which accompanied Liverpool GP, Dr John Hill

Abram on his house calls in the late nineteenth and early twentieth century. The bag and its contents was my favourite exhibit. His arsenal included a phonendoscope (a type of stethoscope that magnifies sounds), a silver nitrate pen (for cauterising things like nosebleeds), an artery forceps to stop haemorrhages, lots of lancets and tweezers to remove foreign bodies likes peas from ears and noses. There were a variety of biaural and monaural stethoscopes, a battery powered ophthalmoscope for looking deep into the eye, a spirit burner and two sets of re-usable syringes and needles (one for putting things in and one for taking things out). No laboratory request forms I'm afraid, but he had his own supply of microscope slides and some endolytic tubes to conduct urine tests in. Annoying little things which would otherwise tend to gravitate towards the margins of the bag were stored in his branded tobacco box! Amongst his favoured drugs were morphine and strychnine. Dr Hill Abram practiced for forty years in Liverpool's Rodney Street and also held down a position as professor at the city's university medical school.

ONE DOCTOR TOWN
January 2000

With all this talk of collegiality and fancy colleges, you might think that all family doctors have moved out of the dark ages. Well think again. A well respected young GP assistant recently set up his own surgery in what was until his arrival, a one-doctor town. Despite the presence of an existing family doctor for some years, there was a perceived and oft-spoken need in the village and surrounding mountains for a new physician with 'a bit of personality'. On what was supposed to be a social courtesy call to the existing doctor, the young pretender was swiftly ordered off the premises and told that he was trespassing. Reports of this startling reaction went around the town within hours. I am reliably informed that it made to major contribution to the fact that the new doctor's surgery is bustling already with hundreds of mightily relieved patients.

FOOD INTOLERANCE
June 2012

There is mounting annoyance in medical circles about the proliferation of so-called 'food intolerance tests', particularly in pharmacy settings. Family doctors deal with much of the fall-out, mainly in the form of patients claiming to be intolerant of broccoli, or kiwi fruit or whatever. The fact is, and any qualified specialist in allergy or immunology will tell you, that there are no reliable and clinically validated tests for so-called food intolerances. Clear advice was given to doctors and pharmacists by the science and technology committee of the United Kingdom's parliament not to offer these tests to patients. Irish politicians seem keener to promote the tests and have their photos taken having them than examining whether they are of any benefit to the communities they serve. Consumer magazine *Which* did their own research and found highly inconsistent results which 'play on people's phobias' and 'could potentially be risking people's health'. They advised patients who are concerned that they may have a problem to keep a record of symptoms and a food diary, and speak to their family doctor.

ROOM RATE
April 2004

A mature couple arrived at their GP's surgery. The doctor asks, 'What can I do for you?' The man says, 'Will you watch us having intercourse?' The doctor raises both eyebrows, but is so amazed that an elderly couple are asking for his advice on sexual matters that he agrees. When the couple had finished, the doctor said 'There's absolutely nothing wrong with the way you do it'. He thanked them for coming, wished them good luck and charged 40 euro before saying goodbye. The next week the couple returned and asked him to watch again. The GP is a bit puzzled, but agrees. This happens several weeks in a row. Finally, after six weeks of the routine, the doctor said, 'I'm sorry, but I have to ask. Just what are you trying to find out?' The old man says, 'We're not trying to find out anything. She's married and we can't go to her house. I'm married and we can't go to my house. The Holiday Inn charges 98 euro. The Shelbourne charges 139 euro. We do it here for 40 and get 20 back from BUPA!'

GERSHWIN'S TUMOUR
November 1998

The National Concert Hall hosted a very entertaining concert last weekend to celebrate the 100th anniversary of the birth of George Gershwin. You would have to wonder what the renowned composer might have achieved if he had a full innings. His short life ended at the age of 38. Gershwin's final diagnosis, and events leading up to his death are interesting, and doctors could still learn from them. In 1937, having left his native New York to work in Hollywood, he suddenly became dizzy during a rehearsal for *Damsel* and almost fell from the podium. He recovered quickly, and refusing assistance, returned to the stage. During the evening performance, he fumbled some notes but the orchestra covered for him and the performance continued without further incident. The following day Gershwin had a medical with his doctor and reported that he had been suffering from vertigo and one momentary blackout associated with the smell of burning rubber. Perhaps a vital clue was missed for his doctor reported that there was no organic cause for these symptoms. Over time, his brother Ira and some friends would say that they found George to be occasionally irritable and complaining about headaches. Most attributed this to his growing unhappiness with film work. He often talked about leaving Hollywood to return to New York. It was suggested that what he needed was a psychiatrist, rather than a physician. His condition had little effect on his work for some of his greatest tunes such as *A Foggy Day*, *Nice Work If You Can Get It*, and *Things Are Looking Up* were written at this time. In June, as he finished *Love Is Here To Stay*, the vertigo and headaches returned and George spent four days in hospital for a series of tests. Nothing was found, and his final diagnosis was 'most likely hysteria'. But one doctor had noticed that George exhibited photophobia - a strong intolerance of light shining in his eyes. He suggested conduct a spinal tap (lumbar puncture test), which George refused. Just days later, Gershwin suddenly slipped into a coma. He was rushed to the Cedars of Lebanon Hospital where it was decided that surgical intervention was required. He was suffering from a brain tumour in the temporal lobe and died after five hours in surgery. We doctors should always be wary of applying neurosis labels to patients with unusual symptoms. It ain't necessarily so.

YOUNG SCIENTISTS
January 2013

Once we have seen the new Bilbo Baggins film and the Christmas wrapping is recycled, there's just one staple on our new year calendar to look forward to each January. It's a jaunt over to the Royal Dublin Society in Ballsbridge to marvel at the Young Scientist Exhibition, which is going now almost as long as I am. Thousands of clever young folk crowded in a jamboree of science. And not one of them daft enough to go into politics. There are always exhibits to catch a roving medical eye. This year there were two projects dealing with the ill effects of lady's shoes. 77% of an average doctor's working day is spent looking after bad feet that are directly caused by shoes with high heels, narrow toes and all round bad engineering. OK, I made that statistic up, but you catch my drift. Foot fashions cause serious disability down the road for ladies who mistake their feet for shoe-horns. They also make orthopaedic foot surgeons very wealthy specialists.

I particularly liked a project this year that looked at lunchtime in French schools and compared them with Irish ones. Irish schoolchildren horse down their lunch in about ten minutes whilst their French counterparts take the best part of an hour (sometimes two) to consume theirs. The French lunch has more courses and a greater variety of fare. The Irish lunch is all about carbohydrates, convenience, speed and not a lot else. The comparative obesity statistics between the two races of children were indeed stark. I went away wondering if our obsession with keeping the school day short as possible, and mealtimes even shorter, might be affecting the future shape of our nation.

THE LOURDES REPORT
March 2006

I picked up a copy of the *Lourdes Hospital Inquiry* report the other day. This is the one that looked at unnecessary hysterectomies in a Drogheda hospital. Anybody who cares a fig about Irish healthcare has to read this publication in its entirety. It's simply riveting, and had me awake most of the night. I'll limit myself to just a few observations. The eye for important detail of Judge Harding-Clarke and her team is extraordinary. It's fascinating to watch how lawyers and judges clinically dissect medical practice, particularly in lengthy inquiries and tribunals. As a profession they are organized to their best advantage. They will not undertake work without all the resources, all the staff and all the time required to be as forensic and fastidious as they are. This marks them out as quite distinct from medical folk. We can learn from the mistakes of pilots. But we could learn how to manage, how to administrate and how to demand only the best in facilities from lawyers.

A salient point struck me on reading the report into Dr Neary who performed far more hysterectomies after birth than he needed to

And it was a point which I had not discerned before. It dealt with Dr Neary's seven years of training, which took place entirely in the United Kingdom. It included lots of gynaecology and precious little obstetrics. According to the report, gynaecology was very much the higher status skill in the 1960s and early 1970s, and his specialist training took place under the tutelage of gynaecologists rather than obstetricians. The report notes quietly that 'there is a suspicion that his obstetric training was considerably less developed than his gynaecology'. This meant simply that he was very good at doing hysterectomies, but not so good at recognising that they don't need to be done so often after delivering babies. Sadly, for all those patients of Dr Neary who had unnecessary hysterectomies, it was poor quality training and a very blatant educational hiatus that seems to have cost them their wombs.

PEPTIC ULCER
July 2007

A surgeon in Dublin took the trouble to write to me with some excellent malapropisms of his own. One patient of his had taken one anti-inflammatory tablet too many, and perhaps a fizzy drink too, for he ended up with a painful stomach condition that he called *pepsi ulster*. The surgeon also recalls a conversation with a mother who thanked him for examining her son who 'seems to have lost one of his *tentacles*'. He also told me of a rather serious transcription error in a solicitor's letter to a client. The lady was supposed to have been instructed to have an independent medical examination. She wasn't too pleased when the letter gave her the name of a doctor to contact for an *indecent* medical examination!

HIGHER EXECUTIVE POWER
February 2004

The Department of Health doesn't bother itself about employment embargos. They seem to place them on everyone else bar themselves. In the same month that our new pilot primary care centres announce that they are unable to employ enough clinical staff because of ceilings on staff, the minister has filled some new positions in Hawkins House. His department has a brand new change management unit with no fewer than one principal, four assistant principals and three higher executive officers. These will be ably assisted by the new strategy implementation unit with yet another one principal, two assistant principals and four higher executive officers. If they get into trouble there is a new strategy legislation unit with another principal and two assistant principals. Doubtless they will be ably assisted by the pre-existing acute hospitals division with their three principals, eight assistant principals and six higher executive officers, not to mention the three principals, nine assistant principals and six higher executive officers of the primary care division. God forbid, if sick patients ever show up at their door, bandages could be wrapped around them by the principal, four assistant principals, two higher executive officers, chief nursing officer and nine nurse advisors of the new nursing policy division. They might even manage a dressing or an aspirin too.

QUACKWATCH & VITAMIN PUSHERS
March 2004

Dr Stephen Barrett is a retired American psychiatrist who has dedicated his life to the debunking of medical myths. He exposes misleading health claims and quack medicine. *Quackwatch* is the name of his project. One of Dr Barrett's hobby horses is the less than honest promotion of vitamins and supplements and he has written a seminal essay on the subject titled *Twenty-Five Ways to Spot Quacks and Vitamin Pushers*. Most doctors in Ireland never see patients with true signs of vitamin deficiency. That's because most of the nutrients we need are present in our everyday diet. Even if your diet is relatively poor, classic vitamin deficiency diseases such as scurvy, beri-beri and rickets are rare to the point of extinction in the western world. The vitamin industry prefers to suggest that everyone is in mortal danger of deficiency and should therefore take supplements as a form of insurance. Dr Barrett likens their pitch to that of a door-to-door rogue trader who states that your perfectly good furnace is in danger of blowing up unless you replace it with his product.

Another myth regularly peddled is that most diseases are caused by a faulty diet. In fact this is far from true as aetiologies of the vast majority of diseases in medical textbooks don't mention anything about food. Your diet perhaps has minor influence on your risk of developing coronary artery disease and diabetes, but Barrett suggests that everyday maladies like tiredness, aches and pains, poor sleep and lack of energy are far more likely to signify a reaction to stress. In which case you should be at the door of a doctor or lifestyle coach, rather than the supplement counter at the supermarket or chemist. It's important to state that not all vitamin supplements and fortified foodstuffs (so called functional foods) are worthless. It's just that those of us who consume most of them, probably need them least. The converse is also true. It was claimed recently that only 20% of pregnant women in an Irish maternity hospital had been taking folic acid at the time of conception when there is ample evidence that this simple supplement can help prevent catastrophic birth defects such as spina bifida. Whilst there is some data suggesting that probiotic bacteria can limit one form of viral gastroenteritis in infants, many of the claims you will hear about probiotics are not scientifically substantiated. A recent editorial in the *British* Medical *Journal* claimed that many functional foods are plain quackery and suggested that products are being marketed on the basis of no more than vague allusions. Twenty years after the European Commission began deliberating on these issues, misleading health claims have now reached epidemic proportions. If you have any gaps in your knowledge in these areas, I'd strongly recommend a visit to www.quackwatch.org to eliminate any deficiencies.

CLINICAL RODENTS
October 1998

Fawlty Towers isn't the only hospitable institution to get its trousers in a knot about rats in the kitchen. An unfortunate staff member in St Camillus Hospital in Limerick sighted such a rodent last week and a follow up pest control operation discovered three such whiskered rodents, or pedigree Siberian hamsters. The mid western health board was quick to act and ordered the immediate closure of the canteen and kitchen. Bait and traps were laid all around the campus and all foodstuffs that might have been exposed to the visitors were disposed of. There is heightened sensitivity about unwelcome hospital visitors since last year, when it was reported that rats in the Ghaziabad District Hospital in India were eating the flesh from bodies on the mortuary. What interested doctors most was that the Indian rats exhibited a particular fondness for snacks of ear lobes, nose tips, eyelids and male genitalia. Gives a whole new sense to the medical skin condition known as a rodent ulcer. Administrators the world over are less interested in researching the eating habits of hospital rats, and have a zero-tolerance no-nonsense eradication policy when it comes to these whiskered clinicians.

SEVEN YEAR ITCH
July 2007

I had an interesting chat the other day with somebody closer than myself to the business end of nursing homes. There are quite a number of very large green-field facilities being built around the country on the back of seven year tax incentives from government. And a pertinent question arises, what happens in seven years time when the tax relief is gone? Might some developers convert their spanking new tax-designated buildings into luxury apartments for younger residents instead? Might other developers suddenly raise their prices for residents? Worth bearing in mind if older patients are looking for a longer term placement. The history of retirement villages in Ireland is littered with shame. I'd hate to think there could be worse to come.

JUICY PROMISES
May 2012

A fondness for juice has grabbed me in recent months. The electric juicing machine has been dusted down and the local greengrocer is trying valiantly to keep up with demand for industrial-sized lemons, ruby grapefruits and over-large oranges. I'm not claiming any health benefits, but I do find the whole process of slicing, squeezing, filtering and pouring quite therapeutic in itself. On a recent trip to Canary Wharf, a little piece of New York in London, I sampled the wares of a fancy juice bar and laughed heartily at the claims they were making for their produce. One of them was wheatgrass juice and this is what they say it does:

It energises you, reduces fatigue, suppresses appetite, speeds metabolism, improves digestion, enriches blood, removes blood disorders, lowers blood pressure, cleanses and purifies the liver, is an antibacterial, prevents tooth decay, improves the complexion, treats acne, is good for other skin problems, stops hair going gray, reduces dandruff, calms the nervous system, boosts the immune system, washes drug deposits from the body, neutralises toxins and prevents ageing.

So I opted for the plain and orange juice instead. Guff-free, honest and absolutely delicious.

CRUISING
November 2007

The HSE has recently announced that doting couples may now get married in venues other than registry offices. Not any old venue mind you. HSE wedding inspectors must visit, validate and approve every premises in advance. Some years ago I asked why 55 members of all the Dublin health boards were offered a free bus trip (refreshments included) to Dublin Port to watch an inspection of a massive cruise liner that had docked along the Liffey. I was told the appraisal of visiting ships was a crucial function of health authorities, just one of a litany of daft functions that politicians passed onto the HSE. If Captain Drumm and his thousands of first mates in the HSE retain any hope of getting health services into ship-shape, it's high time they got their own boat in order and threw all this unnecessary historical baggage overboard. Is it too much to ask for a health service that focuses on health?

MY NEW DENTISTS
January 2012

My old dentist took well-earned retirement last year after decades of trojan archaeological work in my cavern. It took many dentists to replace him and of late, I have become quite expert in the nomenclature of their specialities. I have met a succession of endodontists, prosthodontists and periodontists. The first thing you will note, is that high end specialist tooth pullers substitute the 'e' in dentist in favour of the 'o' in dontist. The endodontists are the root canal experts. Their tools are drills, sprays, x-rays and burrowing instruments. Work is painstaking, some would think monotonous, where hygiene is all. A good endodontist is worth their weight in ivory. The next category is the prosthodontist. These are the experts in dental materials. The word is very similar to the medical 'prosthesis' so these are the crown, plate and denture specialists who fit missing teeth, repair dodgy ones and act as architects, quantity surveyors and on-site foremen for those who are planning new sets of gnashers. The periodontists are the gum disease specialists and recently their field has been revolutionised by the arrival of dental implants. To help my new dentists relax, I won't be writing any more about my treatment. Suffice to say I'm having it at home. Some of you may be happy with lower prices abroad. But I have heard from staff in hospitals here about the other side of the dental care abroad equation. Believe me. It's not wine and roses, or perfect smiles for everyone.

CIRCUMCISION WARS
June 2004

Controversy is raging in the medical press over the tender issue of male circumcision. This follows in the wake of the death of a 29 day old infant in Waterford last summer, after a botched home circumcision. In the aftermath of the tragedy, some senior medics gave vent to the view that routine removal of the infant foreskin was both barbaric and potentially dangerous. Whether performed in a modern hospital setting or on the kitchen table was immaterial to them. The liberal wing of the profession was incensed. They declared that this age old practice, usually of a religious nature, should be freely and easily available on demand at children's hospitals all over the country.

Male circumcision is nothing new. The religious rite holds the honour of being the only surgical operation mentioned in the old testament. Its origins were once believed to coincide with the reign of the pharaohs, some two millenniums BC.

Medical texts that were unearthed at the Valley of the Kings by a 19th century American explorer prove that circumcision was carried out in ancient Egypt. Other sources declare that the procedure began in west Africa and that male circumcision has a 5,000 year history. In Ireland, circumcision was long associated in the public mind with the Jewish faith, but in the 1950s and 1960s, it became quite a fashionable operation in maternity hospitals for Christian parents to have performed on their newborn male children. It was performed on request, for an extras fee, as a part of the obstetric service. Demand fell dramatically by the 1980s, as the birth rate fell too, and modern mores looked more favourably on the male foreskin. Now, the rate of Irish circumcision has taken off again with the rising ethnicity that has accompanied our economic boom.

Recently, Dr Terry Russell of Queensland in Australia told Irish doctors that the city of Brisbane now has a circumcision rate of almost 50%. Citing well-informed parents for the boom in this work, Dr Russell claims to have carried out more circumcisions than any other doctor in Australia. Amongst his list of credits for routine circumcision is a lower risk of urinary infection, HIV acquisition and penile cancer. Not to mention a lower rate of cervical cancer in later partners of circumcised males. Two years ago, an anti-circumcision lobby group reported him to the medical board of Queensland, citing an excessive rate of non-therapeutic circumcision. However, each and every one of the eleven complaints was thrown out. Dr Russell was hailed a hero by his supporters for 'standing up against crackpot anti-circumcision activists' and 'winning in the face of a vocal minority of extremists'. Such language doesn't do a lot to win over neutrals. The founder of Clane Hospital and pioneer of male medicine in Ireland Dr Andrew Rynne, said recently that the high priests of both sides in this debate have no real interest in listening to each other. That's very much the sad truth.

PROFESSOR WARD
February 2011

There is a wonderful interview with retired children's heart specialist Professor Conor Ward in this month's edition of the medical magazine *Scope*. He left Irish shores for London twenty years ago, after a lifetime's commitment to his young patients at Crumlin Hospital. The article records that the professor is one of very few Irish doctors to have a medical condition named after him, namely the Ward-Romano syndrome. Parents of children with Down Syndrome will have particularly fond memories of his diagnostic skill and devotion to their health. In the 1960s Professor Ward was very involved in Catholic causes. But in this look back over his career, he had some very interesting things to say about the interference of bishops in medical and hospital affairs. He had a major run-in with Archbishop John Charles McQuaid when he protested to the archbishop about the treatment of a consultant colleague. He records that McQuaid, unaccustomed to any confrontation, delivered a withering response before turning on his heels and storming out of the room. On another occasion, Professor Ward sought permission to send a mother to Britain for an ante-natal test called amniocentesis, should she ever become pregnant again. There was good reason, for her first child had been born with a serious condition called gargoylism. Such tests were then banned here on religious grounds. When Archbishop Dermot Ryan got wind of this, Conor Ward's professorship at University College Dublin came under threat. Only the intervention from the president of the College forced Ryan to back off. Professor Ward says he remains a committed Catholic, but feels that religion should be a private matter. He goes on to quote a famous phrase from Cardinal Newman 'Conscience should prevail'.

WESTERN ISLE
January 2006

A story making medical headlines this week is the tale of the Scottish doctor who swapped a healthy list of 1,500 patients in the town of Livingstone for a slightly more manageable population of 175 souls on the remote western isle of Jura. Dr Murray Grigor stepped up to the bar and has taken on the onerous task of taking care of an island that's more renowned for its deer, salmon and home-made whisky than its human population. You may recall that Jura's most famous resident was George Orwell, who lived there briefly in the 1940s whilst writing *1984*. With a trifling salary of £100,000 and a free bungalow next to the school with just sixteen pupils, Dr Grigor says he is going to take up the bagpipes. That should keep his waiting room quiet.

NAME CHANGERS
January 1998

When is a chemist not a chemist? When he's a pharmacist of course. I stifled a laugh at the recent letter from a druggist to a medical newspaper asking that his profession henceforth be known as pharmacists rather than chemists. It's all a bit academic really. Like a doctor asking patients to call him a physician, a butcher asking customers only to refer to him as a victualler or a secretary/manager in a hospital who dreams of being called chief executive. For some strange reason pharmacies have not alerted the Golden Pages who continue to list them under 'C' and not 'P'. I scanned Webster's dictionary to ascertain the origin of the new-fangled pharmacist title and discovered that *pharmakos* is a Greek word for a person condemned to death as a means of purification and atonement for the rest of us. I think I prefer my chemist.

DELIVER US FROM DADS
January 2006

Twenty years ago, there was a great fashion in obstetric research to play up the role that fathers could play in the delivery of children. The labour ward Dad was born out of this trend and the practice of men attending their baby's births entered Western culture. It's now so embedded in maternity practice that he who shows the slightest reluctance to attend is regarded with much opprobrium. Today's men have little choice in the matter. In the past year I have of read three studies, and there may well be more, which suggest that the most advantageous clinical position for the male partner during childbirth may well be flexing his elbow at the local alehouse. The latest paper is published in *Psychosomatic Medicine* and it suggests that anxious fathers who attend caesarean sections, pass on their fears to their partners, increasing their post-operative pain, hindering recovery and perhaps even influencing breastfeeding and bonding with the new baby in a negative way. The researchers conclude that would-be Dads should be prepared for elective caesareans during antenatal classes. Missing the point that the obvious solution is to alter the timing of deliveries to fit in with six nations rugby or live premiership football.

APTLY-NAMED
May 1998

More aptly named specialists are on hand this week. How about the two dentists called Dr Payne and Dr Blood. Patients found it hard to choose between them. And I am reliably informed that there is an undertaker in rural Ireland whose initialled name reads Mr C.O. Finn. Research in *New Scientist* magazine has come up with some new gems of nominative determinism such as Mr Lust who is a sex counsellor in Queensland, Australia. Dr Angst is a well known Swiss psychiatrist and a renowned stationery firm based in Northern Ireland is called Reid and Wright. Other favourites are the principal authors of a recent NHS paper on *The Need for Surgeons in Rural Areas*. They were Mr Black and Mr Decker.

FLYING HIGH
April 1999

All doctors dread airline flights for that all too regular cabin crew announcement 'Is there a doctor on board?' Not quite as frightening for passengers as 'Is there an engineer on board?' But many doctors are fed up with being asked to make life and death clinical decisions 30,000 feet up with very limited resources. Last month somebody pressed a wrong button on a British Airways flight into Heathrow. A pre-recorded emergency announcement was inadvertently played stating that the plane was about to crash into the sea. Almost 400 passengers suffered the most stressful couple of minutes of their lives and were told to adopt the brace position and get their life jackets on for an unexpected trip to heaven. Then the chief steward checked with the captain who was as surprised as the passengers, and announced a false alarm. So what did they do next? They asked if any doctors on board might identify themselves so that they could administer assistance to distressed passengers!

DENTAL WAITING ROOMS
January 2012

The waiting rooms of dentists are pleasant bolt-holes in which to while away half an hour. They have a lot less traffic than doctors' surgeries and the chances of picking up nasty bugs or of paediatric patients vomiting on your shoes are very much reduced. The magazines are better too. I was at the endodontist this month and he had a January 2012 edition of *GQ* magazine, *Irish Tatler Man* from autumn 2011 and more *Hello* magazines with skinny princess Middleton than you could wave a bone at. These high standards are not universal. One dental practice in Dublin, popular with the horse and hound set, has (and I have photographic evidence) the August 1978 edition of *Country Life* magazine on display. If anyone spots anything older than this, please do get in touch with me and the *Guinness Book of Records*.

CRANKY OLD JUAN
June 2011

Not everyone in the public eye is as keen to talk about personal health difficulties as chat show guests on RTE. Spain's ageing monarch, King Juan Carlos, has long been a bit sensitive about his fading good looks and declining health. This reluctance to share his clinical case notes with subjects has sparked many column inches in the Iberian press about his state of wellbeing. When asked recently by a journalist how he was, the King replied 'Terrible, terrible. Can't you see it? What you want to do is kill me and put me in a coffin every day in the press!'

You don't need a psychiatric training to tell that he's a bit sensitive. The king had a nodule removed from his lung last year. It was reported as benign. Then earlier this month he was back under the knife for a knee replacement in Barcelona. His doctors reported that after surgery their royal patient would undergo a course of intensive physiotherapy which was 'equivalent to that which would be given to a professional sports person.' That should throw a corpse-sniffing Spanish media off the scent for a week or two.

BIGGEST HOUSE IN TOWN.
June 1999

The days of doctors living in the biggest houses in the town are on the wane. Only the dermatologists now have enough patients to afford them. I see the Dublin home of the late Dr John Shanley, founder of the Irish Red Cross, is going under the Lisney hammer next month. The property is on the north side of Merrion Square at number 17. Dr Shanley, who passed away recently, qualified from University College Dublin in 1919 and lived well past his hundredth birthday. He practised mainly as a paediatric surgeon and according to medical directories of his day, wrote papers on congenital hypertrophic pyloric stenosis (still a relatively common stomach tightening condition amongst first born males) and thoracic empyema (a collection of pus in the chest) in children, now thankfully quite rare. The *Acute Abdomen in Childhood* was perhaps his best known publication. Dr Shanley served as deputy coroner for Dublin at one time and was also president of the Irish Medical Association. Of historical interest is the fact that he was one of the doctors in attendance at the autopsy on Michael

Collins. The 6,000 square foot house is as fine a Georgian building as you'll find in Dublin, and the auctioneers describe it as having a gracious, if somewhat faded interior. Viewing is by appointment. Bring about £2 million in cash with you.

A LADY'S BRAIN
August 2007

Late one night at St Attracta's Hospital, the Murphy relatives gathered in a waiting room, not far from where Granddad lay gravely ill. An exhausted and sombre looking doctor came in.

'I am the bearer of bad news,' he announced. Their faces furrowed. 'The only hope left for your loved one at this time is a brain transplant. It's an experimental procedure, very risky but it is the only hope. Insurance will cover the operation, but you will have to pay for the brain yourselves'. The family members sat around quietly and absorbed the news. After a while Granny Murphy asked, 'Well, how much does a brain cost?' 'Its €5,000 for a male brain, and €100 for a female brain' replied the doctor. The men in the room smiled to themselves. 'Why does the male brain cost so much more?' asked Granny. 'Well' said the doctor, 'the price of female brains has been marked down. Because they have actually been used'

MEET THE HAMILTONS
December 2001

Last week's BBC documentary on disgraced former Tory MP Neil Hamilton and his wife Christine was a television gem. The ninety minutes of captivating footage taught more lessons in life than a membership exam for the college of psychiatrists. It's not often that the trials and tribulations of the middle classes get spewed out for visual consumption by the great unwashed. But this is precisely what took place in one balmy month of August this year when the hapless couple were paid a pittance to allow the world intrude on their space. What followed was compelling.

Most alarming from a medical viewpoint was the sheer volume of white wine consumed, a pastime that ran through their tedious daily lives like a river. The other frequent visitor to the Hamilton's domestic life was stress, with afternoon dips, a flippant attitude to tranquilliser medication, that well known tendency for alcohol to disinhibit and a chronic inability to distinguish good friends from rotten cads. As with many wayward daughters, Christine's biggest crime perhaps is that she didn't listen closely enough to her mother. It struck me as the programme ended that far too much medical training deals with the woes, diseases and foibles of the working classes. This documentary caught a section of a more pretentious upper echelon of society off-guard. Any psychiatrist worth his salt will show it to future generations of students.

FLOGGING PROBIOTICS
October 2012

I had close-hand experience the other day of an attempt by a pharmacist to flog probiotics to the parent of a child who presented with a prescription for antibiotics. This sort of activity makes me very angry, as it has more to do with the healthy profits of a pharmacy chain than the health of any child. The parent resisted this offer of an increase in the bill and was then told that their child could be 'quite run down'. Considering the pharmacist hadn't set eyes on the child, and didn't even enquire as to what was wrong with them or why antibiotics were prescribed in the first place, this surprised me. It suggests that the store's policy is simply to sell as much product as possible. Ireland invested a lot of state money during the so-called boom years into this probiotic promise. To date, they have simply not lived up to the hype. Probiotics may have a rather limited role in minutely reducing the duration of some gastrointestinal infections. But there is absolutely no clinical evidence that every prescription for antibiotics needs an equal and opposite dose of probiotics. If there was such evidence, your doctor would be first in line to pop it on your prescription. The Pharmaceutical Society of Ireland needs to issue some guidance on this matter for their registered members.

BOTTOM DOLLAR
June 2000

I'm not sure how much plastic surgeons pay to insurance companies to cover litigation risk, but those who practice a new procedure known as buttock implants, may be getting a premium rise. Earlier this month, an American jury awarded a former exotic dancer $30,000 for the anguish she suffered when a doctor used silicone breast implants to enlarge her bum cheeks. The 43 year old lady expressed disappointment with the award, claiming that the surgeon ruined her body. The lady's attorney argued that her client would never have undergone the procedure if she had known that breast implants were going to be used. 'I looked like I had two breasts on my butt', testified the dancer. On the other hand, a lawyer for the surgeon said that the lady was a 'plastic surgery junkie' who had undergone at least six surgical procedures in pursuit of perfection and was rarely happy with the results. The lawyer went on to say that 'as malpractice verdicts go, the $30,000 award has almost nothing but nuisance value'. Nice work if you can get it. For any surgeons considering the addition of this procedure to their theatrical repertoire, the fee currently being charged stateside is just over $3,000 per buttock, or $6,000 for full bottom dollar.

A RELATIVE EMERGENCY
April 2004

A retired GP sent me some true stories from his bygone practice days. Once the local curate was visiting his house and was sitting beside the phone when it rang. Without thinking, he lifted the receiver. An agitated young man was at the other end. 'Will you send down the doctor to me Ma, IMMEDIATELY?' he demanded. 'Is she very sick?' 'She's shocking bad. Get the doctor down, IMMEDIATELY'. said the youth. The priest began to get worried. 'Will she be needing the Last Rites?' he asked. 'Ah no'. came the reply. 'Sure she only has a toothache!' The same doctor tells me that his own father was a medic with notoriously bad handwriting. So bad, it was joked that he had trained in Egyptian hieroglyphics. Once when the senior doctor was away on holiday, the son received a completely illegible postcard from his dad. Clever lad that he was, he decided to bring it down to the local pharmacist, the only man in Dublin who could decipher the code. The chemist took the card away for study and appeared from the dispensary five minutes later, holding a bottle of green medicine. It says 'take one spoonful three times a day' he said.

TOURETTE DE FRANCE
January 2007

Channel Four ran a documentary the other evening about a group of foul-mouthed hyperkinetic Scottish teenagers who travelled from home to the Salpêtrière hospital in Paris on an old red double-decker bus. The premise of the programme, with its catchy title *Tourette de France*, was to bring this motley gang of teenagers with their multiplicity of tics to the place where their condition, Tourette syndrome, derived its name. I was very much looking forward to a lesson in the history of French neurology, and a tour of some renowned scientific institutions. Alas, the programme featured little more than swearing at passers-by, complete with unnecessary subtitles. Precious little time was allotted to what was supposed to be the whole learning purpose of the trip. I think they did mention that George Gilles de la Tourette was once shot by a lady patient of his, and that he himself went quite mad towards the end of his life. In fact he died in Switzerland in his late forties from general paralysis of the insane, coded medical speak for the final stages of syphilis. The only saving grace of the programme was the ability to observe such rapid cycling between charm and vulgarity on the part of the Tourette patients. Their shared humanity carried the day.

INTIMATE DETAILS
October 1998

One of the joys of editing the annual *Irish Medical Directory* is the insight one gains into the array of mindsets in all ranks of our profession. I have recently been writing to family doctors asking them to update their practice, personal and clinical details for the next edition. Sifting through the large postbag of entries every morning allows me make some interesting observations. Firstly there is a hardcore of about 10% of GPs who do not appear to respond to any mail. Perhaps this is understandable given the huge daily volume of white envelopes that pour into surgeries up and down the country. Another observation is that a growing number of family doctors, particularly lady practitioners, are happy to fill in every detail except their year of graduation. Some months ago I received a letter from a female doctor suggesting that it was unfair of me to request such 'intimate details' from ladies! There's usually a tale behind every hypersensitivity and this case proves the point. It transpired that she had not minded providing the information for an earlier edition but what had irked her was an indiscreet comment from a visiting medical representative. He told her rather tactlessly that he didn't realise she was so much older than her practice partner.

TROJAN WORK
September 1997

The condom is one of the oldest forms of barrier contraception. Its use has been traced back to ancient Egyptian tribesmen who used sheaths to protect themselves against injury and insect bites more than a thousand years BC. The first published description of prophylactic condom use was recorded in the 16th century by the Italian anatomist Gabrielle Fallopius. He invented a condom made of linen and cut to the peculiar shape of the male anatomy. He conducted trials amongst 1,100 men, none of whom became infected with syphilis. I read today of a new development in the Irish condom market. The Durex Avanti is made from a unique polyurethane material which is twice as strong as latex. This allows for thinner, and more sensitive film to be produced, at twice the price. The Durex range apparently controls three quarters of the home market, whilst in the United States the dominant brand is named Trojan. Peculiar name that for a condom brand. Wasn't there an unusual emission from the Trojan horse?

A BONE TO PICK
January 2011

A Chinese buffet restaurant in Dublin is offering children's meals at half the adult price. Very admirable in the midst of a recession, but their stipulated requirement that all children availing of the offer have be to less than 140 centimetres tall (four feet five inches) is a bit rich. They even have a measurement chart just inside the door. After a recent visit, I dug out my growth charts that were secreted in an old book on paediatric medicine. They reveal that at ten years old, half of all Irish children would not qualify for this special half price meal. Using growth charts for Chinese children, the cut off age rises by about two years to twelve for boys and eleven and a half for girls. Methinks they should raise the bar a bit for our longer-boned Irish children.

A ROYAL GYNAECOLOGIST
November 2000

An eminent gynaecologist spoke out last week about the naming of some of the most venerated and hallowed institutions of the medical landscape. He called on the Royal College of Physicians, the Royal College of Surgeons and the Royal Academy of Medicine to review the titles of their organisations, suggesting that they consider removing the word Royal from their names. He cited the Irish College of General Practitioners as a fine example of what other medical institutions might follow. Heavens forbid that the gynaecologist's urgings would be taken seriously. Give an inch, and next thing they'll be forcing academic luminaries to divest themselves of ermine robes, lumbering maces, funny handshakes, odd sock nights and secret societies. And worst of all, foreign billionaires mightn't be so keen any more to order fifty top notch clinicians around to afternoon tea for honorary conferrals, sovereign proclamations or cucumber sandwiches. Let these anti-royalists go and eat some cake.

ANAESTHETIC WOES
June 2006

The wife of an anaesthetist has been in touch with a lovely tale of family medicine. Her youngest son was about six when he was sent home from school, smothered with a respiratory tract infection. She washed him, helped him into his pyjamas and tucked him into bed with a hot water bottle, extra pillows and a hot lemon drink. 'Now,' said the patient, 'get the doctor'. 'Daddy will be home later' replied the doting Mum. 'Ah, no. I want a real doctor was the reply!' Daddy remains unimpressed by the re-telling of this true story.

BULBOUS LIES
May 1998

I have it on good authority that the following multiple choice question will appear in this year's examinations for would-be doctors. How many medical practitioners does it take to change a light bulb?

a) Depends whether it has private health insurance or not.
b) Five - one family doctor and four hospital specialists.
   GP recommends a bulb specialist, who then finds a bulb installation specialist. He does the job, and arranges for two colleagues to do a colonoscopy and look at some skin moles whilst the bulb is in hospital.
c) One. He signs the death certificate and phones the mortuary.
d) None. The bulb should be told by a triage nurse to take two aspirin and come round to surgery in the morning.
e) All of the above.

BAD BREATH
September 2006

Today's *British Medical Journal* carries a wonderful clinical review of a condition I once knew as halitosis. News to be, but apparently it has been rechristened as oral malodour syndrome. Experts say it affects between 8% and 50% of people in the developed world, depending I suppose on which expert has to do the smelling. I fancy the true figure is closer to 8% and this rises mysteriously whenever products such as tongue brushes and inter-dental scrubbing rods need to be marketed to a wider consumer base. There may be fine distinction between oral malodour syndrome and pure halitosis. Lots of people have mild transient oral malodour when they wake up. It's the smaller number that carry it with them all day who are regarded as the thoroughbred halitotics. Causes of halitosis are generally grouped into three categories. Diseases of the mouth, diseases of the airway and volatile foodstuffs such as garlic, cheese and onion crisps and spice-burgers. OMS (oral malodour syndrome) is not to be confused with OMG (which means Oh My God) or another stinky condition known as trimethylaminuria. This is a rare fish odour syndrome that affects people who either have a defective flavin mono-oxygenase enzyme activity, or live near the harbour at Howth.

The journal's review of oral malodour syndrome concludes with a few lines about patients with halitophobia, an unnatural fear of other people's bad breath. Apparently they all need to be referred to clinical psychologists for investigation and treatment. The authors say that very few halitophobics are willing to attend. Perhaps therapists aren't brushing their tongues as often as they should.

PRESENTS FROM PATIENTS
August 2012

Writing in a medical journal a while back, a Dr Andereck from San Francisco raised interesting questions about the age-old practice of physicians receiving gifts from their patients. He queried whether this custom is ethical in a modern healthcare setting. In his treatise, he cited three possible motives for the giving of gifts to doctors: influence, pure beneficence and appreciation. He suggests that it is ethical to accept unsolicited gifts, but warned doctors against strings being attached, or ever exhibiting favouritism towards donors. He suggested that 'doctors should accept the gift with a smile, send a thank-you note, and move on'. A contrary view emerged on Joe Duffy's *Liveline* radio programme some months ago. Relatives of some patients, and community nurses, were quite distressed to hear that family doctors were accepting cash gifts from older people who had medical cards for free GP care. This week, I had a letter from a lady who was laid up in a small hospital last year. She noticed that another patient on her ward, a lady in her nineties, was handing over fifty euro every week to one particular ward attendant. My correspondent thought it was most unfair but was unsure what she could have done. It's an awkward issue to advise on, because in most cases there are no laws being broken. Guidelines are few and far between. Tokens of appreciation are welcome at all levels of the health service, but they should remain that, tokens. If you do want to give your doctor a wad of cash, a car or leave him your house in a will, there are more deserving cases. Why not ask him to nominate a deserving charity instead? Besides himself.

OLD BIRDS
February 2004

A pharmaceutical visitor to surgery told me the following story about a now deceased doctor who tended his flock on the foothills of north Wexford. Some years ago, he was on a routine visit to two elderly sisters, very hard workers on a small family farm. As was common in the post-war years the doctor had to take his place in the queue alongside the grocer, grain merchant, and other suppliers, for settlement of outstanding bills. The chances of payment were greatly enhanced following the grain or potato harvests, a sale of wool, or the local fair. This doctor was usually relaxed about collecting debts, despite some formidable patients who were always up for a bit of bargaining when it came to settling with him. Well the sisters asked how much they owed him and when he gave them the amount they exclaimed 'We had Mr. Sinnott, the vet here the other day and he didn't charge half that sum. A master of these situations, he retorted, 'Well the next time either of you two old birds get sick, call Sinnott!'

DEEP POCKETS
January 2001

General practitioners the length and breadth of the country might like a cabinet reshuffle. The minister for justice has just awarded solicitors £70 per consultation with prisoners who are in custody, and his fee rises to £100 for each visit outside office hours. These earnest gents with their important briefs have the minister, the criminal legal aid review committee and their own Law Society to thank for negotiating these not unreasonable fees. The problem for general practitioners is that if prisoners are released from confinement into the community, the doctor is paid a one off sum of £29 for their complete care for an entire year. With generous pockets like these for family solicitors, the justice minister might be an even more popular man in the health brief.

LIKE FATHER, LIKE SON
March 2004

A man turned up at his doctor's surgery in Dublin the other day. He asked to be referred to an ear, nose and throat specialist miles away down the country. Having ascertained the precise nature of the problem that needed the specialist opinion, the doctor asked him why he wanted a referral to a hospital so far away. The patient explained that his father had received a letter from the relevant ear, nose and throat department advising that his own appointment had come up trumps. But the poor father had died waiting, four years before. Quick as a flash the son was on the phone to the hospital to ask if he could have the appointment instead of his father. And he was accepted. A real success story for the Irish health service.

CASUAL LOCATIONS FOR ALCOHOL
February 2008

The Royal College of Physicians has been on to the minister for justice requesting a 'radical overhaul' of the sale of alcohol in Ireland. The press release states that 'the country's largest postgraduate medical training body' has called on the minister to implement measures aimed at reducing the availability of 'the substance'. Amongst the many lines of attack suggested by the public health physicians are a reduction in the number of bar extensions, a publicly accessible register of all licence-holders and a ban on alcohol at 'casual locations'. All rather interesting, because the last time I had more than my fill of 'the substance' was at a medical bash in a very casual location. The Royal College of Physicians on Kildare Street. Indeed a flowing bowl held sway in their swanky new function rooms. I do hope this new puritan wing of the college doesn't shoot itself in the liver.

HOWLERS
October 2001

One of my medical correspondents sent me the following signage bloopers from an American journal. First up was the Hong Kong dentist who advertised that his clinic extracted all teeth *using the latest Methodists*. The brass plate of a doctor in Rome stated that he was a *Specialist in Women and other diseases*. A maternity ward in Pumwani, Kenya hung up a notice saying *No Children Allowed*. On the same tack, a sign in a Norwegian cocktail lounge says *Ladies, do not have Children in the Bar*. An unfortunate tourist agency in Prague urges visitors to take one of their horse-drawn city tours with its reassuring slogan *We guarantee no miscarriages*. Finally, a hotel in Tokyo displays a prominent sign in each chamber saying *Guests are requested not to smoke or do other disgusting behaviours in bed*. You have been warned.

UNHOLY SYPHILIS
August 2000

Recent excavations at the town of Hull in the north of England suggest that old ideas about the origins syphilis may well be bunkum. Scientific brethren have long argued that Christopher Columbus and his ilk brought the sexually transmitted disease back from the Americas. Those residing on the other side of the Atlantic disagree, suggesting that European explorers contaminated pure American natives. Skeletons dating from 1300 to 1450 have been exhumed at Hull and according to an archaeological team from the University of Bradford, they reveal clear signs of syphilis. What's even more interesting is that they were conducting their exhumations at a medieval friary. Plus ça change.

CUTTING REMARKS ABOUT SURGEONS
February 2012

Some time ago, I reviewed the book *Irish Surgeons and Surgery in the 20th Century* by Professor Barry O'Donnell. It's a collection of extraordinary human stories, mainly about men, whose dominion was the operating theatre of Irish hospitals. I was perusing it again the other evening and came across a hidden appendix entitled 'Better Left Unsaid'. These were the comments made about surgeons (often by colleagues or junior staff) which on legal advice were left orphaned at the back of the book. Wisely, they remain anonymous in both source and subject.

Many are sharp, cutting and acutely observed. I have included a few examples here:

A lifetime achievement award for the courting of controversy
On the Richter scale of charismatic leadership, the needle barely moved.
A known skinflint and tightwad.
Liver made of brass.
Never put a foot right.

and my own favourite -

His retirement was early, rather than premature.

POWER AND AUTHORITY
January 2008

Soon you won't be able to call a nurse a nurse. Their trade unions remind us regularly that they are 'degree-level professionals' and in the current edition of *World of Irish Nursing*, there is much talk of things called "prescribing power' and 'prescriptive authority'. It features photographs displaying all manner of gowns and graduation hats being tossed up in the air for merriment. Nursing leaders are welcoming the fact that one hundred nurses have completed a six month course in how to prescribe. The Irish nurses organisation went on to 'salute these excellent clinicians'. It's not in my nature to rain on any parade. I am domestically welded to an authoritarian clinician of my very own. But it strikes me, that this is perhaps as much about the acquisition of a new language of power for nurses, more than anything else.

NEW STAMPS
August 1998

The Royal Mail has launched a special set of stamps to commemorate the 50th anniversary of the United Kingdom's National Health Service. The leitmotif is that the NHS touches everyone's life and to this end they have commissioned a themed set of photographs of hands that describe everyday scenes in the delivery of health. Cradling hands adorn the 43 pence stamp, signifying that the NHS delivers two thousand babies every day. Another stamp has fingers on pulse, representing 130,000 hospital outpatients seen every day. Our own health service is expected to follow suit shortly. The 30 pence stamp will feature a skeleton on the telephone with the slogan 'All he wanted was an ENT appointment'. A parking meter will adorn the new £1 stamp to signify the hourly charge for waiting around or visiting in hospitals. And a marathon runner will adorn the new £5 stamp which will carry the public health message: 'Keep fit. Walk between any two departments in hospital'.

WICKED SPELLS
February 2007

The name X-ray doesn't cut it anymore. If you want polaroids taken of your innards you have to seek out a department of diagnostic imaging. But not everyone is familiar with the term yet. The administrator of one Dublin medical school wrote to me the other day to tell me they had just appointed a new professor of *diagnostic imagining*. Medical spellings haven't been too hot over at the Irish Times either. A report on an inquest in today's newspaper makes mention of complications in *post-operatic* patients. I think they meant to say post-operative. And the fat lady hasn't sung yet. The same edition reports that there is not yet a single *Cat Lab* in any hospital in the south east. Before animal rights folk get their claws out, what the paper of record actually meant to say to readers was a Cath. Lab., short for cardiac catherisation laboratory. A place where tubes, dyes and stents are inserted into coronary arteries. Not a pussycat in sight.

ROME IN A DAY
March 2002

I am sipping my coffee today on the Campo di Fiori. It's rather noisy here. All day long, police vans have been soaring up and down the busy streets of the most deafening city in the world. Their sirens screech. Guns are always at the ready. Tanned-looking umbrella salesmen and purveyors of poorly copied Louis Vuitton handbags dive for cover in the Piazza Navona. We are in the midst of Italy's latest crackdown on illegal migrants. In what has been termed a 'calibrated response' to rising immigration, the Italian cabinet has given sharp teeth to a new bill before parliament. A new conservative government took the reins eight months ago with the intention of getting tough with street people. Vendors in Rome could do with their own Tony Gregory. There are constant raids on the city's piazzas. Confiscation of goods, checking of papers and rapid expulsion orders. It's a question of geography. The plentiful seas around this peninsular nation make it a haven for boat people. Polls show that Italians link illegal visitors with theft and many other crimes. Yet statistics reveal that the country has actually one of the smallest settled immigrant communities in Europe.

The Pope couldn't make the Wednesday audience I had promised him at St Peter's. His health is a matter of increasing ecclesiastical concern. He has shown remarkable resilience in the face of a serious assassination attempt, progressive Parkinson's disease and perhaps more seriously, carcinoma of the large bowel. Yet his current disappearance from weekly audiences is being put down by his aides to osteoarthritis in the right knee. This precludes him from standing for any length of time. There is a well known medical condition called parson's knee, but pontiff's knee is a new one on me. Rumours are rife in the eternal city that the health of John Paul II is in acute decline. I managed to get through the throngs at the Vatican museum to see the wonderful Sistine chapel. The cardinals could be gathering there soon.

There is nothing like a good health scare to set the Italian media into over-drive. I was hardly there a few hours when word came through that the minister for health had ordered the suspension of three weight loss pharmaceuticals containing sibutramine. The sale of these medicines had been approved in Italy less than a year ago. Upwards of 70,000 people are reckoned to have taken them in that period. Two obese women aged 28 and 45 had died of heart failure. But the health ministry's surveillance unit was quick to point out that the two fatalities and a number of other adverse drug reaction reports, may just be an anomaly. Nobody takes chances anymore. A consumer hotline was set up within hours of the announcement. It's crazy that individual countries in the European Union continue to take unilateral decisions about product withdrawals. Such measures are not good for either consumers or indeed doctors, who have to stand over products that other countries have suspended.

Mystery, religion or sex create the big news stories in the Italian press. Hailed as the umpteenth miracle of Padre Pio, thousands of Sicilians are flocking this week to Messina, to see the late friar's statue. A man claimed it began to weep blood. In a scene you could only witness in Italy, the local forensic crime team was marched up in their overalls to take samples of the fluid from the marble. Their tests showed that the blood was indeed human and further DNA tests were ordered to ascertain its origin. Up the road in Sant Agata di Mitello a 36 year old lady with multiple sclerosis arose from her wheelchair for the first time in years. She began to walk. Her doctor told reporters that a 'high emotional charge' can improve mobility in multiple sclerosis patients by up to 30%. The woman then threatened to sue any newspaper that reported her case as a miracle. Later in the week a poor mother rang a local radio station in Messina to say that her 17 year old son had admitted smudging his own blood on Padre Pio's statue. It happened on his way home late at night. Padre Pio, whose canonisation due on June of this year, is not the only icon to suffer such humiliations. Italy has had over fifty reports in the last three years of weeping statues. The phenomenon began in 1995 when the faithful began reporting marble statues of the Madonna weeping in Civitavecchia, Lucca, Pisa and Catania. Flocks of pilgrims made their way to each site. Critics suggest these weepings are no more than a ruse to boost local tourism and have called on those responsible to be prosecuted on the grounds of slander against religion. Enough to make us all weep. But you have to love Italy. It demands that you do.

BAD LETTERS
March 2008

There has been much criticism recently in psychiatric and medical journals about the poor quality of referral letters that family doctors send in on behalf of new patients. A suggestion has been made that general practitioners should write four page mental health reports on each and every patient referred to the psychiatric services. I'm not so sure. If doctors were able to write that much in referral, and had that much time on their hands, they may not need to refer patients in the first place. A psychiatrist received a perfectly good example of a short and succinct GP letter recently. 'Thank you for seeing this man who has anxiety, severe kyphoscoliosis and sleep apnoea, for which he uses a C.P.A.P. machine at night. He also wears female underwear and this causes a lot of friction at home'.

119

PAEDIATRIC BABYSITTING
October 1999

Our finance minister's budget is a few weeks away and childcare is the buzz word. If Ireland is to take its place amongst the wealthiest nations on this earth, somebody has to be paid to mind them. It has been reported from one of Dublin's paediatric hospitals, that on Saturday evenings, children are delivered into the care of nurses with symptoms that require overnight observation. Concussion, mysterious rashes and unseen seizures, that sort of thing. The parents then depart for local public houses and nightclubs only to return the next day when the children are fit to be discharged. The same children then re-appear the following Saturday night with variations on a clinical theme, but symptoms that always demand overnight observation. Our all-encompassing state health service now looks after births, marriages, deaths and all babysitting in between. Soon we'll have the same resources as Tom Cruise and his wife Nicole Kidman. During the filming in London of *Interview with a Vampire*, this Hollywood golden couple hired a paediatrician from St Mary's Hospital in Paddington to mind their child. The medical babysitter was paid an hourly rate of £130 plus a weekly retainer of £450. Now I'd settle for that in the budget, provided there's a well stocked fridge.

ANAL CLEANLINESS
February 1999

Care of the human bottom is a matter of concern to a great many patients, but it's a topic rarely tackled face on by the media. Some years ago there was a dial-a-doctor health advice line set up in Dublin, where for a small premium phone charge, you could ring and listen to a doctor pontificate on a variety of everyday ailments. Everything from veruccae to bad breath was covered. There were thirty lines in total but the one which drew the most calls was always pruritus ani, the itchy bottom helpline. It had a full fifty per cent of all the call traffic. The Japanese aren't quite so reticent on talking of their bottoms. A new product that translates as *I Like Cleanliness*, has just been launched in Tokyo. Advertising companies employed by the manufacturer, Taisho Pharmaceuticals, really earned their salt with punchy promotions such as 'Keep your anus clean with *I Like Cleanliness*'. The product is a soft cleansing foam which contains sterilising agents and something called shark lever elements, whatever they are. They sound a bit sharp for the Irish market.

THE PERSISTENT ARCHBISHOP OF DURBAN
January 2002

I seem to have struck up a never-ending relationship with the Archbishop of Durban. Having obviously heard of my long-time activism on world issues and good work against the evils of apartheid in South Africa, the eminent Wilfrid Napier wrote a beautifully scripted personal letter to me last year requesting funds for his mission. Enclosed with his plea was a superb photograph of the venerable clergyman being hugged by the Pope. This irresistible combination has had pride of place on my notice board ever since. In return, I wrote out a small cheque to Wilfrid and put enough stamps on the return envelope to send the donation to Mars. I'm sure the dowry was used wisely, but the downside of making such a donation is that I seem to have risen like cream to the very top of Archbishop Wilfrid's address book. Hardly a month goes by without mission mailbags, candles, paper crosses, brochures, prayer cards, stories of life in his diocese and the latest exciting edition of *Zulu News* filling my mailbox. All come with the obligatory return envelope for a further financial sacrifice. With such marketing persistence, Wilfrid is bound to ascend to Cardinal College or perhaps even a trip to the red leather slipper shop some day. But I am tiring ever so slightly of his begging letters. If he writes again, I may have to fill his return envelope with a picture of his former benefactor, in a loving embrace with the Archbishop of Canterbury.

LOWERING THE SEX DRIVE
September 2000

'You're in remarkable shape for a man of your age' said Dr Murphy to ninety-year old Dan after the examination. 'Ah but I've one complaint that needs curing,' said the old gentleman. 'The wife says that my sex drive is too high. Have you got anything that we can do for that, doc?' Dr Murphy was aghast. 'Your what?' he exclaimed. 'My sex drive,' said Dan. 'It's too high, and I'd like to have you lower it if you can'. 'Lower it?' gasped the doctor, still unable to comprehend what the ninety-year old gentleman was saying. 'Just what do you consider high?' 'These days doctor, it seems like it's all in my head,' said the old man, 'and my wife wonders if it's possible you might lower it a couple of feet!'

DOUBLE-BARRELLED DOCTORS
April 2013

I published a new edition of the *Irish Medical Directory* this month. It's my twentieth year in charge of checking the spellings and it struck me leafing through an advance copy of this who's who at the end of your bed, that we have a real crisis in Irish medicine. There are simply not enough doctors with double-barrelled names. Perusing a much old edition, I was struck by the frequency of hyphenated medical surnames: Dwyer-Joyce, O'Donnel-Browne, Somerville-Large, Sperrin-Johnson, Rogan-Finnegan, Roche-Kelly, O'Reilly-Heffernan, Keane-Royston, Doyle-Kelly, Colleran-Begley, Brooke-Tyrell and many more. There are a simply not enough double-barrelled doctors left in Ireland and it behoves the health minister to take action. The long name has been replaced by a never-ending string of abbreviated postgraduate qualifications which are of much less interest to patients. I was writing recently about the late eye surgeon, Mr Beecher Somerville-Large, who once owned the operating instruments of Oscar Wilde's father, until a nurse threw them out for being rusty. Well a gentleman wrote to tell me that nearly seventy years ago, he remembers his mother delighting in repeating the name Somerville-Large over and over again as their doctor, just for the ears and the pleasure of her neighbours. The power of the double-barrel to impress patients should not be underestimated. With some great, great and greater grandparental assistance, I have now restyled myself as Dr Maurice Léonce Fitzharris-Coyne-Carrick-Egan-Couillard-Cunningham-Guillet-Gill-Pitt-O'Donohoe-Murphy-Moran-Guéret, physician and surgeon and spellchecker to the washed and great unwashed. When I have enough money to pay for the engraving on the brass plate, the queue for appointments will begin around the back.

LATE LATE PIANIST
May 2007

Just over a week to go in the 2007 general election and despite early predictions of a photo-finish, Drumcondra Bertie will be back holding the reins of state. Enda Kenny has finally been given the message that the stuff he sprays around the place whenever photographers approach is not anti-MRSA surgical fluid. He now calls it a medical gel, which is slightly more correct. Over on my leafy pasture of Dublin south central there is precious little excitement. It has been donkey's years since we even had the whiff of a minister, and looking at the mugs on posters this time around, nothing's about to change. But we do have the pianist from the Late Late Show running for the Progressive Democrats. Frank McNamara looks like Ludwig van Beethoven on the posters and his catchphrases are 'A Real Performer' and 'Orchestrating a Better Future'. We have moved our piano just inside the hall door in case the musician knocks in person some evening. Ludwig McNamara will get all our votes if he plays just the adagio from piano concerto number 5 in E flat. Whatever happens, I won't be voting for Sinn Féin this time out. I'd like to think they had fully decommissioned. But I'm a bit perturbed that one of their candidates is looking for a 'Search and Destroy' policy towards the spread of hospital superbugs. It's time all military metaphors were decommissioned from medicine too. There's quite enough trouble on hospital wards without hooded men coming in with armalites in one hand and petri dishes in the other.

ESTONIAN MEDICINE
June 2011

A group of Irish doctors recently visited Talinn, the capital of Estonia, to observe how general practice works on the other side of Europe. GP visits are free to all Estonians. Their doctors are paid an annual sum per patient, and make an extra few bob by providing medical tests or operating theatre services in their own surgeries. If patients need a house-call, or blood tests for prostate or liver disease, the fee is just €3.50 for each item. A blood test for diabetes costs an astonishingly low €1.50. Consultations must be given to patients within one day of request and all urgent cases are seen and investigated by a nurse, before the doctor begins diagnosis. Each surgery employs its own driver who brings doctors on house calls and delivers urgent specimens to the local laboratory. There is no night-time GP service. If you are sick enough after hours, you visit a state hospital. The salary of a hospital specialist is on a par with the salary of a family doctor. Extra duties such as teaching, administrative or academic commitments attract a modest extra payment for specialists. In Estonia they live about five years less than we do here. The high prevalence of smoking is undoubtedly a large factor in this. But they spend just a third of what we do on healthcare, and seem to have developed a service that both doctors and patients are quite proud of. Something that remains quite elusive here.

A CORPORATE IDENTITY IS BORN
January 2005

100,000 health board staff have just been provided with the new HSE Corporate Identity Manual. This 16 page bilingual affair advises them all of strict protocols to be adopted when entrusted with the care of something far more important than patients, the new HSE logo. Described as a 'design of contemporary visualisation with a warm and modern look' the logo promises to 'herald a new dawn in the integration of Ireland's health services'. Now we have heard that line before. Staff are being indoctrinated into the hidden meaning of the pastel colours that will soon adorn each healthcare hellhole they work in. The green colour of the 'H' identifies with and reinforces both our culture and national identity. The warmth of the red 'S' is symbolic of good health and emphasises that service delivery is the core of our business whilst the lighter green 'E' - wait for this - graphically symbolises the three tenets of the Health Service Executive – a better health service, a better place to work and better value for money. There's not enough brown in it for my liking. Following this introduction, we have the most detailed instruction booklet about how to afford proper care to the HSE logotype. I can see a dying patient praying to God that he takes them out of misery and grants him an afterlife as a HSE logo. There are whole sections on fonts, colour, palettes, minimum sizes and separate guides to using logos on stationery and advertising. Another page is devoted solely to Exclusion Zones, or as consultants in health board document translation call them, Limistéar Eisiatachta. At a time when casualty trolleys are packed together as tight as Rudolf Nureyev's jockstrap, our health mandarins have decreed that exclusion zones must pertain to their beloved logo.

Next comes the obligatory 'do's and don'ts' section. The logo must never be printed without the accompanying text. Full colour use is preferable. The two colour or black and white versions are barely tolerated. The logo has been specially designed to work across all mediums including advertising, point of sale, etching, signage and engraving. For those still unclear about how the new logo is to be cared for in a 24 hour health service, the HSE has produced a CD containing examples of stationery they may choose.

A two year wait for a dermatology appointment when you have resistant scabies is fine with the HSE. But woe betide anyone who uses a font other than uncondensed helvetica. Arial or garamond fonts may be used only in case of emergency. The logo must never be used on any photographic or coloured background. A fate worse than death will result if anyone has the temerity to tamper with colours, sizing and positioning of all elements in the logo. Finally the HSE logo must be given equal prominence when used with any other logo. This Lamhleabhar Féiniúlachta Corparáidi is quite the funniest thing you could read this year.

CV FICTION
March 2000

Doctors are people too. And they are as likely as anybody else to use poetic licence on their curriculum vitae. When I was a newly qualified doctor, I had to make up a few hobbies for the CV, just to show future employers that I wasn't quite as dull as the dullard in front of them at interview. Not long into one interrogation, I regretted putting James Joyce down as a hobby. A professor of surgery sitting opposite me knew his literature as well as his scrotal swellings because he seemed to think I was some sort of Joycean scholar. The job materialised, but an uncomfortable few moments of perspiration made me resolve never again to equate scholarship with the single reading of a Richard Ellmann biography and a few short stories from *Dubliners*. I mention this murky episode from my own past following the news of the suspension of a Co Down doctor who lied on her resumé. The General Medical Council in London suspended a 57 year old lady doctor for one year after hearing that many of her claims to have held senior posts at various hospitals were fictitious. The British Medical Association said the obligation was on employers to check the bona fides of potential employees. She was appointed by Kent's Thanet Health Care Trust to set up a prestigious high-tech nuclear medicine unit having claimed previous employment as a consultant at the Royal Hospital for Sick Children and at Armagh City Hospital. She also said she had qualified with honours and won awards. But her performance on a training course caused concern to others and it later emerged many claims on her CV were untrue. The doctor told the hearing that mistakes in one came about because a secretary typed it up for her and she was too busy to check it thoroughly. The General Medical Council did not agree and now the UK's chief medical officer has recommended that 'CV credentialing' be developed further across the health service. Meanwhile, I am now on page two of *Ulysses*.

TAXI OR AMBULANCE?
June 1999

I met a patient recently who told me a story about his recent hospital admission for an angiogram. There were four men on his ward waiting for the same test. It was to be done in a hospital just a few miles away. Early on the appointed morning, a solitary taxi-driver arrived to bring three of them for their test. But my own patient was refused the trip as he had private health insurance. Some minutes later, a bright and shiny private ambulance stopped outside the ward. Two cheerful uniformed paramedics wheeled him out to their vehicle, lay him up on the trolley and headed off on a less than critical journey through the city's traffic. Cost of taxi - a tenner at most. Cost of ambulance - hundreds. Private medicine isn't the answer to everything.

HUMAN TRACES
January 2006

I had a wonderful Christmas, thank you for asking. Managed to visit both Santa Powerscourt and Santa Blackrock and also made a special indentation in the European Union's mountain of mulled wine. A far greater achievement was to finish off Sebastian Faulk's tome, *Human Traces*. My ears overheard two staff members at the post-holiday sale in a bookstore mention that it was not selling as well as expected. 600 pages is a lot to get through, but the trick is to take the fuse out of the television, place cotton wool in both ears and retire to bed soon after dusk. *Human Traces* is a remarkable tale of two young doctors, who in the wake of Charcot and Freud, set out to change the world with their theories about what causes mental illness. It's a story that will resonate with any doctor, the great promise and omnipotence of youth, the clinical impotence that confronts those in mid-career, and the reflective wisdom of advancing age as theories are consigned to the bin and the baton of hopes and dreams is passed on to another generation. A book you should read at least twice before you die, or before you go mad anyway.

BETTER OR WORSE
January 2006

There was a very distinguished Irish surgeon and lecturer, an ear, nose and throat man. And he had a longstanding habit of roaring at each of his patients at the start of each consultation, 'Better or Worse?' His long suffering wife died and he subsequently got married again. On his first lecture back after the honeymoon he glanced up at the blackboard where some wag of a medical student had chalked 'Better or Worse?'

LICKING GOLF BALLS
October 1997

A new specialty is about to break forth called Golfing Medicine. No shortage of pathology - delusions of grandeur, dicky elbows, missile injuries, spasms, sprains and joints of place. Recently doctors at the James Connolly Memorial Hospital in Dublin warned in the journal *Gut* that golfers who lick their golf balls before putting could end up contracting hepatitis. A 65-year-old retired engineer presented to the hospital with a two-month history of lethargy, dark urine and upper abdominal discomfort. Acute hepatitis was confirmed and the man admitted to habitually cleaning his golf balls with his tongue. A weed killer challenge test later confirmed this noxious poison to be the cause. His doctors presented him with a damp cloth to attach to his golf bag for future use. Now I read in the *British Journal of Ophthalmology* a letter from eye specialists at Dublin's Mater Misericordiae Hospital warning about penetrating eye injuries caused by flying golf tees. In the interests of safety, I may have to return to snooker.

A SLICE OF HEALTH
February 2005

If Irish health was a pizza, the Department of Health would manage it thus. The centre of its universe would be a cabinet minister for pizza. Rotating around the minister would be three junior ministers, with responsibility for pizza safety, old pizzas and fresh pizzas. Their real task is to deputise for the cabinet minister for pizza should two pizza photo-opportunities arise at the same time. Junior ministers would not be expected to indulge in onerous activities like taking notes or informing the minister of long-running pizza scandals. The department of pizza would have hundreds of staff - principal pizza planners, assistant principal pizza planners, higher executive pizza officers and masses of underling dough balls. None of them would actually handle a pizza, indeed most wouldn't even know a pizza if it jumped out of a wood-fired oven and scorched them. The department of pizza would appoint an unelected pizza service executive. It would have a pizza board made up of people who wouldn't know a pizza if they woke up on top of one. But they like to talk about toppings.

The country would be divided up into ten pizza delivery areas, and the men and women responsible for shambolic pizza services in the past would all be given the same jobs, the same lousy ingredients and the same baking instructions they had before. 98,000 staff would be re-hired, with just half of whom actually responsible for baking and delivering pizzas. The rest would provide back-up services like translating menus and delivery boxes into Irish and composing answers to endless pizza questions asked by elected representatives of the pizza eating public. Judges, barristers and lawyers would regularly be retained to find out the answers to questions like why Mrs Murphy's pizza was delivered cold and why Mr Byrne's super deluxe pizza had too much sweet corn. All workers in the nationwide pizza service would have a clause inserted in their contracts forbidding them from speaking out at anytime, and not just when they have pizza in their mouths. Sensible customers will take out mandatory private pizza delivery insurance. Complainants will be listened to only if they have high-flying pizza legal teams. If a pizza scandal is proven, free pizza for life will be offered and the number of specialists making whatever pizza was deemed to have failed will be trebled overnight. Bon appétit.

SOCIAL CONSULTATIONS
April 2012

A friend told me about an incident in a rugby club, where a showering medic spotted a nasty looking lesion on the back of another player and advised him to book an immediate consultation with his own doctor. The tip-off had a very happy ending that might not have been so joyous had the wet doctor kept counsel and minded his own business. It reminded me of advice that I received years ago on what to do if somebody uses a casual or social occasion to actually seek medical advice. 'I hate to ask at a wedding/christening/wake . . . but would you mind?' might be familiar a opening gambit that doctors hear on social occasions. The advice we were given as students was to raise your voice to a level where everybody within a hundred metres can hear and say 'No problem, just go upstairs and take all your clothes off. I'll follow up in a minute'. I'm told it works a treat.

LIFE AND DEATH IN VENICE
October 2000

My busman's holiday this year is in Venice, home of canals, broke tourists and *Death in*. It's also the place where English politician Michael Heseltine recently suffered his career-ruining heart attack. Well I'm still alive, though very much the poorer. The omadawns at Heathrow airport forgot to transfer my baggage, so after 24 hours waiting for cases, I began to look and smell like something that had been dredged up from the canals. British Airways provided a minor clothing allowance to freshen up, but neither for love nor money can you find clothes here in the size range of big Irish fellows. Venetian chemists aren't cheap either. 45,000 lira for a razor and shaving foam is extortionate. Ahead of me in the queue was a middle aged lady tourist trying to convey to a young assistant with no English that she had the worst dose of diarrhoea imaginable. After ten minutes gesticulating, complete with gushing noises and the odd pointer to the offending passageway, a box of Imodium was produced. Calm was restored.

I made a mental note to brush up on my Italian. Such a fate will not befall me. I've been fairly lucky with health on my travels. Aside from an asthmatic attack brought on by duty-free cigarettes in a Penang hotel and one tomato soup-induced Spanish gastritis, no other memorable ailments have struck me down on holidays. I can't claim to travel light. One enormous suitcase was full to the brim with guidebooks and assorted cameras. If this keeps up, I'll be due an acute airport lumbago some day soon. The lovely Hotel Danieli didn't disappoint, except for the lack of substance in the breakfast. Each morning we took our tasteless eggs with wonderful views of the lagoon and the renowned Santa Maria della Salute.

The Automobile Association Guide to Venice warned me that likely health hazards include too much sun, an overdose of air pollution and the constant attentions of biting insects. It must have been written in 1890 because the main threats we identified in the city were crowd-induced claustrophobia, pigeon fancier's lung at St Mark's Square and gondolier's thumb. The latter ailment is caused by counting out 250,000 lira for a thirty minute midnight drift up a canal.

A highlight for me was a visit to the canal-side house of the late Peggy Guggenheim, patron of poodles, Dame Edna style eyewear and modern art. Peggy was an American heiress (you'd have to be to live here) who purchased an unfinished palazzo in 1949 and filled it with box loads of strange works by one-time husband Max Ernst, and others like Picasso, Dali, Magritte. Even Irishman Francis Bacon made it onto one of Peggy's walls. The most memorable work in the collection is Marini's *Angel of the Citadel* which stands out on the terrace. For those who have not seen it, let's just say that it's a statue of a man who has taken an overdose of Viagra sitting on a horse. Described variously as provocative, startling and disgusting, the offending piece can be spotted from passing gondolas with a good pair of binoculars. According to legend the brave Peggy used to screw off the standing member from time to time and tried it for size against men that took her fancy.

Postscript: *Fourteen years after my trip to Peggy Guggenheim's house, my brother came down from the family tree to inform me that we are blood cousins of the late Leonora Carrington. She was another lover of Max Ernst and one of the world's great surrealist painters in her own right. I think we share a very great grandfather, a Mr Egan, a minor politician and property developer of the 19th century who once owned half of Howth. Alas he disinherited his family in his final will and testament. Apparently there is a painting in the Venice gallery of Peggy Guggenheim pushing my new cousin Leonora away from Max Ernst. I think we need to go back.*

THE MINDS OF DR MILLER
April 2013

My annual pilgrimage to Hatchards Bookshop in London is over for this year. My prize purchase this season was *In Two Minds*, a new biography of Jonathan Miller, my favourite doctor of the modern age. The jacket of the book has a wonderful quote saying 'If he'd been born French, there would be streets named after him.' The current feeling about Dr Miller is that his own country has never really valued his work, and may only start appreciating him when he is dead. Miller let out his first cry in 1934, just off Harley Street, on London's medical mile. His father was a psychiatrist of some repute from the east end of London and his mother Betty was born in Cork City in 1910. Her family name was Spiro. In the turbulent period between the Easter rising and the civil war, her Jewish father received a death threat, so the family upped sticks from Ireland and by 1922 were settled in London's Notting Hill. Betty became a writer and novelist of some repute, and has been compared with Virginia Woolf. It was felt that an innate shyness held her literary career back.

Not so with her son. The most enlightening part of any biography is the childhood, and *In Two Minds* doesn't disappoint. What fashioned Jonathan Miller as the outstanding polymath of our generation? Like all childhoods, there were hurdles on the way. Miller had a stutter which he said would humiliate him in public and 'deform his face'. He managed to liberate himself from it by trying out foreign languages and becoming a mimic of other people. He remains to this day a patron of the Stammering Association. Dr Miller also wet the bed and in his own words, 'shat himself' too. He was an anxious child. The household he grew up in was comfortable but formal. He once told the late Dr Anthony Clare that his parents loved their children but never kissed or embraced any of them. Any display of emotion at home was 'surplus to requirements'. Miller was gifted with a highly retentive memory which expanded his vocabulary, and he read voraciously as a child. He also had an extremely low boredom threshold, driving nannies to distraction with regularly outbursts of unhappy screams. The book mentions the conflict between today's 'child experts', half of which make hay in the camp of attention deficit disorder whilst the other half thresh to the belief that low boredom thresholds indicate exceptional intelligence, energy, inventiveness and an ability to multi-task. I know which I believe in.

GOOD EXCUSES
June 2000

A colleague sent me a nice collection of amusing excusatory notes, often in a medical vein, received by schools from parents:
Mary could not go to school because she was bothered by very close veins.
My son has been told by his doctor not to take P.E. Please execute him.
Please excuse John for being - It was his father's fault.
and my own favourite:
Please excuse James from P.E. He had very loose vowels.
A GP in Killarney also sent me some strange medical excuse notes used at school.
Please excuse Jason for being absent yesterday. He had a cold and could not breed well.
Please excuse Lisa for being absent. She was sick and I had her shot.
A ruder one was
Please excuse little Jimmy for not being in school yesterday. His father is gone and I could not get him ready because I was in bed with the doctor.
There was another that suggested that the scribbling parent also missed plenty of time at school.
Dear School. Please excuse John being absent on Jan. 28, 29, 30, 31, 32, and also 33rd.

THE GAS MAN
April 2004

A plane is flying over the Irish Sea when there is an urgent message from the captain. 'If there is an anaesthetist on board will he please make himself or herself known'. As it happened, there was. He shot up out of his seat not knowing what to expect - a cardiac arrest that needs cardio-pulmonary resuscitation perhaps or an anaphylactic shock that needs intubation.

'I'm an anaesthetist and expert in critical care'. he told the flight attendant. 'There's no rush,' she said reassuringly. 'it's just that we have a surgeon up in first class, and he wants you to adjust his light.'

SEVEN SPECIALISTS
December 1997

True story. An eminent patient was referred by his eminent GP to an eminent specialist in an eminent private hospital in Dublin for an operation to fix an eminent hernia in his groin. Whilst in hospital, he was seen by no less than seven specialists, including his own surgeon, an eye man, a skin lady, a psychiatrist, an ear, nose and throat man, a prostate man and a plastic surgeon. The first surgeon did repair his hernia and the last surgeon removed a benign wart from his face. But none of the others made any substantial or noticeable contribution to this man's welfare either during his short hospital stay, or afterwards. But the man's eminent GP tells me that the VHI did make a substantial and noticeable contribution to each and every doctor who visited. He suggests that in future, visiting specialists attending private inpatients might at least bring a bunch of grapes or a few *Hello* magazines to patients. It might at least make their visits more memorable.

GORE VIDAL IS DEAD
August 2012

Gore Vidal has shuffled off to no man's land. I knew very little about him as a young fellow, other than the fact that his short, exotic and easily pronounceable name fitted nicely across the cover of many books I hadn't read. Then I saw him being interviewed on television by his friend, Melvyn Bragg. And I liked very much what I heard. A very wise and learned man, a true contrarian, and I became a fan for life. Gore Vidal was celebrated after his death, as is the modern way, with tweet sized sound bites, famous quotations and the showing of televised spats he had with assorted big personalities. But the real making of the man received scant attention. Like our own Flann O'Brien, he tried to enter politics, twice, and failed. Such rejections brush easily off most political hides. But for thin-skinned souls, subterranean consequences rumble on. These failures moulded Vidal's pen into the sharpest of weapons from the last literary century. He dug it in, back and front alike, with passion, delight and the cutting humour of his wisdom. Gore Vidal wrote an awful lot. If you'd like to join his fan club, check out the autobiographies, followed by his essays. We won't see his like again for another few hundred years.

PARTIAL DECOMMISSIONING
August 1998

A recent letter to the *Irish Times* on the subject of weapons decommissioning gave a fascinating insight into the surgery habits of an Irish medical specialist in bygone years. The letter was penned by a former IRA man who decommissioned on the instructions of de Valera's army council in 1923 and subsequently went with a military colleague to study at UCD. The writer studied engineering whilst his friend became a doctor. The medical man was well known as an ex-IRA volunteer and trusted nobody, not even those who presented symptoms to his rooms. Such was the magnitude of his mistrust, that when he installed a couch for examining patients, he fitted it with a secret button that revealed a loaded Thompson machine gun. He prospered in his practice. I'd say he had very few unpaid bills.

LONG WAY FROM TIPPERARY
August 2006

A retired GP has written to me about a Tipperary man who was having a colonoscopy done by a well-known Dublin surgeon. During the procedure he lifted his head and to everyone's delight suggested that it was a most extraordinary way to take out his tonsils. He then suggested to the surgeon that he adopt the motto 'The Longest Way Round is the Shortest Way Home'

SPITZBERGEN
September 1998

I am reading about the current exhumation of bodies of seven Norwegian miners from a cemetery on the Arctic island of Spitzbergen. The object of the exercise is to trap a cryogenically preserved 1918 flu virus that caused the greatest influenza pandemic of the 20th century. In the autumn of that year, an outbreak swept the globe, killing twenty one million people. It seemed to have a predilection for young previously healthy individuals. The virus vanished as quickly as it arrived. After years of research, a geographer from Canada has located the mining graves. The men lie buried in permafrost about two and a half meters down a pit on the hillside above the town of Longyearbyen, just 800 miles from the North Pole. The excavation is being carried out by the appropriately named Necropolis company who are based in London. They have been building cemeteries for well over a hundred and fifty years, including those tailor-made for the burial of cholera victims. Wearing biohazard suits the team take tissue samples from the lungs, brains, throats and livers, and fly them to a facility rated BSL-4, the highest level of biological containment. It is hoped this expedition will assist the development of vaccines in the future. I wish them well, and sincerely hope that none of the diggers is named Pandora.

CHRISTMAS COLIC
January 2007

Spare a seasonal thought for pudding-bowl Prescott, deputy prime minister to Mr Blair's declining government. The croquet-playing boxer, lover of Jags and private secretaries, had to spend Christmas day in the casualty department of Castlehill Hospital in Hull, His complaint? Horror of horrors, it was man's most painful affliction - a kidney stone. Not that Prescott was complaining. 'It was a great pleasure to have my Christmas dinner amongst such dedicated people. What would we do without our wonderful NHS?' There was no corresponding quote from the staff who had to listen to the unseasonal sounds of his Christmas colic.

BOTULINUM TOXIN
February 2005

There are all sorts of tempting nixers and sidelines for doctors who have finished saving lives, but not their life-savings. One is this Botulinum toxin stuff which is being shoveled into the nation's wrinkles at an alarming rate. By all accounts it's a tremendous money-spinner, but a wise doctor once told me that you should never try anything new until those who pioneer it have either died of natural causes or are in jail. I was interested in a recent radio programme that pitted the formidable owner of a chain of traditional beauty clinics against a lady who is some sort of doyenne of plastic surgery in Ireland. What caught my ear particularly was a remark from the beauty chain owner to the effect that she had been approached by a number of injection-happy doctors with a view to linking their service to her boudoirs. But fair play to her, She was having none of it. With no hint of irony, she said 'I thought we trained Irish doctors to save lives'.

SICK REFERENCE
August 1997

I was asked by a patient last week whether he could put my name down as a character referee for a forthcoming job application. Of course I am always happy to oblige such requests, but it set me thinking about whether a doctor's reference might be a poisoned chalice to bring to an interview. A shrewd potential employer might wonder about the health of an applicant whose family doctor knows him intimately.

FEEDING THE DUCKS
December 2010

My officious health twaddle of the year award goes to a council warden in Hailsham, a small market town in East Sussex. Many moons ago the town had a large green common beside it, but all that remains of it after years of development is a small lake known as the common pond. Mothers and their children often visit the tranquil spot to feed the ducks. One rather officious park warden recently spoiled the fun by admonishing a group of feeders for using white bread instead of brown. He strongly advised that on future trips they use wholemeal bread, granary loaf or birdseed and said that families who feed white bread to ducks are the same ones that 'give chips with every meal to their children'. I'd say he is a bundle of fun when he gets home.

TRENCH FOOT
September 2005

Trench Foot was a condition well known to doctors who treated survivors in the early phase of the Great War. More than 20,000 cases were documented in the winter of 1914 alone. Feet immersed for long periods in waterlogged trenches were prone to numb toes, blistered and discoloured skin. In more severe cases, gangrene would set in, which sometimes necessitated amputations.

Isolated cases are still seen here amongst homeless people. I read today that it is resurging across the water amongst festival goers with revellers reporting throbbing digits on waterlogged campsites. The term *Glas-Toe* has been coined to describe the re-emerging condition. I'm too old and decrepit now for festivals but my informants tell me that water levels at Glastonbury camp sites can rise higher than wellies. Festival organisers wash their hands of responsibility for trench foot, by blaming inadequate foot wear.

NUMERICAL OBSESSIONS
January 2011

Santa Claus has wind of my literary pretensions, for the sack he deposited in Terenure last month contained a delightful new biography of Count Lev Nilolayevich Tolstoy. The landed genius, known to his friends as Leo, chronicled Russian life and foibles for the best part of a century. It's by no means a one night read. I have just reached an interesting bit about his obsession for the number 28. Tolstoy's penchant for superstition was apparently inherited from his grandmother. He was born on the 28th and left his home to die on the very same date. He always opened poetry books on page 28 and when his wife went into labour with her first child on the 27th, Tolstoy successfully insisted that she postpone further contractions until midnight had passed. Leo was not an easy man to love or live with. He numerical obsessions wasn't unique. Serbian genius, Nikola Tesla, best known for his inventive work on electricity and magnetism, was similarly afflicted. He did everything in threes and would never stay in a hotel room unless its number was divisible by three. Rather poignantly, he died alone in Room 3327 of the New Yorker hotel at Manhattan. Mathematics sometimes carries a health warning.

BERT AND MONTY
May 1998

I came across a new health insurance policy the other day which costs between £8 and £12 a month. The brochure had a well laid out promotional section outlining the sort of claims that the company settle. For instance Bert suffered spinal problems which required surgery. The insurance company paid out his full bill of £516. Monty's hip was deteriorating and had to be replaced so £1,130 was paid out which included all his hospitalisation fees. Spot was a happy chappy too. He received £236 back for the treatment of a gastrointestinal disorder. You should know that these happy patients with comprehensive health insurance are household pets whose owners subscribed to new policy from Cornhill insurance. I picked up all the documents at a dog show. Alas there is no community rating so if your pet has reached the ripe old age of eight years old, the company is not so keen to issue new business. Bulldogs, Great Danes, Rottweilers and Sheep dogs attract a premium loadIng of an extra £2 a month. I suspect big breeds attract higher veterinary bills for the administration of larger doses of anaesthetics and medicines. Aren't we the lucky ones that the VHI doesn't weigh us or ask for our breed.

DONATING TO SCIENCE
April 2011

A couple of years ago, I was ambling through front square of Trinity College Dublin when I was approached by a nun in a green habit. She was lost on the cobblestones and asked if I might direct her towards the university's anatomy department. It was on the way to my destination, so I invited her to accompany me for the three minute walk past the Berkeley Library and the sports fields of College Park. It transpired that she had the future in mind, her own future. She was intent on donating her body to medical science when she no longer had any use for it. In all my years at Trinity, I think she was the first nun in habit I had ever seen in the place. It transpired that she was a particularly rare species of nun in Ireland, an Anglican sister. I took her to the old front door of this ancient department of dissection and we shook hands to make our farewells. I expressed the hope that it would be a long time before she graced the entrance of the anatomy department for a second time.

Deciding to donate your body to medical science after death is a very personal and kindly act of philanthropy. Some schools of medicine in Ireland have reported a sharp decline in such offerings, though Trinity has a healthier waiting list than others. According to a recent edition of the *Irish Medical News*, University College Dublin and University College Cork are struggling to find sufficient supplies, with only half as many bequests as they need. The problem has arisen because the number of doctors being trained in Ireland for export has risen markedly since the days when I sat in exam halls. It is a delicate decision for any living person to make, so why do people do it? Sometimes it's a practice that simply runs in families. Others feel a gratitude to the profession for treatment they may have received and wish to do something that benefits medical education. In these recessionary times, there may be another motive that is rarely spoken about. A donation to medical science will spare your family the expense of a funeral. Some medical schools will even travel considerable distances to retrieve bodies, and cover the cost. Doctors and nurses are no more likely to donate their own remains to science than any other sector of society. Actors, clergymen, nuns, teachers and gardeners feature more prominently. Few bodies are turned away, but it does happen. Refusals are more likely if a post mortem has already been completed, if the corpse is very emaciated, or it if is quite obese. There is nothing discriminatory at play here. It just reflects the difficulty with preserving such bodies and making them useful for teaching young doctors and would-be surgeons. There is no central application office as such, but a discrete enquiry addressed to the anatomy department at any of the country's medical schools will always be welcomed. With the exception of the University of Limerick. They took an interesting decision at their inception not to use real corpses for their anatomy lessons.

THE PHYSICIAN
May 2002

The National Concert Hall was half-full last Thursday evening when Kevin Haugh's *Theatre Nights* returned for a rousing performance of the words and music of Cole Porter. Highlight of the evening, certainly for the doctors present, was Christine Scarry's enchanting portrayal of unrequited love as a love-struck patient singing *The Physician*. This starry eyed clinical romp might not be regarded as politically correct if sung on the wards today. Goodness gracious me, you could end up beside Peter Sellers in serious trouble up at the Medical Council.

> *Once I loved such a shattering physician*
> *Quite the best-looking doctor in the state*
> *He looked after my physical condition*
> *And his bedside manner was great*
> *He said my bronchial tubes were entrancing*
> *My epiglottis filled him with glee*
> *He simply loved my larynx*
> *And went wild about my pharynx*
> *But he never said he loved me*

CREUTZFELD-JAKOB DISEASE
March 2000

A young English woman had a caesarean section operation last year to deliver her baby. She was later found to be suffering from a rare form of Creutzfeld-Jakob disease of the brain. The surgical instruments used in her child's delivery were sterilised after the birth, but repeatedly re-used afterwards. It is known that the offending prion (an infectious bit of protein) can survive sterilisation of surgical instruments. Seven women may have been exposed during subsequent use of the instruments. But the health authority took the decision that it would be wrong to warn them because they would only worry and their risk of actually contracting the CJD infection was 'vanishingly small'. The woman's baby has since been found to suffer from a neurological condition, sparking fears she may be the first British child to inherit the illness from its mother. The local director of health said that it was not ethically clear if informing the women was the correct thing to do. He pointed out that once patients are told, they can forget about life insurance and may spend the rest of their lives worrying about something that in all probability will not affect them. This sounds eminently sensible to me. But why then do our own hospitals hold public press conferences and start phone lines and inform all patients of infinitesimally small risk every time it is found that they shared instrumentation with a CJD patient? There seems to be very little room for common sense in modern healthcare.

A NATIONAL SCANDAL
March 2004

This country is now paying out €15 million every month on whiplash claims, This fascinating statistic emerged from a recent meeting of the Irish Pain Society. To put it into perspective, the monthly total would be enough to run a small general hospital like Naas for a full year. This scandal of disproportionate pay-offs for soft-tissue injuries has to come to an end. And to be honest, it's within the remit of the medical profession to change it. Doctors share responsibility with our learned legal friends for this national drain on finite resources.

Too many doctors play the compo game. Medico-legal report fees (not to mention consultation charges, scanning costs and court costs) are simply colossal for injuries that should really merit encouraging advice, a handful of analgesics and a spot of physiotherapy. The language of minor sprain is inflated to encompass the words moderate and severe in so many whiplash injuries. Sometimes there is idle talk of nerve root injuries. Prognoses are extended to fit legal timelines, for months and more usually years. Generous fees for updated reports are claimed annually until such a time as the wigged barristers exchange pleasantries and compensation on the steps of the courts. And then all goes quiet. The life-changing injuries rarely get a mention again. Until the next case arrives.

APRIL IN PARIS
April 1998

I am writing my diary this week from a table at the famous café of Les Deux Magots in Paris. The name refers not to a couple of maggots, but to its prominent pair of Chinese figurines. The café was once a fabric shop that sold silk from the east. The city has changed beyond recognition since advancing Prussians caused my Guéret ancestors to flee to Dublin in September 1870. For a start, the three main tourist attractions, the Eiffel tower, Jim Morrison's Grave and the Diana and Dodi crash spot hadn't even been conceived. Gustave Eiffel's monstrous metallica which was built for the universal exhibition in 1889 is a sight to behold for those who have only seen it in photographs. It's a little known medical fact that the Eiffel tower provided the corpse which effected a major breakthrough in pathology in 1911. A daft Parisian tailor, known for posterity as Birdman Reisfeldt, attempted a human flight from the tower using a modified black cape as his pair of wings. A huge crowd witnessed his death plunge which was widely reported in the press of the day. However the doctors who performed the autopsy subsequently reported most extraordinary post mortem findings, namely that he had died of a myocardial infarction before reaching the ground. This must have been some consolation for his terrestrial family.

Speaking of post mortems, one of the most famous autopsies never to rake place in Paris was on Jim Morrison, legendary singer with the Doors rock group. He was found dead in his Paris bath tub in July 1971. He was just 27 years old. The fast life and sudden death of Morrison are big business in the city. Number 57 on Rue de la Seine in the Latin Quarter is the address of the club where he allegedly took a fatal dose of pure Chinese heroin. He believed it to be cocaine. It has been suggested that the man known as the *Lizard King* was already dead when friends removed him to his apartment for recuperation in the *salle de bain*. The death certificate simply stated heart failure. Finding his grave in the city's Père Lachaise was not easy. The wails of three teenage American girls crying inconsolably on a nearby tombstone helped. Morrison's plot was originally leased for a thirty year period, which expires in three years time, and there have been rumours that his body is going to be removed to Los Angeles. Relatives of the deceased at Père Lachaise have long petitioned the authorities to have his body removed because of persistent desecration of tombs and headstones in the vicinity of his resting place. But the French government recognises a money spinner when it sees one and has designated Jim's grave as a cultural heritage site. Somebody has recently tidied up the grave which is unrecognisable compared with photos in Parisian travel books. His remains also have a 24 hour security presence. Cigarettes and petals are now the only luxuries that fans are allowed leave for their idol.

Pavement life in Paris is a sight to behold. The prevailing ailments amongst the many beggars at tourist sites are osteoporosis, vertebral collapse and in some cases abject prostration. Some also do a good imitation of Parkinson's disease. One poor old woman near the Place Vendôme spends the entire day with her face two inches from the pavement, bum to the sun, and her left hand in a permanent waiter's tip position. We crossed palms frequently.

The open air cafes and restaurants explode into life after sundown as thousands of trendy young things indulge in orgies of conversation and gesticulation with each other on the Rue des Capucines. The most common fashion accessory for the chic Parisienne in 1998 is the Marlboro Light cigarette. Eating outdoors late one night we estimated that perhaps 90% of young ladies on nearby tables chain smoked. According to a recent special report on international tobacco habits in the *British Medical Journal*, smoking in public is declining in France, albeit slowly. It has taken legal actions against the authorities to enforce a smoking ban on the Metro and RER stations but few restaurants or bars seem to bother with no smoking areas. Recent statistics show that more women in the 18-24 year age group smoke than their male counterparts and this was certainly born out with our recent experience.

Less than a year has passed since the tragedy at the Alma tunnel that took the life of Diana, princess of Wales. A new book by experienced Time magazine reporters based in the city offers a fairly definitive story of the events on 31st August last year. The weighty Ordre des Médecins, an equivalent to our own Medical

Council, strictly prohibits the discussion of any physician-patient interaction. The authors could not find a single French doctor who would go on the record about any aspect of Diana's treatment. However they did find plenty of North American emergency medicine specialists who had no such hang-ups. They posed some interesting questions. Was Diana's blood sample pregnancy tested? Was the result positive? Where are all the contents of her medical file? Why did it take two hours to get her to hospital when other countries had abandoned the policy of 'stabilisation in the field' many years ago? I'll say no more other than to give *Death of a Princess* a hearty recommendation. Next time you are sipping coffee at Les Deux Magots.

FAMILIAR SHOUT
December 2005

Murphy took a coach to Dublin as he heard that the greatest medical brains of the country resided there. He walked from Busáras to Fitzwilliam Square and surveyed a long line of brass plates. He knocked on the door with the shiniest one. In the waiting room, he tried to find out a bit about the doctor. He asked the man sitting next to him if the doctor was a specialist. 'Oh God and he is' the man replied 'this doctor specialises in everything'. Murphy thought about this and got a bit nervous. He asked if the doctor was expensive. 'Oh God and he is. He charges you one thousand euro for your first visit, but all your visits after that are just fifty euro each. For the rest of your life'. Murphy was about to leave when he got called by the nurse to go in to see the doctor. He ran into the consulting rooms and shouted over to the specialist 'Yoohoo doctor, it's me again!'

UNSPOKEN FEARS
May 2000

Doctors were told this week that the first three things they say to a patient could be of paramount importance to the success of any consultation. New research shows that many doctors are missing the real worries that underlie many surgery visits. Apparently the three most common unvoiced concerns of patients are worries about the possible diagnosis, fears about medication having side effects, and a desire not to get a prescription. So now we know. I'm ready for surgery to re-open tomorrow.

'Hello madam. You are looking well. There's no cancer around to worry about. The tablets I gave you are all placebos and have no side effects. In fact you don't need them and I'm not going to prescribe anything anymore'.

'Oh thanks doctor. Assume I don't owe you anything for that'.

HAEMORRHOIDS IN LANZAROTE

January 2011

I have just arrived home from a week's rubification in the winter sun. Arrecife Airport in Lanzarote bustled with so many Irish passport holders, that I began to wonder if the Israeli secret service were planning an assassination. Holidaymakers were glad to escape the clutches of snow at home. Like Dublin, Lanzarote's airport has two terminals. Unlike Dublin, both terminals operate smoothly and I'd say cost a hell of a lot less than half a billion euro to build. Dublin airport is pre-occupied with creating a shopping experience. At the expense of efficient travelling. It took eight minutes to offload luggage from the plane that took us to the Canary islands. The same plane took us back, and almost an hour later passengers were still waiting forlornly for suitcases. Nobody seems to care in Ireland. As long as the tills keep ringing.

Enough moans. We had a happy holiday, disease-free, and we dined handsomely for half the price at home. The same could not be said for a middle-aged Belgian who sat beside us at dinner one evening. He was seething at the price a local English-speaking clinic charged him to treat aberrant haemorrhoids. Our friend had severe pain in a delicate area where the Lanzarote sun doesn't care to shine. Without clinical examination, I took an educated guess that his problem had been a thrombosed or clotted pile.

It had obviously swollen to such a size that he couldn't sit, nor walk nor even lie down with any ease. A quick consultation with a Spanish lady doctor, two injections and a prescription for anti-inflammatory medicines had added a bill of €525 to his holiday budget. His treatment worked wonders. But Belgians don't part easily with their money. He asked me what such a consultation might cost in Ireland. I was pleased to inform him, with insider knowledge, that for a Sunday consultation including a few jabs, change from €100 might not be plentiful. We are often told how expensive our family doctor service is compared to our European counterparts. The truth is a little more complex. There can be surprise stings in the tail.

URINE TRAFFIC
February 2003

High insurance is not the only downside to living in a country with more lawyers than sense. You have to live with some very strange laws too. The state of Arkansas in the United States passed a bill last week to ban the sale of urine. 'Traffickers' in urine can be sent to the penitentiary for three months and also face monetary fines for their illegal activities. So what's going on? Well the great land of the free is becoming increasingly neurotic about health-checks. Pre-employment urine tests are now routinely used across the country. Workers are also being subjected to all sorts of on-the-spot urine tests for illicit drug and alcohol. Clean urine has therefore become quite a valuable commodity. Websites now offer special kits with discrete tubing, heating pads and vacuum packed clean urine samples so that devious employees can provide doppelganger pee for nosy employers. The trafficking of 'clean urine samples' is reckoned to be a growing problem. Business interests, as they always do in America, has lobbied politicians to bring in this law. Yes, ye shall know them by the laws that they pass.

CORNER BOYS
June 2006

I turned on the radio last Tuesday morning to hear that President McAleese was on her way back from darkest Africa to attend 'the funeral'. What funeral? Must be a big one to bring Queen Mary back from her world tour. The newsreader started reading out some earnest words from the President's tribute. 'Great faith . . . pride . . . dignity . . . grace . . .' Oh my Gosh, I thought – we've had another of those quickie Popes. Benedict has tripped over one his favourite cats and all the Swiss Guards and neurosurgeons couldn't sew him back together again. But then they mention a wife, Maureen it is, and four children, and Bertie, and then it dawns on me.

It's Charles J. Holdings, the Kept man of Kinsealy. 'Enough of that' says Charlie, as he trotted off skywards to touch another big fella. Seeing as half the country has already eulogised the most crooked sixpence of them all, I'd like to offer my own ha'penny on the man I spent two decades years admiring and the last few years wondering just how deluded I was. Garrett Fitzgerald rightly apologised for improper use of the word 'pedigree', but he had no need to withdraw the accompanying 'flawed' adjective. All this nonsense about Haughey being Robin Hood, a complex genius, a visionary and sperm donor for the celtic tiger is absolute guff. Charlie was an artful chancer and a first class actor. He trod the boards of Leinster House, a playhouse that pays leading lights and dim ones much better rates than the Gate or the Abbey. His favoured role was hypocrite, for it required little make-up or disguise for Charlie. Telling us to tighten our belts when his own monthly running costs were a hundred grand. Legislating that contraception was only for married couples while he conducted a torrid affair with a woman who was married to somebody else. I met Charles Haughey just once. It was in or around 1983 and he was paying a visit to Trinity College. A small line of us were there to shake his hand before his talk was to begin. As it happened, myself and a fellow medic were wedged into a little alcove of the room above the Student's Union shop. 'Ah, the cornerboys' he said as he eyed us up. Coming from him, that was a real compliment.

Charlie was a great man for giving out things that you might use regularly and remember him by. Free bus passes and free tooth brushes were his legacy to Ireland. Except that they weren't free. He used your own money to pay for them. Haughey was the tenth minister to take the health portfolio when he was appointed minister in 1977. Like Micheal Martin, he veered towards the easy public relations stuff like health promotion and steered clear of anything like tough decisions. Perhaps his only notable achievement was extending free hospital services to all income groups. This was squeezed in after a deal with consultants, that allowed them to bill well off patients in public beds. With Charlie, there was always a price to pay. He was the master at disguising it.

Post-Script: *Soon after I wrote this piece, a colleague wrote to tell me of an occasion when Charlie did a 'Boris Yeltsin' during his tenure as minister for health. Haughey was due to visit a well known hospital in the south of the country one afternoon. All the consultant staff, management and associated dignitaries were asked to assemble in the forecourt wearing their Sunday best. Later than expected, the big black car arrived and entered the hospital gates. The throng got a wave of the hand from the back of the car and whoosh the car was gone. Some days later a letter of apology came mentioning urgent business in Dublin. However further local enquiries revealed that the ministerial party had, how shall I put it, 'over lunched' in the locality and the minister was not in a fit position to step onto the red carpet.*

DEMON BARBER
September 1997

On a recent trip to London, the tour guide from the Big Bus Company regaled us with gory tales of Sweeney Todd, the demon barber of Fleet Street. He would slit the throats of unsuspecting customers as they relaxed in expectation of a close shave. British doctors recently warned of another danger lurking in the hairdressing salon. A little-known condition known as *Beauty-Parlour Syndrome* has entered the medical annals. This cautionary advice followed an incident where a woman suffered a stroke while having her hair washed, The unfortunate lady damaged the lining of her carotid artery whilst hyper extending her neck over the sink. That's why I opt for the dry cut.

HSE STATIONERY
February 2005

If there is such a thing as reincarnation, I am going to ask at reception to come back as stationer to the Health Service Executive. Hospitals up and down the country have been ordered by the HSE to dump supplies worth hundreds of thousands of euro so that the new HSE logo gets pride of place everywhere. Not all staff are pleased. There are pockets of resistance scattered about the country, and they are insisting that they will use up their perfectly good paper. I am hearing whispers to the effect that this HSE diktat is both environmentally unfriendly and financially wasteful. Not sure that their new 'value for money' mantra is appropriate. Instead of money following the patient, it has an uncanny knack of chasing supliers.

MARATHON DEATHS
May 2012

The name Claire Squires mightn't mean much to you. Last month, the thirty year old hairdresser collapsed and died at the tail end of her second London marathon. According to her pals, she was 'just so healthy'. Newspapers reported on the shock that someone so young and so athletic, could die whilst jogging, and whilst fundraising for good causes too. One newspaper was so awestruck by the number of donations that came in after her death, they called her a 'one woman totaliser'. They urged readers to keep refreshing her website page to see minute by minute how much money she could raise posthumously.

In the acres of print and photos, not a jot was written about the dangers of marathon running. Nobody wanted to write about the ten runners who have died since the London marathon was founded. When a 22 year old male fitness instructor died in 2007, the news was hardly recorded. Nobody was keen to talk about the four men who died during a single Great North Run in 2005. I have no particular bone to pick with endurance sports, except to say that fundraising for 'healthy causes' is not always good for you.

The event that lends its name to this gruelling twenty six mile race was first run two and half thousand years ago by an ancient Greek courier called Pheidippides. He ran full tilt from Marathon to Athens to advise the city of a military victory against the Persians. But as he delivered his message, Pheidippides collapsed and died. You can prepare as well as you like for endurance sports. You can be screened in advance for every disease under the sun. But there are no guarantees. There will always be sports where not everyone comes home alive, and marathon running is certainly one of them.

CHEMISTS ON THE FIDDLE
September 2000

We all know that Irish pharmacists are as scrupulously honest as Irish doctors. However this may not be the case in Germany, where a major investigation is underway into fraudulent druggists in Lower Saxony. It's being alleged by insurance companies, that millions of deutschmarks have been fiddled by pharmacists in a scam involving compliant, and not so compliant patients. It would appear that in return for the presentation of unnecessary or surplus prescriptions from their doctors, patients have been offered vouchers for cosmetics, perfumes, one hour photography and indeed viagra tablets by their friendly neighbourhood chemists. It's amazing how frequently fraud is uncovered when private concerns are picking up the bills. When governments fund providers directly, skeletons remain firmly under the floorboards.

MALAPROPS ABOUT
February 2005

I have received a new booklet with more tales of amusement, mainly at the expense of patients. A GP received a letter from disgruntled relatives who said they were going to report a suspicious death to the *foreigner*. They meant to say coroner. And a husband who was unhappy with his wife's treatment, wrote to her doctor to say 'I am not of a *lecherous* nature but I am going to sue you'. Litigious perhaps. A patient once demanded 'a refund or my money back' and a hospital secretary received a letter stating that 'your reply is not good enough so I am writing to the *omnibusman*'. Errors from medical notes included a patient whose behaviour was attributed to 'his *metal* disorder'. A wound once oozed '*melodious* fluid'. Missing letters and superfluous ones can be problematic too. Notes recorded that a lady 'removed her undergarments to reveal a *scared* abdomen'. Another doctor said he 'contacted the surgeon under whose *car* the patient was at the time'. And pity the poor intern who wrote that the patient was breathless with a *severed* heart condition. A doctor tells me of a couple who once attended his surgery. The husband had a lump somewhere on his leg, and his wife, who had quite a phobia about cancer, looked worried about it and asked the doctor if he thought it was *ligament*. After a few seconds, the doctor realised she meant to say malignant.

ALZHEIMER SPOTTING
February 2011

'Teacher leave those kids alone' was a favourite chant of oppressed schoolchildren in the 1980s. The line came from the Pink Floyd track, *Another Brick in the Wall*, which sold four million copies and became an anthem for teenagers disillusioned by regimes of rigid and unimaginative schooling. In apartheid South Africa, the song was banned when it was used to promote a boycott of segregated schools. Perhaps they should re-release it in Hong Kong. According to the *British Medical Journal* this month, schoolchildren on the island are to undergo training in how to spot key signs of dementia in elderly relatives. History projects interviewing Granddad about his experiences during the Japanese invasion might take on a whole new perspective. Any doctor or nurse will tell you that dementia is notoriously difficult to diagnose with any certainty in its early stages. And when you do make the diagnosis, well there's not an awful lot to look forward to. I'm sure that the schoolchildren of Hong Kong have quite enough to worry about without being trained as surrogate Alzheimer specialists. Yes, please leave those kids alone.

HEALTH STORES
December 1998

There is an urgent need for some health store regulation in Ireland. For some time now I have had suspicions about the quality of staff, products and practices in some of these outlets, but my evidence tended to be anecdotal, gained from the spoken words of patients who had purses relieved rather than symptoms. The UK based Research Council for Complimentary Medicine recently investigated 29 health food shops, chosen at random. They sent a researcher in claiming to be suffering from severe daily headaches of recent onset. Her symptoms were carefully chosen so that they could well indicate more serious pathology. Less than one in four stores advised consultation with a doctor. All but two recommended a purchase, and just one was said to have followed the ideal course of action which was to ask for more symptoms and then recommend an immediate medical consultation. The study was published in the *Journal of the Royal College of Physicians* and its findings should be made widely known amongst members of the public. Diagnoses from shop assistants ranged from altered blood sugar levels. liver and colon blockages, toxins circulating in the blood, dehydration, weakened immune system, using the brain too much and the weather. Not one of the health food outlets employed a pharmacist. Staff training, if any was given at all, was in the form of seminars by remedy and vitamin companies. One finding of particular concern is that young people are three times more likely to consult these shops than the over 50s. They also rate the advice provided more highly. So much for a bright well-educated future.

MIDLANDS MALES
October 2001

The board that looks after medical card payments issues a report on its expenditure each year. My copy of the most recent edition is now well dog-eared as I have been doing some sums to see which patients are being followed by the most money.

My conclusion is that the patient in Ireland who costs the state pharmacy more than any other is the midlands male. Pensioners in Birr and retired turf-cutters from Edenderry are now the most medicated patients in Ireland. Each costs an annual average of £466 to keep in tablets, rubs, patches and gels. The ageing men of Cavan and Monaghan come in a very close second. For the record, school going boys on the east coast cost the state least in terms of medicines consumed, currently just £32 a year.

MEDICAL BOOKPLATES
January 2004

Patients who attended the now retired neurologist Dr Eddie Martin to have their patellar tendons tapped and sensations mapped, invariably had fond memories of the man. For many years, Dr Martin served patients with neurological illnesses at the old Adelaide Hospital and at St Vincent's in Elm Park. He has been busy in retirement too. Dr Martin has produced a book that would delight any doctor either on his birthday, or simply as a gift for a good cure or impeccable behaviour. His *Dictionary of Bookplates of Irish Medical Doctors* offers a fascinating insight into the private and public lives of generations of Irish physicians. Those who treasured their book collections would have personalised plates designed and printed to adorn the inside covers. Today we toss our paperbacks around with abandon, but as Dr Martin points out, books were once a valuable commodity whose cost represented a sizeable proportion of the average wage. One hundred volumes was a respectable collection for any doctor. Five hundred was above reproach. A thousand was considered to be a library of some magnitude. This hardback book is beautifully illustrated with dozens of extraordinary bookplates and it contains detailed pen-pictures of doctors over many centuries of medical history.

Whilst perusing this book. it dawned on me that the modern Irish doctor has become a terribly dull boy. The biographies of medics past reveal characters that were a lot more rounded than we are. Their out of hours interests were certainly a lot more wide-ranging than the upright bearers of today's bad news. Take

Sir Francis Cruise, son of an ancient family in the county of Meath. Prior to his death in 1912, Cruise was a surgeon in the Mater Hospital. But he preferred inventing to cutting and made many advances in scoping equipment (tubes for looking around inside) and the design of chest bandages. Then he got interested in hypnosis, studying the new-fangled practice with well-known *professeurs* at the Charité and Salpetriére Hospitals in Paris. He studied the medical springs of Europe, became an expert of ancient Christian texts, composed pieces for the cello and edited classical works and Irish airs. He did much to popularise chamber music in Dublin and apparently the National Museum has a double bass viol that used to belong to him. The best known party piece of Sir Francis was to shatter the necks of champagne bottles by rifle shot at the annual booze-up (aka picnic outing) of the Dublin Biological Club. He had learned this gun skill in the wild west of America where he was sent as a youth for health reasons. Nowadays the club would probably host a lecture about the effects of lunchtime drinking on liver function tests. Today's profession is sadly reducing to a one-size fits all.

OPTIMAL NUTRITION
June 2012

As a dog owner, I am fascinated by the manner in which pet food is now being sold to us. In the good old days, by which I mean 1974, it was all lean mean meaty chunks in gravy poured from stinky tins that had been sealed in factories somewhere in the midlands, off the road to Galway. Now it's all designer portions, food pyramids, antioxidants, nutrients, essential fatty acids and immune system boosters. I saw a dog's dinner the other day claiming it had up to seventeen times more vitamin C compared to other leading cat and dog brands. The really expensive ones seem to like the exclusivity of being stocked only by 'veterinarians' or 'pet establishments'. They look down their long wet whiskered noses at the mutt's stuff sold in tins or sacks at the supermarket. 'Precise Pet Nutrition' reads one of the slogans, as if the manufacturer knows just how your beloved spaniel likes to be wined, dined and tickled under her chin. Putting the words 'vet' or 'science' in the name of the brand, and adding inanities like 'optimal care' or 'clinically proven' is popular too. And here is a question for the vets out there - why do neutered dogs need their own special food? The logical extension is that neutered owners would need their own diet too. Perhaps doctors, and restaurants too, are missing a trick.

MATRON'S NEW POWERS
September 2007

Gordon Brown's first conference speech as the British Labour Party leader was every bit as damp as the hair gel his handlers had enveloped his head with. Promising to 'bring back matron' and give her the power to order more cleaners will hardly endear him to a new generation of graduate nurses who gave up such ward duties long ago for careers in diagnosis, therapeutics and clinical research. More interesting was his new promise to advance the outer age limit of breast screening to 73 and bowel screening to 75. In Ireland, politicians use medical cards to win extra votes. In the UK, where care is already free for all, they play Santa Claus with screening instead.

ADVANCE FEES
September 2011

This practice of doctors demanding money before a consultation begins is spreading. In fact it has seriously infected parts of the specialist sector. Last week I heard about a psychiatrist who demands credit card details (or a cheque) for a couple of hundred euro before agreeing to see the patient at all. This upfront demand for the entire consultation fee is simply for the privilege of making the appointment with the specialist. Doubtless doctors have their debtors, their expenses, their no-shows and their unpaid bills like everyone else these days, but good manners and old fashioned trust are priceless commodities in medicine that should never be allowed go out of date. A now deceased GP of my acquaintance only billed his patients once a year, in guineas. Often long after their visits. He trusted his patients, and they trusted him. He had no bad debts. When doctors you have never met before, write personal letters to you focusing almost entirely on the amount of money you are going to pay them and how you are to going to pay them, you might be wise to question whether that doctor is the trusting person for the job in hand. I hope it's only a minority of doctors who run their 'businesses' this way. But if this is how some correspond with patients they have yet to meet, it's little wonder that litigation is on a steady climbing curve.

UGLY IRISHMEN
June 2011

A mortal wound has been delivered to the sensitive egos of Irish men with the news that we line up beside our Polish buddies as the least attractive masculine species in the world. This crucifying disclosure, heralding perhaps the discovery of a national gene for male ugliness, emanated from beautifulpeople. com, an international dating agency. These on-line matchmakers have the sort of entry rules that only golf club bores could dream up. New members are screened for facial attractiveness by existing members. The nub of our predicament is that less than 10% of Irish men desperate enough need on-line introductions are accepted. This contrasts unfavourably with Swedish men and Brazilian hombres who have an acceptance rate of closer to 70%. It may take a generation or more for Irish men to re-locate their confidence after such a devastating blow. Our fair Irish ladies won't be sniggering behind our backs, for they don't appear to perform any better.

BOB GELDOF F.R.C.S.I.
May 2007

I have been dipping into the Bob Geldof autobiography *Is That It?* which was published a bit prematurely in 1986. It has a very touching description of the death of his mother from a brain haemorrhage and how he responded as a young boy to her demise. He donned his favourite Nazi helmet, painted white to exorcise the ghost of the storm trooper who had worn it, and ran off to a friend's house to play. Geldof is a most interesting man. I noticed for the first time in this book a wonderful little quotation on the title page from the Story of St Vespaluus by Saki.

'I don't mind being reverenced, greeted and honoured' said Vespaluus. 'I don't even mind being sainted in moderation as long as I'm not expected to be saintly as well'.

Geldof lived up his billing last week when he returned to Dublin to receive an honorary fellowship at, in his own words, the 'Royal F***ing College of Surgeons'. Always true to his word.

HEALTH SCREENING
January 2005

I have a long-standing personal scepticism when it comes to screening mass our population for illnesses. My prejudice probably has all to do with the fact that our crumbling half-finished jigsaw of a health service is incapable of looking after the illnesses that have been discovered already. You shouldn't throw more patients into the flood water when you cannot cope with those already drowning. When you watch a lady wait the best part of a year to get an ultrasound of her tummy and then receive a radiology report suggesting that she has an ovarian cancer that has advanced beyond salvation, it has the effect of steaming up the most rose-tinted of spectacles. Let's look after those who know they are sick, before rounding everyone else up off the street.

GREEN TUREEN
June 2001

Veteran journalist Cathal O'Shannon appears to be recovering well from his recent surgery for oesophageal cancer. He spoke to Vincent Browne last week about his diagnosis, treatment and more importantly about his long career in reporting and broadcasting. What particularly caught my attention in the interview was the reference to the Mohangi case which O'Shannon covered as a young reporter. He also featured the murder trial in his television series *Thou Shalt not Kill*. Shan Mohangi was a young Royal College of Surgeons medical student from South Africa who received a death sentence for the murder of his young girlfriend Hazel Mullen in 1963. The sentence was later commuted and Mohangi returned to his native country after serving three years in Mountjoy prison.

The case was known to Dubliners as the Green Tureen murder, after the restaurant on Harcourt Street in which Mohangi dissected and cremated his girlfriend's corpse in a clumsy attempt to hide evidence. I have read extensively on and around this case, and was less than surprised that O'Shannon should claim in this interview that he believed Mohangi was not the murderer. Reading between the lines of the forensic evidence led me many years ago to that same conclusion. O'Shannon went on to say that he could not name the person he believed was involved, because the person is still alive. I wonder how long we will have to wait for that particular revelation.

Post-Script: *Cathal O'Shannon survived ten years after his oesophageal cancer was diagnosed. He died in October 2011. He never revealed his suspicions about the Green Tureen case in public.*

POST TRAUMATIC DISSENT
January 2001

A Dr Summerfield of St George's Hospital in London has published a paper that makes an interesting case against the over-diagnosis of post traumatic stress disorder. He describes how the condition was 'discovered' in the aftermath of the Vietnam war and how it infiltrated medical and medico-legal culture in years to follow. He claims that it is now latched onto everything from childbirth to verbal harassment to receiving bad news from a doctor. Dr Summerfield describes a 'veritable trauma industry' comprising all manner of experts, lawyers, claimants and assessors. He calls it 'a social movement trading on the authority of medical pronouncements'. The lure of compensation for perceived stress or denial of counselling means that what were previously everyday work situations are now viewed as traumatogenic for those who are simply doing their everyday jobs - paramedics, policemen, nurses and doctors. His brave pronouncements make for challenging reading in the *British Medical Journal*, particularly for doctors who double clinical earnings every year by hiring out their souls to the medico-legal industry.

BIRO DIRECTIVES
November 2007

A dicky-bird tells me that a new *Biro Directive* has been issued by the Health Service Executive this week. Some hospital managers are no longer considered senior enough to order their own stationery. HSE regional headquarters have decreed that only grade 8 hospital administrators can sign for biros, rubbers and photocopy paper. The problem arises because not every hospital in the country has grade 8 personnel, so orders for rubber bands, paper clips and treasury tags have to be sent off to the personal assistant of the local hospital network manager who then has to locate her travelling boss for a signature. The average time for such a request to be processed is apparently two weeks, such is the amount of scanning, photocopying, posting and rubber stamping involved. One wonders what chance a hospital manager has with hospital hygiene if he or she doesn't even have the authority to order a ream of paper. This HSE *Biro Directive* explains all we need to know about a centralised health service gone mad.

Another HSE circular has also come my way. It concerns a one day seminar for staff on *Mid-Career Planning*. It deals with 'work-life balance, a guide to personal taxation, investment & savings, income protection' and a host of other nonsense that has nothing whatsoever to do with the health of patients. Applicants are asked to fill in a detailed application form, outlining dietary requirements and what they hope to achieve from the course. Then they must 'have a discussion with their line manager in relation to how this course will enhance their role' before passing the form over to their line manager who will fill in a section about 'how this course satisfies the applicant's learning and development needs'. The completed forms are then to be returned to the local performance & development unit of the HSE for appraisal. My correspondent on this matter wonders how in the midst of a total recruitment ban, with every department running on core staff numbers, a roomful of people can spend a whole day (if 9.15am to 4.45pm with an hour for lunch can be considered a whole day) doing this sort of thing. But hey, this is the HSE. They can do anything they like. Just as long as it doesn't impact on the health of patients.

GEORDIE NURSE
February 2006

A Geordie nurse was struck off the register last week for placing a patient's glass eye in a cup of coca cola and offering it to her ward sister to drink. Another staff nurse, a sprightly 53 year old, was struck off for drawing a smiley face on a male patient's umbilical hernia. Whilst the headlines in the newspaper were very much along the lines of *Carry on Matron*, the underlying truths weren't quite so funny. Closer reading shows that there was more to these cases than meets the eye. The disciplinary panel of the nursing and midwifery council heard twelve charges in total, including drug error, rough handling, slapping of patients and racial taunting of fellow nurses. This included use of abusive terms like *chinky* and *nig-nog*. Sounds like the authorities at the infirmary in Newcastle were indeed correct to seek disciplinary action.

FIFTIETH ANNIVERSARY SURPRISE

August 2000

Dr Mick and his wife Betty were out celebrating their 50th wedding anniversary.

Dr Mick turned to his beloved and asked, 'Betty, have you ever cheated on me?'

Betty replied, 'Oh Mick, why would you ask such a question now? You don't want to ask that question'.

'Yes, Betty, I really want to know'.

'Well, all right. Yes, three times'.

'Three? Well, when were they?' he asked.

'Well, Mick, remember when you were thirty years old and you really wanted to start your own surgery and no bank would give you a loan? Remember, then one day the bank manager himself came over the house and signed the loan papers, no questions asked'.

'Oh, Betty, you did that for me! I respect you even more than ever, to do such a thing for me. So, when was the second time?'

'Well, Mick, remember when you had that last heart attack and you were needing that very tricky operation, and no cardiac man would touch you? Then remember how Surgeon O'Brien came all the way up here, and offered to the surgery himself, and then you were in good shape again?'

'I can't believe it Betty, that you should do such a thing for me, to save my life. I couldn't have a more wonderful wife. To do such a thing, you must really love me darling. I couldn't be more moved. So, all right then, when was number three?'

'Well, Mick, remember a few years ago, when you really wanted to be president of the golf club. And you were 54 votes short. . . '

UNHEALTHY WIKILEAKS
December 2010

The Wikileaks story that dominates this week's newsprint has serious ramifications in healthcare, especially in the realm of electronic medical data. If an entire database of diplomatic cables from the world's most secretive superpower can so easily be compromised, it raises serious questions about how we store and share healthcare records, and how easy it might be for them to enter the public domain. I have been sifting through some early leaks in a quest for medical data and gossip, and there's plenty of each. It's now clear to me why embassies the world over spend so heavily on cocktail parties and diplomatic soirées. They are cheap sources of useful hard information and everyday tittle-tattle that are relayed back to big brother at home

France's President Sarkozy is described in the leaks as hyperactive and on permanent overdrive. His politics are erratic and hard to predict. Barack Obama was once briefed on the fact that Sarkozy, like our own dear leaders, is somewhat summit-prone. His lackeys go to great lengths to avoid his legendary outbursts of tyranny. They once diverted his plane to avoid him seeing the Eiffel Tower lit up in Turkey's national colours. One French diplomat suggested that 'just being in a room with him is enough to make anyone's stress levels increase' whilst another suggested that where African politics were concerned, much work was needed on his 'bed-side manner'.

The USA had no embassy in North Korea's capital Pyongyang, and relied on friendly local sources like the former prime minister of Singapore. His medical report on the rogue state's leader Kim Jung-Il stated that he was a flabby old chap who is overly fond of the drink and likes nothing more than prancing around stadiums full of his supporters receiving adoration.

The mental health of Cristina Kirchner, glamorous president of Argentina, was a particular source of interest to Hillary Clinton who considered her 'thin-skinned' and 'intolerant of perceived criticism'. Clinton's department asked diplomats for a personality profile of the left-leaning leader who Americans suspected of suffering from 'nerves and anxiety'. In particular, the embassy was asked to find out what medication she was taking to calm herself down.

American listeners in Libya were interested in Colonel Gadaffi's medical arrangements. They discovered that four Ukrainian nurses were employed to travel with him tending his daily health needs. One in particular, Galyna Kolotnytska, was described as a 'voluptuous blonde' who knows his routine better than anyone else. She knew just how to calm his phobia for heights and his long-standing fear of flying.

NORWEGIAN SENSE
July 2000

A medical colleague visited Scandinavia recently, Norway to be precise, and reported back some interesting facts and figures from the land of Grieg and high fjords. Doctors in Oslo pay about £38 a year to cover themselves against malpractice claims. It would appear that Norwegians don't really sue their doctors. They have very great difficulty understanding the thousands of pounds that doctors pay here annually. On the other hand, a consultation with a Norwegian family doctor costs a very modest £11. So how do they manage this? Well in Norway, the practice premises, equipment and all the ancillary costs of being a doctor are all paid by the state. Service and facilities are of a universally high standard. And the harder the doctor works, the more he or she earns. Worth investigating here I would have thought.

NEW STANDARDS
February 2013

The Royal College of Surgeons in London has published some new standards they would like to see in the cosmetic therapy industry. The president of the college expressed two serious concerns. Not all of those who offer cosmetic procedures are qualified and secondly, patients may not be getting accurate information prior to treatment. I thought we'd run through a few of their suggestions here as it might speed up some action in this particular backwater, and help some Irish patients in this unregulated world. The college suggests a cooling off period of at least a fortnight between deciding to have a procedure and actually having it done. They say doctors should avoid telling patients they will feel better or look nicer, suggesting that a simple 'bigger' or 'smaller' should be adequate descriptive terms for medics to use. They want time-limited special offers or discounts to be stopped and botulinum toxin parties to be outlawed. They want real photographs and subjects to be used in all advertisements, with a ban on airbrushed models. They also want to make sure that anyone who administers laser treatment, botulinum toxin or intradermal fillers is qualified and registered either as a doctor, a dentist or a nurse. That might just put a nicer face on this unregulated industry.

AN ITEMISED BILL
June 1998

The wife of a well known tycoon fell down at a wedding and broke her hip. The businessman enlisted the best orthopaedic surgeon in the city to do the operation which consisted of lining up the broken hip and putting in a screw to secure it. The operation went fine and some weeks later the surgeon sent the business man a fee for his services of £5,000. The businessman was outraged at the cost, and sent the doctor a letter demanding an itemised list of the costs. The doctor sent back a short invoice:

One screw	£ 1
Knowing how to put it in	£ 4,999
Total	£ 5,000

The bill was paid in full.

ERRATIC SPELLING
July 2004

A psychiatrist has been in touch with a medical typo he spotted. Recorded on the Dictaphone was the consultant's letter to a GP describing an 83 year old lady who presented with a history of very erratic behaviour. Alas, by the time his secretary had finished typing it, the lady had presented with history of very *erotic* behaviour.

MEDICAL SUICIDE
August 2006

The latest journal from the Society of Medical Writers carries an interesting article entitled 'Doctors who Kill Themselves'. Written by Dr Henry Tegner, a London medic with a long background in training general practitioners, he felt inspired to write it after the suicide of a young and dedicated lady doctor who took her own life three summers ago. Dr Tegner suggests that there is a danger sign to watch out for, namely the doctor who accumulates a very large retinue of patients who 'will not see anybody else'. He advises a close eye be kept out for young GP trainees who attract more than what might be regarded as their fair share of overly-personal patients. He mentions dropping prescriptions off to houses on the way home and an inability to switch off as particular warning sins. Tegner says that the remedy is never easy, but a word in the ear is wise if you feel the danger is sufficiently grave.

ORTHOPAEDICS BY CHANCE
May 2013

A reader of my Rude Health column in the *Sunday Independent* brought me back to 1945 when he was a boy of six living near Temple Street Children's Hospital in Dublin. He remembers being taken by his mother to a basement room on Merrion Street where he was stood on a table and examined in his birthday suit by a medical man. There was no pain or injury that precipitated the visit, but the outcome was a prolonged stay in the Clontarf Orthopaedic Hospital where he remembers a view of the Pigeon House from the windows. X-rays showed that the ball of his left hip had departed the socket that was intended to house it. The treatment was a special bed that would stretch the leg and slowly move the joint back into position. He remembers it as a steel frame set at an angle with a sliding support on rails to support his upper body. His legs were taped inside and out and attached to steel shoes with spring balances mounted high on the bed end. He was billeted outdoors on the ground floor veranda. He recalls that his bed was in the corner, so that by the time the urine bottle came around it was always full! After a full two years in Clontarf (hard to believe now), he was discharged on two crutches with his leg in a strap. Later he wore a shoe lift for a few months. An active life followed of swimming, badminton and Dublin city marathons. Assisted by this excellent case history, and a little geographical research through old medical directories, I surmise that my correspondent was probably treated by Mr Arthur Chance (1889-1980) who was the first ever professor of orthopaedic surgery at Trinity College. Chance was a legendary teacher on bone conditions across all medical schools and according to Professor Barry O'Donnell's biographies of Irish Surgeons, was 'a warm, chuckling rounded figure with a great love of life and surgery. He was a well-recognised expert witness in the theatre of Dublin's courts, and his prop was a monocle which he polished carefully before consulting his notes. The monocle could then be allowed drop from the eye with perfect timing if he felt the opposing evidence was any way inconsistent. The Chance family lived at Nullamore in Milltown, just above the Dropping Well public house. The Chance family also played an important charitable role in the early life and education of Dr Noël Browne when his family fell on hard times. And when Arthur Chance had a stroke late in life, it was Dr Noel Browne who attended him and arranged admission to hospital.

CAN I JUST HAVE A NOTE DOCTOR?
June 2001

A family doctor in Glasgow was asked recently by a patient to sign a certificate saying that she was too ill to take her pet to the sick animal dispensary. Another was asked by parents to certify that their four year old child was fit to appear in an advertisement. These are just some of the examples of spurious uses of medical time that were drawn to the attention of political parties during the recent general election across the water. Doubtless the same sort of thing goes on here, but we don't hear as many complaints. Probably because doctors charge for these sorts of errands.

CRIME AND PUNISHMENT
May 2006

This is a true story. A young mother was at a surgery and was making zero effort to restrain her five-year-old son, who was ransacking an adjoining treatment room. An extra loud clatter of bottles did prompt her to say, 'I hope, doctor, you don't mind Johnny being in there'. 'Not at all' said the doctor calmly, 'He'll be quiet as a mouse any minute now that he's found the poisons'.

BRAM STOKER'S BROTHER
September 2007

I see that the Royal College of Surgeons is taking legal advice about the provenance of a Walter Osborne painting in Beaumont Hospital. *Milking Time* was donated by Mr Thornley Stoker to his fellow consultants at the Richmond Hospital at the turn of the 19th Century. I have been doing some research on surgeon Stoker, whose fame in life was eclipsed by the fanged creation of his brother Bram. Thornley Stoker had a huge private practice and his neighbour, the writer George Moore, was able to ascribe each and every lavish furnishing in his Ely Place home, to the proceeds of particular operations. In 1878 Stoker performed Ireland's first abdominal hysterectomy (taking the womb out through an incision in the tummy). He was the quintessential general surgeon performing operative procedures on brain tumours, abscesses in the brain, varicose veins and obstructed bowels. He was meticulous about recording details of these operations. Once his afternoon consultations were over, he would set off for Grafton Street to peruse antique shops and galleries. A long-time member of the board of the National Gallery of Ireland, Stoker was knighted in 1895. James Joyce included his name, amongst many other doctors of the day, in *Ulysses*. Alas, it was not in any heroic role. Merely a mention that a carriage arrived outside his house during a cold snap in 1893.

WHAT'S IN A NAME?
October 2000

New Scientist magazine has started to collate details more appropriately named personnel from the medical field. There are two plastic surgeons in the UK called Mr Carver and Mr Hackett. And family doctors there include Dr Hurter, Dr Stiff, Dr Coffin and his locum Dr Graves. I've been trawling through some old medical directories here, and whilst the Republic is short of good names, Ulster doesn't disappoint. There was a lumps and bumps surgeon in Newtownards called Dr Moles, a retired GP in Antrim called Dr Boddie and a Belfast neurologist called Dr Swallow. South of the border I did find Dr Faul a Geriatrician, a Dr Dyer in Castledermot and a former brain surgeon, Dr Pate.

NO PAPER TOWELS
November 2005

A microbiologist with the Health Protection Surveillance Centre went to the Dáil last week to tell TDs that most of the country's hospitals are in the dark about their own rates of MRSA infection, as they simply don't have the staff or laboratory facilities to compile them. On the same day I had an email from a rural doctor who does his surgeries in a number of local health centres. He told tell me that he now has to resort to drying his hands 'on the seat of his pants'. Two weeks prior to writing to me, one health centre on his daily circuit ran out of towels. He lost his rag completely when a second health centre also failed to provide paper towels. He rang the local HSE administration office to be told that the forms to requisition paper towels hadn't been filled out. He despairs of health bureaucracy. In his own words, he says that 'the very basic tenet of health care is to provide somewhere warm and dry with basic hygiene to see patients – the present HSE can't even do that'.

THE PRESIDENT'S KNEE
June 2012

On his recent *Late Late Show* appearance, President Higgins confirmed that he is the proud owner of a new knee joint. I wasn't surprised. Minor surgery on a knee does not usually need a ten day admission to hospital, whether it's public or private. During the course of his election campaign, questions about the state of his knee were deflected with talk of a slip on wet tiles during a visit to Colombia and a resulting fracture of the kneecap. There was no mention of impending replacement surgery of the entire knee. I am not clear whether President Higgins went into the election knowing there was a prospect of surgery immediately afterwards. Something for his biographers perhaps to tease out in the future. Watching his gait and difficulty moving after alighting from of cars, I certainly formed the impression that the knee situation was a lot more serious than something caused by a slip on wet tiles. I'm happy to see that knee replacement surgery has given us a much happier looking and more mobile President.

In Ireland, there was always a kind of consensus that the health of our leaders and ministers is a personal and private matter. This unwritten rule was ignored in 2009 when a television station announced just the day after Christmas that then minister for finance, Brian Lenihan junior, had a 'serious condition'. The minister waited eight days before issuing a personal statement confirming that he had a tumour in his pancreas.

Politicians stand over a system that demands fitness assessments and medical examinations for many less well-paid jobs in the public service than their own. It seems to be one rule for poorly waged jobs, and quite another for the executives. If you look upon the presidency as a seven year contract with a €2 million cumulative salary plus a house for seven years and expenses, you might rightly wonder why medical fitness for the job is not assessed. I've seen cleaning ladies sent for clinical examinations for badly paid part-time work. Why this discrepancy?

The release of the medical records of presidents, and even presidential candidates, is now the norm in America. There is history there of course. An extraordinary event happened in 1893 when President Grover Cleveland asked White House medic, Dr Robert O'Reilly, to examine a soreness in his mouth. O'Reilly sent biopsies off from a nasty looking ulcer. Word then came back that it was a tumour, but perhaps not malignant. America was in the midst of a major depression, and it was decided to hide potentially bad health news from the electorate. A plan was hatched to pack President Cleveland off on a cruise holiday near Long Island. He secretly had major oral surgery on board his yacht. Part of his palate and left jaw were removed and the press were fobbed off with a story about two bad teeth spoiling his vacation. Further surgery followed as doctors had to fit Cleveland with a rubber prosthesis that allowed him to speak properly again. It also helped make him more presentable in public. Only in 1917, nine years after President Cleveland had died, did the full story come out. One of the medics on the boat that day, Dr William Keen, America's very first brain surgeon, wrote about the secret surgery. Interestingly, Cleveland's pathological specimens had been retained and were re-examined in the 1980s. Pathologists confirmed that he had a low-grade cancer that could have spread if it had not been treated.

URGENT BUSINESS
November 2000

A consultant in a rural hospital wrote to me last week with details of the latest scam to come his way. He received a letter from a west African military widow who was searching for a reputable person to assist her in an urgent business deal. Her son was in prison and she had millions of dollars in frozen bank account. She asked him to act as a beneficiary for a 20% fee by sending her his bank account details. He was cautioned only to use email as her telephone line was being bugged by security agents. The surgeon wrote back and told her that whilst he was indeed a reputable person, he had little financial acumen, as he spent most of his days surgically removing haemorrhoids. And anyway he told her, the percentage for a hospital consultant of his standing should be at least 35%.

DEAR BERTRAND
August 1997

Bertrand Russell's autobiography contains many fruitful observations on the human condition. Allow me one quote.

'One of the symptoms of approaching nervous breakdown is the belief that one's work is terribly important. If I were a medical man, I should prescribe a holiday to any patient who considered his work important'.

I nod my head in agreement with Bertrand. A medically-approved holiday is a very under-valued cure, particularly by doctors themselves. Other non-capsulated and alcohol-free prescriptions that modern doctors fail to appreciate are divorce, murder and a change of occupation. The former are moral issues on which I plead ignorance, but a change of job is a different. An interesting position has arisen in my local health board for a director of complaints with a salary somewhere between £28,000 and £34,000 per annum. Now I'd complain about that for starters.

DOC RUGE
September 2005

Sad to report the death of Dr Daniel Ruge. The name mightn't mean much to you, but he did an awful lot for Ronald Reagan. Ruge was the president's physician for the first of his two terms at the White House. A spinal neurosurgeon by training, he found the four year long stint with a single patient distinctly unglamorous. Ruge described the position as vastly overrated, boring and not in the least bit challenging for any self-respecting medic with good qualifications. Doc Ruge spent his days preparing for emergencies that never happened. Evenings were passed in his office in Washington dressed up in a tuxedo doing crossword puzzles. The White House telephone directory once listed him as chief usher and curator of artifacts. Unlike Ronnie, he wisely refused a second term, though he was widely praised for the way he handled of Reagan's near fatal assassination attempt in 1981.

GREEN BACK
May 2001

Mick the vegetable man finished his weekly rounds before making his way to Dr Murphy's surgery one evening. 'I'm in a bit of trouble, doc. A stick of lettuce seems to have taken root, and it's growing out me back passage! ' Dr Murphy looked puzzled and told Mick to open his belt and hop up on the couch. Following a careful examination, Dr Murphy shook his head. 'I'm afraid it's much worse than you think Mick', he said solemnly, 'this may be just the tip of the iceberg'.

MEET THE WIGGLES
June 2007

I should be canvassing support for another senate election at Trinity this week, but instead, at eleven on a Saturday morning, I am in the Helix theatre in Dublin City University. The place is packed to the rafters. Balloons, streamers, jingles and merchandising are everywhere. No, it's not my campaign rally. the My three years old daughter secretly conspired with her maman to bring papa to a Wiggles concert. For those of you in the dark, the Wiggles are four ascetic-looking Australian men who perform repetitive ditties and high drama for kids whilst wearing Star Trek uniforms. Apparently they are the highest paid entertainers in the Antipodes, earning more than Nicole Kidman and AC/DC combined. We paid handsomely to see Greg, Jeff, Murray and Anthony, but Greg never showed up. Apparently, he now suffers from a chronic condition called orthostatic intolerance. Also known as POTS, short for postural orthostatic tachycardia syndrome, this rarely diagnosed disease was first described in 1993, and can sometimes be misdiagnosed by doctors as panic attacks. Greg was forced to leave the Wiggles a few months ago because every time he stood up, he suffered from vertigo and tiredness. He has been replaced by Sam who does a lovely versions of 'Yummy Yummy', 'Fruit Salad' and 'Big Red Car'. My new campaign songs.

DEADLY SAUSAGES
November 2010

There are an awful lot of speculative and frankly daft scientific scare stories in the newspapers these days. Today it's the turn of sausages. Friends of the Earth, guardians of righteous living and self-appointed judge and jury on planet-friendly practices, have been mouthing off again. They decree that 45,361 lives every year could be saved in the United Kingdom alone, if all of her majesty's subjects reduced meat consumption to less than three times a week. In fact they suggest an arbitrary limit of 210 grams of meat per week. That's one solitary 8 ounce sirloin steak. Newspapers across the UK know that very few readers can afford steak so they dutifully carried the story about restricting yourself to half a sausage a day could save the population of a medium-sized town from extinction. Their figure of 45,361 pricked up my ears, especially when they further broke it down into 31,000 less heart attacks, 9,000 less cancers and 5,000 less strokes. Not a single question was raised about where these figures came from. Thin air I'd say. The representative body of twenty thousand British pork producers was asked to comment on the research. They used the phrase 'over-simplistic'. I'd say that's putting it mildly.

BIGOREXIA
January 2000

Oscar Wilde was on the dollar when he said that we have everything in common with America except language. This quotation prefaces what I write about today, namely the reported discovery state-side of a new-fangled illness called bigorexia. Otherwise known as reverse anorexia, or worse still, weightlifter's woe. Bigorexia, we are now being told, is a body dysmorphic disorder which drives body builders on to greater engorgement of their veins in fitness clubs. Just as anorexic patients mistakenly believe they are too fat, bigorexics think themselves too small, no matter how big they are. A doctor in New York's Mount Sinai school of medicine claims that as many as one person in fifty suffers from the illness. Of those interviewed in a recent study about ten per cent of male bodybuilders and over eighty per cent of female ones had symptoms of the disorder. No matter how much they work out, they still feel puny. This leads them to hide from other people, or wear baggy clothing to disguise their body shape. Surprise, surprise, it responds well to new antidepressants. A new niche market is born.

STRONG COFFEE
February 2008

Mrs Murphy visited her GP to ask for help in reviving her husband's libido. 'What about trying Viagra?' asked the doctor 'Not a chance', she said. 'He won't even take an aspirin'.
'No problem', replied the doctor. 'Just pop the pill into his coffee. He won't even taste it. Give it a try, and call me in a week to let me know how things went'.

Seven days later, Mrs Murphy was back in the surgery.

'Well,' said the GP, 'How did it go?'

'Terrible, just terrible, doctor!' she replied, near to tears.

'Didn't it work then, Mrs Murphy?'

'Too right it did. He'd barely put the coffee mug down, when he turned into a raging, unstoppable love-machine. It was his best performance in twenty years'.

'So what on earth is the problem?'

'Oh doctor. I'll never be able to show my face in Starbucks again'.

SHORT COURSE
January 1998

There's a nice little report in the *Lancet* today suggesting that an old-fashioned consultation with your family doctor can be just as effective as a short course of psychotherapy. Researchers at the Royal Free Hospital in London looked at patients with emotional and stress related problems and found that routine treatment from the family doctor gave as much relief from symptoms as a twelve week course of fifty minute psychotherapy sessions. But we knew that already, didn't we?

DUBLINESE
December 2006

There's a wonderful new book on the shelves this month called *Dublinese – Know What I Mean*. Published by Collins Press in Cork, it's penned by Bernard Share, an English graduate from Trinity College, and a bit of an expert on slang. There are some very nice medical snippets in it. I didn't know for instance that requesting a pint *from the lung* meant one that was poured from a new barrel. Nor did I know that a Dublin man could request a half pint of Guinness by asking for a *GP* (glass of porter). In the days before Mary Harney's smoky coal ban, Dubliners would regularly suffer from *bad bronichals*. The book will help psychiatrists in the capital to brush up on the language of their patients as the book clearly distinguishes what a Dubliner means when he uses various clinical appellations. A *head* is not to be confused with a *header* which in turn is not be mixed up with a *head-the-ball*. When you have mastered these important mental health terms, you can then tackle *thoolermawns*, *thullabawns* and *looderamawns*. A great stocking filler for any *medical skanger* or their *concernded (sic) parents*.

DR LAURA DILLON
October 1999

I have been perusing the third edition of *A Dictionary of Irish Biography*, and can report that it's still a work in progress, as I'm not in it yet. Amongst its many thousands of entries, it has all the usual medical suspects such as Collis, Stokes, Graves and Stevens, but perhaps the most unusual physician is Laurence Michael Dillon. Laurence Michael was born Laura Maud Dillon in May 1915. Her mother died soon after birth and she was raised by two aunts in Kent. Anatomically a healthy female, Dillon's deep voice and facial hair confirmed her feelings that she was emotionally and physically a man. In the early 1940s she had a mastectomy and went on male hormone pills prescribed by a sympathetic doctor. In 1945, Dillon entered medical school in Trinity College and during summer holidays continued to have protracted and painful operations under the legendary plastic surgeon Sir Harold Gillies. Dr Dillon graduated in 1951 and served as a ship's surgeon on voyages all over the world. In 1958, his secret was discovered and he was outed by the *Sunday Express*. Dr Dillon fled to a Buddhist monastery in Bengal. He was ordained a Tibetan monk and lived a generous and primitive life until his premature death in a Punjab hospital in 1962, the same year two books by him were published in London. Dr Dillon was just 47.

RHINOPLASTY IN ROSCOMMON
May 2013

A kind librarian has sent me a fascinating description of what must be Ireland's very first nose job, or rhinoplasty. The operation took place not in Dublin, but in Roscommon. In a book written by Isaac Weld in the 1830s, he describes a ward round at the county infirmary in the company of its surgeon and physician, a Dr Lysaght. During the visit, the writer met an out-door servant of the same doctor, who had lost his nose. Dr Lysaght admitted him to his own hospital, and refashioned a new one for him.

He did this by cutting an incomplete triangle of skin from the forehead, reversing and peeling it downwards to where the nose should have been, before shaping and attaching it to each side. A lock of curly hair was then grown downwards to hide the forehead scar. The servant was so pleased that he still fancied himself as 'a favourite amongst the women'.

The general description of Roscommon's infirmary and the ailments that afflicted the local population at the time is fascinating. The people of the town have a very proud medical history to uphold today as they struggle to maintain their hospital. The writer, Mr Weld, was told that feverish patients were not admitted to the main hospital and that any patients who came down with a fever, were removed to an 'outer apartment'. Such isolation facilities and policies would be welcome in Irish hospitals today. On his appointment, Dr Lysaght managed to double bed numbers from 25 to 50 and the hospital always reserved six empty beds for emergencies. His 'good management' is mentioned as there was no material increase in expense to the public. This signifies that doctors acted in an administrative capacity long before the modern era of professional managers. We are told that amongst the poor of Roscommon, inflammatory and bowel complaints were rare. The writers tells us that Connaught people, like Italians, did not 'stand for bleeding' so this common practice of the time was rarely performed there. Frequently seen diseases included scurvy (vitamin C deficiency, scrofula (tuberculosis in neck glands), dyspepsia (indigestion), dropsy (swelling caused by heart pump failure) and skin diseases, including one oddity called the Connaught button. This seems to be related to the mythical Aleppo button, a disease to which visitors to the towns of Aleppo, Baghdad and Damascus were prone. Aleppo button was a skin affliction, a hard swelling, often on the face, which was painful for a few weeks, prone to secondary infection, and finally burst open leaving behind it an ugly scar. It was particularly disliked by women who at one time would avoid travel to these towns in case they were afflicted. Legend had it that the diseases could start any time up to two years after your visit. In Iraq it was better known as the Baghdad Boil. In medical terms this condition is known as cutaneous leishmaniasis and is caused by a parasite carried to the skin by a biting sand fly. I have my doubts as to whether Roscommon had many of these.

PROVOCATIVE PATIENTS
June 2000

The Italian medical magazine, *MD*, is warning ladies in Adriatic and Mediterranean climes to dress less provocatively when visiting the doctor. Apparently the *belle signore* are leading handsome clinicians astray in the afternoons by overcoming them with aphrodisiac perfumes, expensive underwear, exaggerated make-up and horror of horrors, fish-net tights. One male medico was quoted as saying that their behaviour 'makes men think more about bed than illness'. One hears rumours of this sort of carry-on in obstetric practice, but I don't foresee see a rush of Irish general practitioners to the sunnier shores of bella Italia. They are more than happy with current modest levels of exposure which allow full concentration to be maintained on bunions, leg ulcers, varicosities and rams-horn toe nails.

PISSING IN THE SNOW
August 1997

I am reading the wonderfully titled *Pissing in the Snow: Ozark Mountain Folktales*. It concerns a high altitude part of Missouri in which many Irish immigrants settled in the 19th century. One story tells of a wizened old country doctor who could treat anything. Well it seems one time, a patient from the hills came into his office with three complaints. 'Doc,' he said, 'I can't taste nothin', I can't tell the truth, and I can't remember nothin' besides'. Well the old doc thought about this for a minute and went back into the apothecary. He made up two capsules full with cow hooey, and gave them to the man, telling him to take one immediately and chew it well. Well, the man did as he was told, bit down and started chewing, then yelled out, 'Yeachhhhh... this stuff tastes like shee-it'. 'Uh huh,' the doctor said, 'Well I see that you can taste, and you're certainly telling the truth now. And the next time that you're memory is acting up, just take the other pill'. And the old doc charged the man fifteen bucks and sent him on his way, and never did hear no trouble from him after that.

KIDZ HEALTH
August 2007

Some holiday reading left me a bit cold this summer. For two euro I picked up a new magazine called *Kidz Health*, tagged as 'Ireland's first health magazine for kids'. I do hope it's the last. Packed with tips on 'making plans and working out how you are going to get there' and 'feeling happy that your body is working well', it's perfectly packaged for parents who want to pass congenital health neurosis onto their offspring. If you want your kids (six to ten year olds to be precise) to start worrying about exactly how many minutes exercise they do each day, the precise nutritional content of what they eat, warts, rashes, scars and a host contagious diseases, *Kidz Health* is perfect. The strangest page was one that tells children how to increase their carbohydrate intake. Our children have a whole lifetime ahead of them of worrying about health matters. But I don't it does any good to kick-start them at just six years old.

NOCTURNAL FLOWERS
October 2010

An American happened upon a piece I wrote about medical terminology, and how it varies from country to country. She sent the following tale which she heard from an aunt who attended a New York city nursing school in the 1940s. The urine bottle provided to male patients for night-time emergencies in the training hospital was known colloquially as a vase. However one of the student nurses was quite unaware of the terminology. When a man asked 'Nurse, may I please have a vase?', she hesitated for a second and replied 'Well yes of course sir, how big is your bouquet?'

WHERE THERE'S A WILL
September 1997

I have to say, there's not an awful lot of public sympathy out there for the financial worries of hospital consultants. And they are not helped by positioning in today's newspaper. I am reading an article which says consultants are going to dig their heels and sturdily reject a government offer to increase their pay by 9% in return for a change of working conditions. Just below the news item is this week's wills. Led by a late ear, nose and throat surgeon from Dublin who has just left a net estate of one and a half million pounds. Ouch!

W.H.AUDEN AND OBESITY
April 2012

Though he died almost forty years ago, the poet Wystan Hugh Auden has yet to be forgiven in his native England for heading off to the United States in the same year that the second world war broke out. The fact that he sailed into New York a full eight months before Hitler invaded Poland never cut mustard with those critics who labelled much of his work as that of a deserter. The fact that Auden leaned left and was bisexual too, perhaps tipped the balance on these scales of injustice. The hundredth anniversary of his birth passed in 2007, and it received barely a mention. Little of his work is celebrated, with the exception of *Funeral Blues* which stopped all the clocks in the celebrated film *Four Weddings and a Funeral*. The shabby treatment of Auden contrasts with the endless honouring of John Betjeman who worked in Dublin as a press officer (some even claimed he was a spy) during the war. W.H. Auden was the youngest child of a doctor and nurse who fell for each other whilst training in a London hospital. His father had a successful general practice in York and left it to become a pensionable school medical officer. Later he was to be appointed professor of public health at Birmingham University. Moderate obesity was quite the fashion in Auden's time and that of his father. A healthy baby was a fat bonny one and a man's prosperity was judged, not by his pearly orthodontics, but by the girth of his waist. Auden wrote a lovely short poem about doctors, which I suspect his father might have approved of.

> *Give me a doctor, partridge-plump,*
> *Short in the leg and broad in the rump,*
> *An endomorph with gentle hands,*
> *Who'll never make absurd demands*
> *That I abandon all my vices,*
> *Nor pull a long face in a crisis,*
> *But with a twinkle in his eye*
> *Will tell me that I have to die.*

A BLOODY MISTAKE
April 2007

A nurse phoned the *Liveline* radio programme the other day to defend the decision of her colleagues not to take blood tests. This was a non-nursing duty, she said. When asked who would be able to take them, she suggested that this was the job of a haematologist! I suspect this may have been a nurse who never saw the inside of a hospital. Surely everyone on the wards known that a haematologist treats blood disorders like anaemias, haemophilias, leukaemias and lymphomas. The person who takes hospital blood tests during the day is a phlebotomist. At night it has traditionally been the job of the nurse, the junior doctor or the man from Transylvania.

FEEDING VITAMINS TO BIRDS
November 2012

I recall very little Irish from my 1970s school curriculum, but I do remember a short story by Patrick Pearse, about a small boy who is visited each year by birds in his garden. *Eoghainín na nÉan* was a sentimental yarn that ended with the death of the boy. I think tuberculosis caused his demise, though perhaps this was not stated in the text. The story came to mind the other day when I was reading an article, as doctors do, about the bird feeding industry. This lark is big business now, worth £200 million a year in the United Kingdom alone. Every year there is growing competition amongst seed merchants to capture new market share. I was thrilled to read the views of a scientist who said that although all birds need to eat, there is no evidence that wild birds are deficient in any vitamins. So if like me, you have taken to hanging cages and pots from the apple and pear trees, the plain non-vitamin stuff will probably do fine. You just have to decide between the squirrel proof mixture with chilli extract, the garden songbird blend or the finch energy mix with added niger seeds. Soon they'll be selling probiotics to the magpies.

MRS ROBINSON'S CANDLE
November 1997

'Tell our roving President that her fatuous low-watt, low-powered, cheapest available, warmly welcoming electrical candle in her window, brought no comfort to our diaspora and could now, permanently, be switched off. Those exiled by hunger, joblessness and poverty . . . those sleeping rough in London's cardboard city, in the prisons, the jails, the mental hospitals, the alcoholic wards, the brothels, the kitchens of cheap-labour hotels, the building sites, the dole queues, and skid rows of the world, too poor to come home for Christmas'.

Bitter comment indeed for Ireland's former president Mrs. Mary Robinson from the late Dr Noel Browne who was less than enchanted with the 'roseate black-tie Waldorf Astoria Dorchester Hotel expatriate black-tie diaspora' that received the patronage of our former president. Dr Browne's own light went out not long after he wrote these words. He might have been pleased to know that Mrs. Robinson's electric bulb soon followed him into the darkness.

AMERICAN HEALTHCARE
February 2005

The Spectator magazine claims to be the oldest English language magazine continuously in print. It's currently edited by a bonking blonde called Boris who spends his days pedalling his bicycle between Doughty Street and the houses of parliament at Westminster. Last week there was a leading article which lavished praise on the American healthcare system. Apparently they keep their cancer patients alive for far longer than their British counterparts. The statistics quoted in the piece, if indeed they are true, are quite startling. 60% of Americans with colon cancer survive five years compared with 40% in the UK. In the more difficult to treat oesophageal cancer, the Americans get twelve in every hundred patients beyond the five year mark compared with just seven in Britain. In prostate disease, their figures are even more astonishing. *The Spectator* claims that just 19% of those diagnosed with prostate cancer in the United States die of the disease compared with 57% in the United Kingdom. The article was challenging, and didn't shy away from the fact that shiny apple skins of the American system can hide a rotten core. Their doctors may well keep you alive longer, as long as you don't a mind price tag flirting with bankruptcy.

The Lancet has also been looking across the Atlantic for the good, the bad and the ugly of American healthcare. Their recent commentary demonstrates the folly of either criticising or lauding the United States health system as a whole. The same doctors who warn against the dangers of health league tables at home, often delight in the fact that the World Health Organisation awarded the USA a miserable 29th place in the premiership of healthy nations. But *The Lancet* points out that it is the study of individual states in America that reaps rewards. Why does Minnesota have health parameters much better than Canada and Europe? Why does Louisiana have healthcare attributes of a third world despot nation? Race, ethnicity, class and wealth are undoubtedly major factors. The wealthy white American avails of superior health services precisely because they are offered to him and he finds them affordable. But the key finding in this report is that Minnesota spends eight times more per person on public health than Louisiana. $185 a year versus $22 in the poorer state. States that plough money into acute hospitals at the expense of primary care services, reap fewest rewards. There are lessons for us to learn in Ireland from these statistics. But learning is never enough. We don't seem to have a capacity to change. With our track record, all that ever happens with extra public health spending is that it's swallowed up by extortionate pay claims and obese salaries.

BLESS ME FATHER
May 2005

'Bless me Father, for I have sinned, I have been with a loose woman'. The priest asks, 'Is that you, little Tommy Shaughnessy?' 'Yes, Father, it is'. 'And, who was the woman you were with?' 'I can't be tellin' you, Father. I don't want to ruin her reputation'. 'Well, Tommy, I'm sure to find out sooner or later, so you may as well tell me now. Was it Brenda O'Malley?' 'I cannot say'. 'Was it Patricia Kelly?' 'I'll never tell'. 'Was it Mary Shannon?' 'I'm sorry, but I can't name her'. 'Was it Kathy Morgan?' 'My lips are sealed'. 'Was it Fiona Connors, then?' 'Please, Father, I cannot tell you'. The priest sighs in frustration. 'You're a steadfast lad, Tommy Shaughnessy, and I admire that. But you've sinned, and you must atone. You cannot attend mass for twelve weeks. Be off with you now.' Tommy walks back to his pew. His friend Sean slides over and whispers, 'What did you get?' 'Three month's holidays' says Tommy 'and five good leads'.

WINTER MEETING
November 2005

At the recent winter meeting of the Irish College of General practitioners, the new professor in charge of the Health Service Executive told family doctors that they need to become more like GAA clubs in the community. I am acting on this advice and will soon be converting my waiting room into a drinking den at night. When I'm on house calls, my surgery chair will be used by Fianna Fáil TDs and councillors for their constituency clinics. I will discourage patients from having non-Irish treatments and refrain from preaching alien healthcare philosophies or joining foreign medical forces. My lottery applications for floodlights, a fully equipped gymnasium, orthopaedic camogie equipment, a dance floor and staff changing facilities are in the post. And I'll be asking the Gardaí to sanction bar extensions twice a month. Now I just need to find a sponsor for the tweed jacket.

BURMESE DAYS
March 2013

I found last winter to be a particularly long one, and cold too, despite relatively little snow in the suburbs. It didn't get any warmer, or shorter, when I set myself the task of reading the entire canon of George Orwell. Having devoured all the facts I could gather about him from biographies, the next logical step was to digest his fiction, from the early *Burmese Days* to his final seminal works, *Animal Farm* and *Nineteen Eighty-four*. Orwell's first job was as a policeman in Burma, and *Burmese Days* is a fascinating account of how a corrupt local magistrate sets out to ruin the reputation of a well-respected Indian doctor. The plot thickens against the background of a lazy British colonial community who do little but drink through the afternoons and engage in casual racism. I enjoyed the description of Dr Veraswami's dusty hospital with its bad water-supply and 'the inertia of sweepers and half-trained assistant surgeons'. Its outpatients department had just one table, two chairs and a crooked portrait of Queen Victoria. A procession of patients queued at the table which had one drawer to house the doctor's cigarettes. Examinations were quick and perfunctory. All patients who attended Dr Veraswami got a prod in the back and an ear laid on their chest for a quick listen. A compounder across the yard filled prescription bottles with water and various vegetable dyes. The compounder was so badly paid that he kept the real medicine to sell illegally on the street. Dr Veraswami's assistant surgeons were less thorough. They simply demanded 'Where is your pain - head, back or belly?' And depending on the reply, one of three prescriptions was pulled from three pre-prepared piles. Another world class health service.

AN ORTHOPAEDIC CHASTENING
September 2006

The General Medical Council in Britain has become rather tetchy. It's all part of the Dr Shipman legacy of a certain which has threatened to scupper the Council and the whole concept of self-regulation. You can get yourself hauled up and thrown out these days for more or less anything. There was a case reported in the press recently of an orthopaedic surgeon being suspended for six months because he told a young teenage patient to 'pull himself together'. At least that what was the newspaper reported. But there was a little bit more to it. The surgeon had dismissed the boy's parents as 'pushy Americans' when they suggested to him that their son's fractured elbow might have gone septic after a stabilisation procedure. No antibiotics had been prescribed, and as luck would have it, the parents were quite correct. They also pointed out that the boy should not have been prescribed aspirin by the surgeon, as it was contra-indicated in his age group. The surgeon told the Medical Council that he was unaware that it was no longer suitable for use in children with fever. Both parents also told the enquiry that the bone surgeon told them that 'a British patient would sit back and read the Sunday papers and let the doctor do his job'. Wise parents, chastened doctor.

ENERGY OF THE FLOWER
September 2011

A young pharmacist of my acquaintance is a man of rigorous science. He is also a witty observer of the flora and fauna of the 'natural therapy' world that come into his shop flogging magical wares and angel cures. Now he is in the happy position of not owning the premises. He is a pharmacist employee, so he is not the final arbiter of what universal remedies make it onto the shelves. Recently he was busying himself behind the dispensary when a lady representative propelled herself in to the shop announcing she was from a 'naturalist' company. Given her slightly dubious title, my pharmacist friend dared not turn around, lest his visual field be filled with the resplendent form of a lady sans fig leaf. He did eavesdrop however as the sales lady and the counter assistant launched into an intense tête-à-tête about the benefits of the snake oil that she was peddling. The counter assistant was assured that the line of products was totally safe and without side effects as, and I quote, 'they do not actually contain the flower itself but rather the energy of the flower and that's why they are so safe'. Ah the natural world. Sure you couldn't even make it up.

FURTHER MEDICAL TAXONOMIES
April 2002

I am still receiving plenty of collective nouns for medical specialists. We have a hot-flush, an islet and a secretion of endocrinologists, a cluster of medical epidemiologists and a cell of microbiologists. Or how about a paralysis, a ganglion or a seizure of neurologists and a drill of neurosurgeons. Kids could be treated by a centile, a croup or a bawl of paediatricians. Mental health could be improved by a confusion, a brainstorm, a couch or a soothing of psychiatrists. And if all else fails, call in an army of general surgeons, a finger of proctologists and a mindset of psychologists.

THE CHOSEN DOCTOR
July 2011

An outstanding obstetrician and gynaecologist, who had retired from practice in Dublin, died last year and received a lovely obituary in the medical newspapers. The tribute said that he was especially well regarded by his colleagues in the maternity services who had universal respect for his skill and judgement in the labour ward. Exemplifying the high regard in which he was held, the obituary said that a very large number of fellow medics entrusted their wives to his care when they were pregnant. He was known as the 'chosen obstetrician' of the medical profession. It set me thinking that there really is no greater honour that you can bestow on a colleague than to entrust him or her with the care of your family in time of need. A question that patients rarely ask, and one which they certainly should ask a good deal more, is 'where would you go yourself with that, doctor?'

ALTERNATIVE PRACTITIONERS
August 1998

An elderly lady told her family doctor recently that her daughter would like to make an appointment with him to get her thyroid gland treated. He asked about the precise nature of her glandular ailment and was told that she had no symptoms, but that the 'foot specialist' had advised getting her thyroid treated. The doctor pulled her file out to see what foot surgeon the daughter was attending. She wasn't seeing anyone. He asked the mother if it was a chiropodist that the daughter was attending. 'Oh no doctor, it was one of those foot specialists who read your feet and then tell you what's wrong with you'. The doctor sat back and let out a sigh. How he has grown to detest that new breed of alternative practitioner, the diagnostic reflexologist.

NEW ETHICS
August 2003

Pat Kenny's radio show took a medical twist the other morning when he interviewed the author of a paper on the dying art of medical slang. I think the article was published in a journal called *Ethics & Behaviour*. Politically correct it was not, as the ears of patients up and down the land were treated to dozens of disrespectful acronyms, execrable rhyming slangs and other odious terms that generations of doctors once used to describe them. Diabetics are no longer called *Betties*. Nor are highly malignant tumours described as *cheeriomas*. A puddle of blood is not *house red*. Long stay wards for older patients are not known as *departure lounges*. Anaesthetists no longer suffer the indignity of being known as *gassers* and nobody prefaces the surnames of any surgeons with *slasher*. And woe betide any casualty officer who refers to psychiatrists as *pest control* or the *freud squad*. Only saints now tread the corridors of health.

LETTERS FROM OUTPATIENTS
July 1999

The letters that hospital clinics send back to family doctors have become a bit sterile in recent years. Everyone is so worried about where the next lawsuit or tribunal is coming from, that there seems to be no room in the medical inn for poetic licence or verbal spontaneity. Thankfully there is still the odd consultant whose humour and insight pours forth from their clinical pens. Last week I received a lovely concise outpatient letter from an ear, nose and throat surgeon which read simply: *Dear Doctor, This lady gets the prize today for her tonsils - they are enormous! Surgery required.* Two sentences that say it all. No jargon. No padding. No 'thank you for allowing me to share in her care'. Just plain language that we all understand.

FORENSIC EVIDENCE
November 2010

I read a fascinating interview the other day with Dr Stuart Hamilton, a well-respected forensic pathologist who works all over the United Kingdom from his base in Newcastle. Forensic pathology is an unusual medical speciality in that it rarely has waiting lists. Only patients who have met with suspicious ends appear on their trolleys. Dr Hamilton was asked how his job makes him feel and he came up with quite an appropriate word, fatalistic. He spoke of how he meets patients with the most dreadful lifestyles who live well into their nineties and others who live by all the rules of health promotion and yet perish at fifty. Most interesting were his comments about Sir Bernard Spilsbury (1877-1947), England's most famous pathologist. Spilsbury was known to generations of medical and criminology students as 'the father of forensic medicine'. Though not highly regarded by academics in his day, he was known as being pretty well unchallengeable in court. He carried judges and juries with him wherever he went. Spilsbury also devised the 'murder bag', a case of equipment required by any forensic investigator in the aftermath of a suspicious death. Famous trials to involve Spilsbury include the case of Dr Crippen and the Brides in the Bath murders. Dr Hamilton suggested in his interview that much of Spilsbury's evidence would simply not stand up to scrutiny in a modern courtroom. A solid argument against the death penalty.

ANOTHER DOSE OF DR DOG
December 2007

Happy to report that after thirteen years, the children's book Dr Dog has a worthy successor. Babette Cole's follow-up is called *A Dose of Dr Dog* and the diagnoses are every bit as disgusting as in the classic first book. This time Dr Dog has his tropical holiday disturbed by the Gumboyle family and sets off into the jungle to search for herbal medicines. He meets Professor Hund, a bit of a quack merchant, and what follows is a veritable feast of travel medicine with pooh flies, insect bites, sunburn, motion sickness, and really venomous looking spots on the bot. The sturdy hardback is an absolute must for the paediatric wing of any doctor's waiting room. I wrote to Babette Cole a few years ago asking if it might be possible to purchase an original drawing or sketch from Dr Dog. In a very pleasant reply that I didn't really expect to get, she told me they had not been sold but were a constituent part of her rainy day pension fund. Sensible lady. Should they ever come to market, I'll let you know after the day after the auction.

COLOUR-CODING HOSPITAL DOCTORS
May 2001

It's very easy for patients to get confused by the different categories of specialist that visit them in hospital. A lady wrote to the *Journal of the Canadian Medical Association* recently and suggested that doctors should start to wear colour-coded coats. Red ones perhaps for haematologists who specialise in blood diseases, stripy pink and blue for obstetricians who deliver babies, and black overalls for pathologists who consult with their patients *post mortem*. It's a very interesting idea, but I'm not so sure that infectious diseases specialists or proctologists are going to appreciate the particular shade of uniform we have in mind for them.

SUCCESSFUL OUTCOME
January 2004

True story from a GP colleague. A delightful older lady from south Dublin had a cardiac arrest at home and was rushed to the emergency department of the Adelaide and Meath Hospital at Tallaght. She was successfully resuscitated, or at least that is what she meant to tell the GP on her discharge from hospital. What she actually told her family doctor was that the doctors in the hospital had to *resuffocate* her twice.

THE CURSE OF MITTERAND
January 2001

No new year celebrations for Dr Claude Gubler. He learned just after Christmas that France's highest court has ruled against his return to medicine. Gubler was the doctor who depicted the final years of his most eminent patient in a book called *The Great Secret*. The deceased patient was the enigmatic French President Francois Mitterand, who hid ten years of prostate cancer from a respectful public with the connivance of his doctor. Gubler was summarily struck off the French medical register for what was seen as a betrayal of confidence. He was also penalised back in 1997 for falsification of the President's regular medical assessments. Maybe it's just as well we don't subject Irish leaders to annual palpation, percussion, auscultation and digital examination of their prostates.

CENTRES OF EXCELLENCE
January 2006

At a health board meeting some moons ago, a breast surgeon was invited in to lecture county councillors about the many advantages having specialised breast clinics and centres of excellence. Survival rates were far better than in a system where every tumbledown county hospital with a surgeon was trying to provide the same service. After carefully explaining how the clinics work, how expertise is built up, and how it is vital to concentrate resources in one regional centre of excellence, a councillor stood up to congratulate the surgeon. He spoke at length about the perils of breast cancer, the great value of these centres and then went on to urge that one be set up in every town in the country.

CINEMA ADVERTISING
February 2012

There is a group of women out there, perhaps larger than we think, who aren't happy about the use of cinemas to worry and nag them about their risks of getting the big C. One lady told me recently that advertisements from cancer screening services are spoiling her enjoyment of her rare nights out. It would appear that targeting of particular groups is the order of the day. If it's a film for younger women, then they are likely to be urged into screening for cervical cancer. And if it's an adaptation of the Brontë sisters or Jane Austen, with Colin Firth in the starring role, then the advertisements warn about the dire consequences of not having mammography for breast cancer. All very important I am sure, but it might surprise health screeners to learn that there are still some people in this busy world who attend cinema to escape from the daily worries of life. They don't mind powders that get your whites whiter, the delights of the happy ring house or previews of forthcoming attractions. But they don't wish to be reminded of cancer, mortality, diagnosis, illness, screening and death every single time they pay for a cinema ticket. They have a valid point.

PACKETS OF TEN
June 2007

I had an interesting chat with a newsagent the other evening about the ban on packets of ten cigarettes which has now come into force. The shop is selling more tobacco than ever and its owner has lost count of the number of 'ten-only' customers whose consumption has quietly risen since they were forced to buy bigger packets. The muddy thinking behind this ban was that it might discourage children from starting. If that was true, there might be some merit in the measure, but I can't help thinking it's a bit like banning a half pint of beer to cure a nation of alcoholism. I would favour a reduction of the number of cigarettes. Why not have packets with two cigarettes, or five? It's illegal to sell them to children anyway and if this was adequately enforced, the argument for a minimum of twenty in every packct is simply not there.

NEW YEAR RESOLVE
December 1997

Doctors are rarely happy with the number of patients under their care. Younger ones complain that they haven't enough and older practitioners always pine for less. With new year upon us, we have been devising some January new year resolutions that senior doctors could adopt to reduce their onerous lists.

- Every time a patient asks you to sign something, get into the habit of asking them to sign a waiver.
- When a particularly demanding patient asks you to do an extra favour for them, ask them if they want fries with it.
- Give names to all of your pens and insist that consultations can't begin until they're all present.
- Come to work in your pyjamas.
- Put a picture of your mother-in-law on your practice brochure.
- Don't put up your prices. That has been known to attract patients who think you must be good. Drop your price, drastically.
- Develop an unnatural fear of staplers.
- While sitting at your desk, soak your fingers in Dettol.
- Schedule every fifth appointment for 6am on Saturday mornings.
- Make up nicknames for all your patients and refer to them only by these names. 'Your heart sounds good, Bonzo' or 'there's something for yourself, Big Lass!'

SAMSON'S MENTAL HEALTH
March 2001

Psychiatrists from the University of California have been assessing the mental states of some famous biblical figures and have published their early clinical findings in the journal *Archives of General Psychiatry*. These patients have been on a waiting list for 3,000 years which is probably about the same length of time as it takes to get an orthopaedic appointment in Mayo. First up on the couch was Samson. The modern day inquisitors pondered his setting fire to Philistine fields and his reported cruelty to small animals. They looked into his bullying, his fighting and his reported use of the jawbone of an ass to inflict hurt on others. With his failure to conform to social norms, constant lying, impulsivity, aggression, reckless disregard for safety and lack of remorse, Samson easily met six of the seven criteria for antisocial personality disorder. They had no effective treatment to offer, so if they have any sense, I'd say they'll find him a good woman and let the barber surgeons at him.

WORST JOBS IN SCIENCE
September 2003

Popular Science magazine is doing some splendid research into the most unpopular jobs in science and medicine. Pig farms that go in for a spot of breeding and fertility work are always on the look-out for a good barnyard masturbators (gloves supplied free of charge). And I cannot imagine that dysentery stool sample analyst on your curriculum vitae would appeal to potential new employers. Another strong contender is flatus odour judge. An American gastroenterologist recently hired a team of two of these, otherwise known as full-time fart sniffers, for his research laboratory in Minneapolis. Runners up for science's most unpopular jobs are Brazilian mosquito researchers, isolation chamber testers, bovine fistula feeders, prison rape researchers and corpse flower growers.

GENTLE BEN
August 1997

One of the world's greatest golfers has moved on to the 20th tee. Ben Hogan, who was 84 years old, has died from a massive stroke. He had been in failing health for some years with a diagnosis of Alzheimer's disease I believe. No golfer worked harder at his trade than Hogan and his haul of nine major titles ranks him well up the all-time order of merit. Hogan's writings on the mechanics of golf, in particular his anatomical study of the golf swing have stood up well to the scrutiny of the computer age. Looking through his textbooks on the mechanics of golf, I feel he would have made an excellent clinician. His career was all the more remarkable for the tragedy he endured. His father committed suicide in Dublin, Texas when Ben was just nine. Then in 1949, the golfer himself suffered horrific crush injuries to his legs in a car accident that left him with chronic pain for the rest of his life. In the immediate aftermath of the crash, doctors wondered whether he would even walk again. But just sixteen months later, Hogan lifted the US open title. Even as his memory declined, Hogan still remembered to practice his golf each day. A golfer well worth remembering.

OVERHEARD IN DUBLIN
September 2007

A little book called *Overheard in Dublin Again* is a real treat. Its authors specialise in recording the off-stage wit of Dubliners - on buses, queues and even in doctors' waiting rooms. My favourite story was of a rather narked young man who wasn't too happy with the triage system at a hospital casualty department. He told the nurse in no uncertain terms 'I'm bleedin' bleedin'!'

Two older dears were chin-wagging about multicultural Dublin when one spotted a row of ethnic shops and turned to the other with a 'Jaysus, there's bleedin' Chinese embolisms everywhere'. I think she meant to say emblems. And there was another conversation from the emergency department of St Vincent's Hospital where a visitor overheard a girl replying to the question 'What religion are you?' with 'normal'. In St James's Hospital a doctor was sent in to calm a particularly difficult patient. His entreaty 'would you relax' met with an unexpected reply. 'I'm gonna f***ing relax your head against the wall in a minute'.

A charming book from a not always charming city.

CAT SCRATCH FEVER
April 2002

I don't recall a condition known as Cat Scratch Fever ever being mentioned on differential diagnosis lists at my medical school. But this feline-acquired indisposition features in the clinical review section of this week's *British Medical Journal*. Pussy Cat, it would seem, is a potential villain in all cases of unilateral lymphadenopathy. In English, this means one sided swollen glands, perhaps in the groin, the armpit or in the neck. Finding one-sided swelling of glands is not uncommon in general practice. A 29 year old lady with a painless swelling in her groin was referred to hospital where she underwent blood tests, scans and a biopsy of her lumpiness. A condition called sarcoidosis was initially suspected, but blood tests, particularly one for a bacterial bug called Bartonella, gave clues as to the origin of her problem. This bug was named after a chap called Barton, not an Irish scientist, but a south American, I believe. Cats can contract the infection from ticks, sand flies, fleas, mosquitoes or lice. There is usually an element of bloodsucking going on here. This particular patient improved over time without antibiotics. She later helped confirm the diagnosis by recalling that a neighbour's cat had scratched her in the groin about a month before she became unwell. They say 24,000 people get cat scratch disease each year in the United States, the majority of them children. Patients with cat scratch disease are likely to own a young cat (under 12 months) or to have been scratched or bitten by someone else's kitten. A well named ailment. And worth remembering in any household dominated by a cat.

TOO MANY VOICES
February 2012

It's high time we had some rationalisation of health promotion services in this country. Last month, the cross border SafeFood agency came out of the oven all hot and bothered about the hidden health dangers of twelve inch pizzas with meat toppings.

And before you could add spicy wedges to it, the Food Safety Authority of Ireland were out of their traps boasting about the 11,000 food complaints they handle each year. The HSE have their own vast army of healthy food promoters too. And the Department of Health hardly lets a day go by without putting a minister and bananas in the same sentence of a press release.

Then we have all these bodies sponsored by the food industry, that have worthy titles but are in effect vessels for the promotion of a particular sector, be it milk, meat, fish or whatever the food of the day is. Methinks our health promotion foodie room has far too many voices in it. And when they all speak together, nobody listens and nobody gets heard.

HEAT IN THE KITCHEN
April 2004

I had a letter from a GP in the north west of the country detailing a true story from his surgery. He had an elderly man in who was beginning feminising hormone injections for prostatic cancer and was warning him about possible menopause-type side effects like hot flushes, heavy sweating and enlargement of the breasts. The man returned four weeks later for his second jab, not at all pleased. 'Oh yes, everything you told me might happen, did happen' he said 'but you failed to warn me of the worst one of all.' 'And what might that have been?' enquired his doctor. 'Every time I went into the kitchen the smoke alarm went off!'

MISSING NOTES
September 2011

You cannot turn on the news these evenings without hearing tales about the whereabouts of confidential hospital notes. I've lost count of the number of incidents, but safe to say that when your records are turning up in graveyards, bogs, disused building sites, landfills, new estates and household bins, it's little wonder they're never there at the time of your hospital appointment.

Medical record management in Ireland is still very much in the dark ages. Last week I heard of a case where a general practitioner had sold his surgery premises many years ago, but the family who purchased the old house are still receiving confidential records from local hospitals to this day. These include appointment letters, consultant reports, blood tests, x-ray reports and even cancer diagnoses. The worst thing about this sort of event is not that it is happening. It is happening, and it is taking place countrywide every single day. The worst thing is that nobody in the health service actually cares.

DR BIGGLE'S JOURNEY
January 1998

The next time your doctor gets a house call from Mrs Murphy to say that Mr Murphy has collapsed over his Weetabix, he may pause to think before racing through the rush hour traffic. Dr Anna Biggle is a 55 year old family doctor from Locks Heath in Hampshire. She had such an emergency recently and was caught by the police doing 51 miles per hour in the early morning traffic in a 30 miles per hour zone. For her diligence she was fined and had her driving license endorsed by three points. On hearing of Dr Biggle's case, a spokesman for the British Medical Association, bemoaned the fact that there are no exceptions for doctors when it comes to speed limits, no matter what the emergency. This is an unsatisfactory state of affairs and I dare say that Ireland is no different in this regard. One wonders why it's all right for visiting politicians and dignitaries travelling for non-essential work Dublin Castle to be given such fast liberties with the traffic laws, whilst doctors on emergency call-outs is hindered rather than helped by police motorcycles. Just for the record, Dr Biggle's patient sadly passed away.

LEAS CROSS
November 2006

I have been perusing the report of Professor Desmond O'Neill into the Leas Cross nursing home scandal. My particular interest was to find out more about how medical cover at this nursing home operated. This section of his report makes for particularly unnerving reading. At any one time, just a single off-premises general practitioner was providing cover for its one hundred and eleven patients. Professor O'Neill saw no documents outlining training for the post. He saw no policies in place for medical cover. Nor did he see any other policies on areas such as immunisation, infection control or medication review. Professor O'Neill spotted two instances in the nursing notes where there was difficulty in contacting a doctor, in one case extending for three days. Nearly all prescriptions were written in a different handwriting to that of the doctor's signature. There was no record of any pneumococcal vaccines having been prescribed on patient notes despite a significant number of residents with heart and lung diseases who required this immunisation.

The professor made some very worthwhile recommendations in his report about medical cover in nursing homes. For care centres that do not use patients' own GPs, he suggests that a minimum qualification of a diploma of medicine for the elderly or equivalent should be instituted. He insists on better team work with multi-disciplinary support and specialist back-up from consultants in geriatric medicine and psychiatry of old age.

Some GPs have now abandoned nursing home work entirely, leaving a paltry service even more stretched than it was. A family doctor has written to tell me of some of his nursing home experiences. Recently he was called and notified that a patient didn't eat all of her cheese and crackers at the finale of her supper. He tells me this was classified as an 'adverse event' by staff, and the HSE dictates that all adverse events are now to be notified to patient's GP. He then had a request to examine a man who 'may have fallen and injured his hip'. 'Where is he now?' asked the doctor. 'Oh, he's gone out to buy a newspaper,' was the reply. Then he was asked for a visit to approve and sign a form so that a nursing home could use cot sides. These are now deemed to be restraints. He was also asked to confirm that a resident (of five years standing) does not have coeliac disease and could continue to have toast for his breakfast. He was requested to visit and examine a patient who had not passed a bowel motion for just two days to see if he might benefit from a laxative prescription. Finally he was asked to visit a feverless patient with a headache. The nurse had refused to give her paracetamol without a handwritten prescription. He ended his letter on a cautionary note. 'Much more of this and I'll be declining to treat any patients in nursing homes in future'. I suspect he won't be the only one.

Before there is any more talk of beefed up inspectorates, somebody needs to develop a set of medical standards for all institutions that provide long term care of the elderly patient. As I see it, Irish general practice simply doesn't have the manpower or resources to provide 24/7 cover to nursing homes.

Some family doctors might welcome the opportunity to close up surgery, do further training and take on full-time positions covering one or two nursing homes only. That would be a worthwhile development. But they will need to be replaced in day to day practice. They will also need to be paid a salary, either by nursing homes, or by a state that feigns interest in the plight of aged residents. If things don't move quickly, conditions for patients in Irish nursing homes could get a lot worse.

MEDICAL JOURNALISM
March 1999

Market competition is cut throat amongst American newspapers. Recently a famous actress was hospitalised. Keen for a scoop, the Post sent a lady reporter out to get the story. She was to dress up as a nurse, sneak into the hospital, and interview the actress. The next day the reporter returned to the office. Her editor asked, 'Did you get the story?' 'No' she replied, 'I got thrown out by the doctor from the Daily News.'

IRELAND'S FIRST PACEMAKER

January 2003

For some time now I have been trying to uncover the story of the very first patient in Ireland to receive a cardiac pacemaker. The only response we had initially was from a retired Dublin doctor who told us that he used to remove early pacemakers from deceased patients and send them on to the veterinary hospital in Ballsbridge. Second hand human models were a great bonus for specialists in both equine and canine cardiology. Just when I had given up hope of finding the story of the first pacemaker used here, I received a very kind letter from a retired anaesthetist. He was able to give me all the relevant facts. We had wrongly assumed that the procedure might have place at the cardiac centre of the old Royal City of Dublin Hospital on Baggot Street, but our assumptions were incorrect. The first pacemaker was inserted in Dublin's Mater Misericordiae Hospital in the late 1960s. The patient was a very deaf lady in her late thirties. She also had a rare and very serious auto-immune disease - her body was attacking its own organs, including the heart. She was in the intensive care unit at the hospital and her heart had stopped a number of times. Being of a relatively young age and being in a good place to have a cardiac arrest, she was successfully resuscitated each time. A senior registrar at the hospital, who later went on to become an excellent cardiac surgeon, suggested that one of these new pacemaker devices might be the answer to protect her from a fatal heart cessation. The registrar was not long back from training in Birmingham. It was decided to proceed as something had to be done. The pacemaker was, by present day standards, very basic. A metal ring was placed in the tissues under her collar bone from which two wires were attached to the right beating chamber of her heart. Following the closure of her wound a second ring was strapped to the skin overlying the embedded ring. This was connected to a machine that sent out an electrical impulse every second or so, inducing a current in the embedded ring which was connected to her heart. The pacemaker was about the size and shape of an 1980s vintage mobile phone and was attached to the lady using a belt. There were no Duracell bunnies in those days so the batteries had to be changed every three days. The operation was hailed as a great success. The lady did not live as long. But this was more on account of the underlying seriousness of her disease. She played a role in Irish medical history and deserves to be remembered. The world's first pacemaker was given to a Swedish man, Mr Arne Larson, in 1958. He died in 2001 at the grand age of 86.

MILKY MESSAGES
April 2012

The milk section in the supermarket leaves me rather cold these days. There are milks to help you sleep, milks for your heart, milks for your teeth, milks for your bones and funniest of all, milks to help you keep in shape. If I live long enough, we'll probably soon have milk for the menopause, whipped cream for the prostate gland and hard cheese for male erectile dysfunction. For many years now, doctors have been bombarded with hard sells and vague information about the health benefits of cow juice, but I have yet to peer into a medical fridge that has succumbed to the charms or high prices of these therapeutic liquids. Call me old fashioned, but I prefer my medicines to be administered by a good pharmacist rather than a prize dairy herd. I drink milk. Ordinary milk. Not as much as I used to, but I am a fan. But I recommend daily fortification against falling for these new-fangled promissory milk products.

MODERN NURSERY RHYMES
October 2007

I have received a very fine collection of Nursery Rhymes that have been updated and annotated for modern children. The news on *Jack and Jill* is not good. Subsequent to their respective fall and tumble, both passed away during the ambulance ride. The HSE set up an enquiry, which came to the following conclusions.

The 50 mile journey to the nearest Emergency Department was in the couple's best interest. The fact that there was no local bed in which Jack could mend his head was unfortunate, but no targets had been breached. The lack of vinegar and brown paper was not material to the death as the Health Quality Authority had yet to decide whether it was cost-effective, and in any case both the brown paper nurse and the vinegar nurse were away doing off-site university courses. The GP was clearly at fault and should be suspended and referred to the Medical Council, as he had not reported Jack and Jill's lack of water to social services. He also failed to recognise that anyone going up the hill to fetch a pail of water might have serious and enduring mental health problems. Furthermore, he had not engaged the services of a falls co-ordinator which resulted in Jill tumbling after Jack.

Doctor Foster didn't fare a lot better. Readers will recall that Dr Foster went to Gloucester in a shower of rain, but stepped in a puddle right up to his middle, and never went there again. This resulted in a major public debate in the British parliament and media. The tabloid press said it was outrageous that doctors earning over a hundred thousand pounds for a 30 hour week should be put off by a mere soaking. Prime minister Gordon Brown wanted to know why so many doctors were going to Gloucester in the first place. It was an over-doctored middle class area that has never voted Labour. The Royal College of Nursing said doctors weren't needed as nurses could now do their job just as well. What's more, they were holistically trained and would have no problem with puddles as they could now walk on water. Indeed local nurse practitioners agreed that they would go to Gloucester, but only after receiving extra money to do the appropriate diploma course. The managers decided to have an away-day multi-disciplinary meeting one hundred petrol miles from their offices to discuss rain and puddles. The next time there was heavy rain in Gloucester, it coincided with a stake-holder conference in Marbella. Nobody was available. The NHS Direct phone line advised calling the nearest GP. That was Doctor Foster. But he refused to attend as he could no longer afford malpractice insurance premiums, and had in any case, given his solemn word never to return there.

CELLULITE NONSENSE
June 2011

Quackery is alive and well. I love the way it assumes the mantle and vernacular of modern medicine to throw less discerning patients off its dodgy scent. The latest example that I encountered on my travels is something called the 'quadruple thighpass'. This 'non-invasive anti-cellulite treatment' is now on offer in the United Kingdom for a mere £115 per hour. If you have infinitely more money than sense, and don't mind your upper legs being coated in oils and egg cups while a 'therapist' massages them with a vacuum cleaner that 'sucks out fatty cellulite particles' then the quadruple thighpass could be just for you.

MO MOWLAM
August 2005

Mo Mowlam died this week. Obituaries focused on her general bonhomie, her work in Northern Ireland, rows with Tony Blair and the brain tumour which curtailed a promising political life. Five years ago, my wife brought home a biography of Mo Mowlam. A sure sign that this was a rare politician for her, as he doesn't suffer many of them gladly. I got second read and what I remember best from Julia Langdon's tome are the many happy snaps of Mowlam's childhood that litter the book. But photos don't tell the whole story. Mo Mowlam's early life was far from idyllic. Her father crucified the family for many years with his problem drinking. The teenage Mowlams would often arrive home from school to the humiliating scene of their Dad staggering from side to side on the pavement. Mo Mowlam made little attempt to hide the dysfunction that afflicted her family. She was patron of the National Association for Children of Alcoholics and had a rare empathy with the silent many in this club. The book quotes a psychiatrist, who in a pigeon-holing way peculiar to the speciality, says there are three possible routes for the children of alcoholics. The first shuts the door and escapes as early as possible. The second takes refuge themselves in drink. And the third positively rejects the drinking parent. The psychiatrist decided that the 'healthy option' was the first one – the path it is claimed Mo followed. One night Mo Mowlam's manipulative father cornered his wife and was abusing her verbally. Their seventeen year old son could take no more. He pinned his father down on the floor and smacked him. Things changed that night in the Mowlam household, for the better. Another interesting fact to emerge from the death of Mo Mowlam is the news that she had made a living will. It has been widely reported that she had a bad fall hitting her head off her bed a few weeks ago and had not regained consciousness despite brain scans showing no acute injury. The *Guardian* newspaper, in a piece written before her death was announced, claimed that life support had been withdrawn three days before, and that she was not being given food and water. One could read and write more between the lines, but it won't bring her back. We'll just acknowledge our poverty with her passing.

END OF LIFE
November 1998

It's hard for any middle ground to be heard in the euthanasia debate. One side talks about the culling of old people whilst the other speaks as if they monopolise dignity in death. France's airwaves have been alive with talk of death since health minister Dr Bernard Kouchner called on his countrymen to alter its existing methods of dying. 'I want us to invent in our country a special environment for the passage of death, a new ritual for the end of life. Without dogmatism, without certitudes, with humility and love, let us allow our loved ones to die with less pain and less brutality'. In short, Dr Kouchner wants to avoid legislation like the plague. What he urges instead is a new moral flexibility based on the wishes of patients and the consciences of doctors. He shares my belief that when lawyers get involved in moral affairs, an imbroglio tends to ensue that is impossible to disentangle. Our own sad and tortuous experience of abortion referenda should teach us that devising remedies without recourse to law has a lot to be said for it.

NAILING THE HARD DRIVE
September 2007

Across the pond, there are very red faces at the Dudley NHS Trust, and it has nothing to do with acne rosacea. One of their hospital computers was recently sold on the eBay auction website and the lucky purchaser was able to access all sorts of personal data about cancer patients. The hard drive had not been wiped clean. Discussions are taking place about how this might have happened and suggestions are being sought about the best software for wiping hard disks clean. According to one technology consultant, the gold standard in this endeavour requires not a computer programme, but an electric drill or a nail. Sounds like another job for the department of orthopaedic surgery.

PRAGUE SPRING
April 2001

I'm in Prague this week. It's like the queen mother of Europe, a majestic benevolent old dear of a city, every bit as keen on protocol as it is on gin. I feel very much at home here. As for its healthcare, tourists are advised to make maximum use of 24 hour chemists for their ails. Their apothekes are pretty good. I managed to get an anti-fungal cream called Lamisil over the counter but was refused a cortisone cream to go with it. Emergency care is provided by the Na Homolce Hospital or the Motol out in the suburbs. Most English speakers receive their health services from the American Medical Centre. Family membership costs £250 a year entitling you and yours to a 24 hour house call service, one annual free check-up and reduced rate consultations with any of the clinics' GPs, paediatricians or dentists. That means a visit to the GP will only cost you £100 instead of the £150 paid by non-members. Not cheap, but it's the annual service you pay for. I'm surprised some of these family medical clubs haven't caught on back home.

Prague is not without its chancers. Tourists are often approached by shifty looking gents in cheap suits who whisper 'Sheik Yomani,

Sheik Yomani'. After forlorn discussion about mistaken identity, it transpires that these gents are in fact the Prague equivalent of financial services advisors at home. 'Sheik Yomani' is how Czechs pronounce 'Change Your Money'. Dollars are still popular. They even have a yen for sterling. But show them Irish punts and they run a mile. These street bankers offer excellent exchange rates for dollars and sterling, provided you don't mind using fake bank notes for the rest of your stay.

There are medical chancers in the city too. I trawled its phone directories for mention of human transplants but all organs in the Czech republic seem to have gone to ground. It's not that long since there was a serious scandal of live organs being traded from Prague. A company called TransPlacent managed to get hold of a database of German dialysis patients and sent them all a mail shot offering hassle-free kidneys from live donors. Doubtless fava beans and Chianti might have been thrown in too, had Interpol not got onto the case of the queue-free kidneys.

I liked the Czech Airlines folk who offer almost daily flights out of Dublin and returns from Prague. They have introduced measures to reduce 'air rage' such as complimentary (good sized) bottles of wine and cans of pilsner beer. Nicotine replacement gum is now also available for those who miss their weed during the two hour flight.

So how does one describe Czechs? Well, the average lady of Prague, let's call her Martina will live to 78, six years longer than her prolific beer drinking husband, Franz. She lives in a suburban flat complex where she has reared three lumps of sons. Milos the youngest is an atheist who brings home £100 a month as a junior doctor. The middle son Jan is a general practitioner who puts in a sixty hour week for £500 a month (not lucky enough to work in the American Clinic). Her eldest and favourite son, Tomas, takes after his father. He was a professional Davis cup player before the great unspoken doping scandal put a giant smash on Czech tennis. Now he sleeps between Pils bottles outside the Church of Our Lady Victorious that houses il Bambino di Praga. His mother prays every day for another miracle. At Easter time Franz and Martina indulge in a local custom that has pagan origins, and might help explain the fact that Prague has the highest rate of marital breakdown in Europe. Easter Monday is a public holiday, one on which Czech men are allowed beat their wives with willow sticks, supposedly to keep them fertile well into the summer season. Women are allowed to retaliate with buckets of water, thrown over any part of the male that needs cooling down. This strange ritual has probably been tolerated for so long only because it is traditional to make up afterwards. The woman apologises by gifting her beloved a hand-painted egg. A recent survey found that 70% of Czech women are unfaithful, but happy. A safe bet that this painted egg business is a good one to be in.

NUTTY NAMES
August 2003

A few more examples of nominative determinism have come my way. They include a colo-rectal surgeon called Mr Butts. Other well-named surgeons who might engender a smidgeon of fear in their patients are Mr Butcher, Mr Slaughter, Mr Hacker and Mr Killingsworth. I quite like the sound of Mr Dart the vascular surgeon and two obstetricians, Dr Waterfallen and Dr Concepcion. There is a Mr Flood in urology and another well titled expert in prostatic diseases called Mr John P. Long. Dr Lipman is a dermatologist and no prizes for guessing the sort of clinical setting that Dr Toothman works in. Not so sure I'd be keen on surgery from the ophthalmologist called Dr Blinder, but Dr Goodenough the neurologist should be just fine. There are two aptly named orthopaedic surgeons in the west of Scotland called Mr Bone and Mr Cartlidge. Neurology once had two eminent stalwarts called Lord Brain and Sir Henry Head. And there was a gynaecologist called Dr Mann, who was a lady. I am told but have never been able to verify whether there was an Irish psychiatrist called Dr Nutty. If there was, I'm sure he was kept very busy.

LABELS ON CHILDREN
February 2012

The debate about whether we are over-diagnosing children with fashionable ailments is not exactly boiling, but it quietly simmers on the back ring. What is clear is that modern psychiatry has become rather too obsessed with classification. Depositing human characteristics in neat boxes greatly simplifies the work of doctors, therapists, researchers, educators and health planners. But positive outcomes for patients, parents and society, from often perfunctory classifications, are less clear. I had a letter the other day from parents whose son had been diagnosed with a 'mild form of dyspraxia' by his primary school teacher. Now when I qualified in the 1980s, dyspraxia didn't even merit a mention in my largest psychiatry textbook. Now it's everywhere. It began as a medical term used to categorise children who were perhaps more clumsy than their peers. Over the years it has broadened out to include children who don't brim with sporting talent, who forget to pack stuff in their schoolbags, or who lack some social graces. Dyspraxia has become a new catch-all condition. It is lobbed like a grenade at ever-increasing numbers of families, without resources to adequately diagnose, grade, treat or follow it up. The old medical adage, when in doubt, observe closely and do nothing, has been forgotten. The condition has fuelled a boom in private occupational therapy and associated 'aids' which can run into hundreds and thousands of euro. The family who wrote to me went to their family doctor, whose opinion was that there was nothing wrong with their son. They were subsequently told that because of cut backs in resource teachers, it is in the interest of schools that as many pupils as possible are waiting on HSE assessments or 'labeled' by therapists. As I write, the health minister is looking at sticky labels for foodstuffs to say whether it is good for you or not. Maybe he should have a look at deficiencies in our child-labeling system instead.

UNPROVEN DEATH THREATS
April 2008

We were told recently by a visiting 'expert in weight loss' that for the first time in Ireland we have a generation of children that will have a shorter lifespan than their parents. This ludicrous prediction is nothing new. It began four years ago when a select committee of the British House of Commons included it in a report as an idle and unproven threat that might happen if nothing was done about childhood obesity. I have never been able to source any scientific data behind the forecast and the reason for that is because there is none. Versions of this statement are widely reported across the internet. Everyone from politicians to celebrities to famous chefs throw it out there as if it's fact. In my humble opinion, it's a bogus claim and has no place in science.

NURSING COMMISSION
March 2005

When a state board says they are going to keep a watching brief on something, it usually means there are no plans to do anything. Cosmetic surgery, the proverbial wild west of healthcare, is a case in point. There isn't a regulator in sight. The medical council say they are going to have a look at it. While they are at it, the nursing board might do well to join them. I am looking at a newspaper advertisement today saying that a 'prestigious' Dublin clinic is looking for a nurse and is offering to pay 30 thousand euro per annum. What alarmed me were the two little words that followed the salary - *plus commission*. I would have thought that the nursing board might have one or two things to say about a practice where a nurse's salary is dependent on how many medical procedures she can sell to patients.

CANCER CURE
June 2011

Overheard in a cafe in Dublin's ILAC Centre recently. Seven year old child chooses a pink bottle of Ballygowan as her refreshment. It's the one with the Breast Cancer Awareness label. A donation is made to the Marie Keating Foundation for each bottle sold.

'So why do you want the pink one?'

'It's healthier than the other water, this one cures cancer!'

BIRTH CERTS
November 2007

HSE officials wrote to a family doctor of my acquaintance recently about renewing his vaccination contract. They told him that they could not do so, unless he provided them with a copy of his birth certificate. He is still wondering whether they are just plain nosey-parkers with nothing better to do, or whether they are considering him for a booster injection. It reminded me of a recent meeting with the husband of a lady who has been entombed in an HSE office for more years than she cares to remember. Eight years after the Eastern Health Board became the Eastern Regional Health Authority and three years after Eastern Regional Health Authority became the Health Service Executive, she still doesn't know what her job description is. She goes to work five days a week and conducts research on whatever tickles her fancy. Nobody ever queries her about what she does. And nobody bothers to look at her research. Maybe she's the one who collects birth certificates of general practitioners.

MEANINGLESS BODIES
April 2008

I am grateful to a friend who sent me a little extract from a new book on the Northern Ireland Peace Process. It neatly sums up how we conduct business in Ireland. The writer was a participant on that long Good Friday when nobody got any sleep at Stormont.

According to the author '*the Irish dug their heels in, and David Trimble came across as appallingly rude to Bertie Ahern, who came within an ace of hitting him. In the end I had to appeal to Trimble on bended knee to add a meaningless body ensuring co-operation between the health services of the two territories that the Irish wanted, and he agreed*'.

Another meaningless body in Irish healthcare. Who would believe it?

BOTOX BOTTOMS
March 1998

A wise old professor of surgery at Sir Patrick Dun's Hospital once poured forth to us on the topic of sick bottoms. He told his students that there are two groups of patients who attend his rectal clinics. Half are panic-stricken about cancer and the other half are as sure as night follows day, that they have piles. His own favourite disease of the posterior passage was the anal fissure, an exquisitely painful tear in the lower half of the anal canal, first described as a clinical entity in 1934. This was probably around the time our learned professor qualified. Such fissures can become chronic and a widely used surgical treatment was anal sphincterotomy, where the valve in the area is cut or stretched to prevent spasm. This is not risk-free and has the potential hazards of anal deformity and incontinence.

Last month, a team of doctors from Rome reported a breakthrough in the *New England Journal of Medicine* with their use of injections of botulinum toxin into the anal sphincter. Fifteen patients were given botulinum toxin and the fissures healed in eleven of them. A control group of another fifteen patients were given injections of salty water (poor souls) as a placebo and just two of them healed successfully. With the exception of one botulinum toxin patient who developed a temporary incontinence of gas, there were no adverse reports and the injections were easily performed and painless. I think the professor would have approved. A much better medical clinical use for botulinum toxin than the face of matron.

YORKSHIRE'S FINEST
October 2005

Bernard Ingham, Mrs Thatcher's former press guru, still has all the marbles that his former boss is now losing. Last week he published an excellent book, celebrating the fifty greatest Yorkshire men and women that ever lived. Featuring prominently are figures from literature and sport – Emily Brontë, JB Priestley, Ted Hughes, Freddie Truman and my own personal favourite, the late Brian Clough. Just one medic made the pudding mix, and it as Dr Almroth Wright, a very distinguished Trinity College Dublin graduate. Almroth was born near Richmond in Yorkshire where his Irish father, like the father of the Brontë girls, had been appointed curate of a small parish. In those far off Victorian days, university education gave a much more rounded preparation for life, so Almroth took a first class honours in arts as well as medicine at Trinity. His research and clinical activities were varied, ranging from coagulation and immunology to vaccinations and war wounds. Wright was a close friend of George Bernard Shaw. Indeed he was the model for Sir Colenso Ridgeon in *The Doctor's Dilemma*. Ridgeon was the private medical practitioner who developed a cure for tuberculosis, and had then to decide which patients are worthy of treatment. Almroth Wright taught himself Russian at the age of seventy, Eskimo language at eighty and only resigned from his research laboratory in St Mary's of London at the age of eighty five. He was succeeded in his laboratory by a much lesser man called Fleming.

WELL NAMED
November 2007

A proud doctor writes from the south east of the country to tell me that his seventeen year old son has just passed his driver theory test. The certificate was signed by the head of driver testing, the wonderfully named Mr Skidmore. The south east is quite a hot bed for appropriate surnames. According to the *Irish Medical Directory*, one hospital in the region has a bed manager called Ms

Argue. Can't complain about that. A general practitioner tells me that there was once a famous firm of solicitors in Sligo town called Argue & Phibbs. And a nurse left a message for me about some military patients she once tended to who all had an ornithological ring to their surnames. She mentioned Captain Sparrow, Private Bird, Captain Gosling, Private Crowe and Private Ahearn – which he always pronounced A Heron.

PREMATURE LITTLE EINSTEINS
January 2012

Today's newspapers are full of bluff and guff about how Irish families can produce little Einstein offspring if expectant mammies are encouraged to eat more fish. The research is early, ongoing and really it's quite premature to be issuing press releases. The European commission's office in Dublin sent out a waffling press release titled 'Fish boosts unborn babies' brainpower'. Scientific slaves in the media did their wedding of Cana act, miraculously turning one piece of paper into hundreds of news headlines. The small study that this 'news' is based on is German and was published last year in the *American Journal of Clinical Nutrition*. Don't get me wrong. I'm partial to a flatfish in lemon breadcrumbs or mackerel in season. I'd also rather that we supported our local trawlers and fishmongers than hawkers of fish oil capsules at wildly inflated prices. But I'd also prefer if selective and preliminary results were pondered and debated, with appropriate input from independent experts, rather than gift wrapped by EU public relations people as brain fodder for our indentured masses.

TAKING AIM AT DOCTORS
February 2003

My American correspondent has sent me some fascinating new statistics that an under-fire National Rifle Association are using as ammunition to defend themselves. Apparently the number of gun owners in the United States is estimated at 80 million and they account for about 1,500 accidental gun deaths a year. The current number of physicians in the United States is 700,000 and the National Rifle Association claim that doctors cause 120,000 accidental deaths every year. Using these figures, my calculator suggests that doctors are statistically 9,000 times more dangerous that gun owners! Doctors have always proven themselves to be a very easy target to hit.

VIVE LA FRANCE
August 2011

A sojourn to France this summer did wonders for a healthy complexion. My own rather than that of the bank manager. In the comfort stakes, air travel loses out badly to boat crossings, so top marks to Irish Ferries and all the crew of their *Oscar Wilde* for maintaining an immaculately clean boat and keeping all our food exactly where it belongs. Irish Ferries is perhaps a misnomer, for aside from the captain and the entertainments crew, it was hard to find a native person on the staff. Perhaps our seafaring islanders have emigrated en masse to work on Baltic Ferries. Not that I am complaining, the service and the smile has improved immeasurably over the last decade.

Our modest art deco hotel on the beach at La Baule was doing its bit for health promotion. On opening the mini-bar we were greeted by a drinks menu that stated 'Pour votre Santé, Attention à l'abus d'alcools'. The hotel's translation genius had helpfully given a simplified version for overseas guests: 'Attention on the Alcohol Abuse!'

We paid close care to the warning and didn't open the fridge again. The policy in this particular establishment was to price you into better health. A gin and tonic from the fridge came in at fifteen euro and a single half-sized can of heineken followed close behind at six euro, one coin more than the small bottle of still water. Outside the room, breakfast was twenty seven euro per person and dinner a cool fifty each before drinks. France ain't cheap. The kid's club was twenty five euro per child for the morning and the same again if you wanted to read a book in the afternoon. The French love nothing more than introducing bureaucracy into childhood. It takes the longer to complete an health questionnaire on your darling child than it takes your ferry to travel back from Roscoff to Rosslare. I was going to fill in one of the omnipresent hotel comment cards, until I discovered that the top lady at our edifice had the grand title of *Directrice d'Exploitation*. That said it all. But the funny thing about France is, we'll be back. And if we win the lottery, it could be back to our favourite hotel in La Baule.

Things work in France. And they could teach us a thing or two about sign-posting roads. They don't make the Irish assumption that everyone already knows where they are going. Their supermarkets and hypermarkets, especially those whose aisles are swept by Monsieur LeClerc, put our own filthy and poorly stocked carbohydrate depots to shame. Even better, we drove a thousand kilometres without meeting a single toll booth. If the French road safety authority play nagging adverts on the radio telling you to have a cup of coffee to combat tiredness, they do so in the knowledge that there are service stations all over the place where you can pull in for ridiculously large ham baguettes, good coffee and a pee. The French also recognise that people all over the world have a strange involuntary desire to use lavatory facilities every now and then. We saw no 'Toilets for Customers Only' signs on our travails. Parking in disabled spaces is also a cultural Non Non. Those who are tempted, have their consciences pricked with an omnipresent warning: *Si vous prenez ma place, prenez aussi mon handicap* (If you take my space, take my disability also). Yes, in France, you can still use the word handicap without being shot down. I'm told that deep down they care more about what you do than what you say. Cigarettes are half the price they are in Ireland, meaning that poor people who struggle with a packet a day habit, don't waste seventy euro a week straight away from the family budget. And I like the fact that by and large they enjoy alcohol sensibly, without needing daft slogans devised by drink companies to keep public health doctors off their backs. Always a bon voyage.

MOSCOW SIEGE
January 2004

Last week, the BBC *Horizon* programme covered the recent siege in Moscow where a vaporised opioid drug was fed into the ventilation system of a theatre to knock out forty terrorists and a thousand hostages. This allowed Russian special forces to retake the building without any bombs going off. Despite the fact that one in eight hostages died, the rescue has been lauded as a relative success. The potential to lose all lives was a very real threat.

Much of the documentary focused on the worldwide search for the exact chemical that was used. The Russians, as always, weren't too keen on volunteering any state secrets. The conclusion reached was that a cocktail of drugs may have been utilised. One was reckoned to be a potent derivative of the painkiller fentanyl, and the other a novel chemical that lessens the breathing depression you can get with opioids at high doses. The most extraordinary claim of the programme was that those who died may have unwittingly caused their own deaths by falling asleep in an unfavourable recovery position. It was suggested that many who did not survive the gas, were likely to have suffered airway compression that led them to choke to death under the effect of the drugs. Much criticism has been made of the rescue efforts that began an hour after the gas was released. A team of just seventeen poorly briefed doctors, without airway equipment or adequate supplies of naloxone antidote, were sent in to triage a thousand overdosed patients. But *Horizon* also raised the possibility that a team of a thousand doctors one hour later mightn't have fared any better. Those who died tragically, did so within minutes, but any earlier intervention by troops might have allowed the terrorists detonate their deadly devices. The Russians forces were in a catch 22 situation, damned if they did and damned if they didn't.

SMALL TOWN DOCTORS
March 1999

The Talk of the Town is a wonderful debut novel from Ardal O'Hanlon, the best known doctor's son in Monaghan. Celebrated for his hilarious portrayal of the gormless Father Dougal in *Father Ted*, O'Hanlon has written a moving fictional tale of loneliness, violence and drink in small town Ireland. There is plenty of the expected, but it's written with a very appealing humour, occasionally subtle, more often blunt. The main character is the feckless Paddy Scully, an awkward young man, whose views on rural general practitioners raised more than a few eyebrows. 'All doctors are the same - they're only in the game because they got the required points. They're all raving alcoholics so they are, with their tweed jackets and a free basket of eggs every Friday from a grateful patient. They're only interested in making money and perks. They can mend bones and staunch the flow of blood. Sure a carpenter or a plumber could so that. But if you go into them with anything seriously wrong with you, they take a wild guess and hope for the best. They send you to somebody else in Dublin to be on the safe side'. Such rare imagination could come from the pen of a doctor's son.

ANOTHER DAY, ANOTHER FORM
January 2006

No more than ourselves, medical colleagues across the Irish sea get all hot and lathered about local issues of world-shattering importance. Take Dr Peter Holden. He is a family doctor in the Derbyshire Dales and a national figure of medical admiration amongst doctors with his campaign to alleviate general practitioners from the need to sign ridiculous forms. What really tickled his goat was a ruling from his local district council that people with steps outside their homes who needed assistance moving their wheelie bins in from the kerbside, had to get a special form signed by their family doctors. The story went from being a local one to the national press and the council were forced to amend the rules about their form. Now it annoys even more busy people as it can be signed by district nurses and social workers too.

EUPHEMISMS IN PSYCHIATRY
October 2007

The Oxford University Press has just published an updated *Dictionary of Euphemisms*. There's plenty of HSE type corporate-speak here like *personnel ceiling reductions* (job cuts) and the like, but it's the older and often defunct entries that are the most interesting. When was the last time you heard somebody who was mentally unbalanced being referred to as *dicked in the nob*? The number of entries devoted to mental illness is very large, the third most numerous category after euphemisms for body parts and sexual references. Some of the less politically correct examples are geared towards asylum buildings such as *acorn academy*, *screw factory* and *state farm*. More personal jibes about mental illness include having *both oars in the water*, *the gears having slipped*, *having bats in the belfry*, *living next door to a padded cell* and the equivalent expression in London which is *living next door to East Ham*. Yes, I had to look that one up. Apparently it's the tube station next to Barking.

A CLOSER INSPECTION
May 2001

I met a man recently who was absolutely convinced that he had picked up a dose in his doctor's surgery. This is a common worry amongst patients that rarely finds a voice. 'He shouldn't be allowed practice from that place' he said 'the waiting room is like a sauna - bugs all over the gaff'. He had obviously never visited my surgery on a busy day, but he does have a point. The state spends huge amounts of money annually on the inspection of abattoirs, crèches, nursing homes, coffee shops and mental hospitals for health and safety breaches. But nobody has ever been handed either the authority or duty to inspect the premises that ninety per cent of illnesses are seen in. All risk is relative and the iatrogenic risks from general practice may be relatively low, but nobody really knows what practices that go on behind surgery walls. Whose refrigerators have rotting sandwiches and milk cartons dripping on their vaccines? Whose loos haven't had a scrub since the arms crisis? Things are so lax here that nobody even checks if there are any bogus doctors masquerading as family practitioners. For a new millennium, I think the general public deserve better.

PRODIGIOUS BELLY AND DOUBLE CHIN
October 2005

Stately plump Ken Clarke looks like he is out of the three-legged race for leadership of the British Tory party. A double-pronged attack on big Ken from unelectable right wing neoconservatives and unelected anti-tobacco campaigners may well force the people's favourite out of the final reckoning. Last week the *British Medical Journal* carried a letter from an Australian professor of health policy suggesting that Clarke's previous links with the tobacco industry make him unfit for any public office. Clarke may not have a proud record in this area but do we really want a political arena populated by non-entities with no medical histories, no flesh on their bones and no skeletons in their closets? If you bow to one such lobby, you bow in future to them all. Last week Clarke was described in the British media as a man with 'a prodigious belly and eye-catching double chin' whose weight 'advertises his origins of a distant age when he roamed Westminster in a herd with fellow Mastodons like Lawson, Lamont and Soames'. It went on . . . Clarke's corpulence 'does not send out a responsible message in terms of public health'. We must be careful these days about bandying around terms like Nazi, but a certain Austrian gentleman, christened Adolph by his parents, sent out very similar messages to his own master race before he got bunkered. I suspect the new Tory leader will be an awful lot thinner, and a great deal duller than Mr Ken Clarke.

DEFIBRILLATOR MADNESS
October 2005

This country is going mad for defibrillators. I have ongoing concerns about this current wave of sudden cardiac death hysteria and the plot to install defibrillators in every building in the country. I was rather taken aback last week to read that an instructor with the Irish Heart Foundation said every community in the country should have 'several defib kits' and that they should be as plentiful as fire extinguishers. Very little research has been conducted and the little that there is, would suggest that the cost versus benefit ratio is too high. In one Wicklow town, parishioners purchased a defibrillator after major fundraising and placed it inside a local church. Even the parish priest has been trained in its use and doubtless had some say in the positioning of the equipment – right beside the statue of the sacred heart. Like most public defibrillators, it will attract ongoing servicing, maintenance, training and replacement costs, and will in all likelihood, never be used.

THE LOCAL NURSE
May 2003

Nurse Moira Cassidy has written an affectionate piece in this month's *World of Irish Nursing*. It's a tribute to her mother and thousands like her who practised as 'the local nurse' in bygone times, toiling twenty four hours a day, and without pay too. She tended to serious injuries on the roadside, dying neighbours, childhood fevers and all grades of cuts and bruises. Nurse Cassidy describes in loving detail how this free nursing care propped up an ailing health service for generations. The contents of the USA Biscuit Assortment tins of local nurses kept casualty departments free for those who really needed emergency help. The biscuit tins were relics of Christmases past, and contained Andrews liver salts, ingredients for bread poultices, pre-loved bandages and rattling bottles of pills. Nurse Cassidy said that the children were expected to be a hardier lot than today. Bandages were only given to wimps or those with projectile haemorrhages and arc-like spurting of blood. A child with a half-severed finger, courtesy of a chance meeting with the garden clippers, was stitched with s heavy black thread and sent to school the following day. A male infant with an umbilical hernia would arrive in nappies at the nurse's living room to have a two-penny bit taped firmly across the offending navel. The article called it a subterranean service, old fashioned nursing care on a shoestring. Unrecognised then and now, but sorely missed. And very well described by Nurse Cassidy.

SPOT DIAGNOSIS
January 2000

O'Brien goes to see his doctor in Dublin. He pokes himself in the arm and says it hurts. Then he pokes his own leg and squeals. When he pokes his tummy he yelps in pain. Jaysus, what's wrong doc - I'm sore all over'.

'Quite simple really, Mr O'Brien,' says the doctor, 'you've a broken finger.'

ORWELL'S RECOVERY
October 2011

I spent much of last summer, and recent months too, immersed in biographies of George Orwell. What started as a treat did turn to a drudge in the end. But on the positive side, reading of his early death persuaded me to give up a cigarette habit of thirty years duration. For that I am grateful. Orwell was a lifelong asthmatic, and one that smoked like a trooper. He finally succumbed to a lung haemorrhage, induced by tuberculosis, a few years short of a half century. When he was thirty, Orwell was admitted in critical condition to a cottage hospital in Uxbridge. He had severe pneumonia and was delirious with a high fever. The sister-in-charge on his 'Lung Ward' reassured family and visitors that Orwell would make it. She told them that those on the ward with red faces were in greatest danger whist those with paler faces tended who pull through. This reminded me of my medical school days when we were taught to distinguish between the 'pink puffers' who had emphysema and the 'blue bloaters' with chronic bronchitis. Tests and textbooks will tell you so much, but you can learn most from the wise specialist nurse. She has seen it all.

WORST INFECTION ON THE PLANET
August 2005

Things weren't looking so good for O'Reilly at the clinic.
'Mr O'Reilly, I'm afraid I've got some really bad news for you. You've got the most infectious disease on the planet' said the doctor.
'Oh, no! What treatment can you give me?' asked O'Reilly.
'Well we're going to take you into the hospital Mr O'Reilly, give you your own private room, padlock the door and put you on a diet of shredded duck and pancakes'.
'Shredded duck and pancakes, doctor? Delicious! Will that cure me?'
'Not at all' said the doctor, 'it's the only grub we can slide under the door!'

SATELLITE IMAGING
November 2002

A medical colleague sent me the following strange news story from Portugal. Police there are investigating a complaint by four women who stripped naked to their waists and stood by their windows so that they could have mammograms by satellite. The ladies, aged between 19 and 45, said another 'woman', identifying herself as a doctor, phoned them about this revolutionary new method to examine their breasts. They were each asked to expose their chests and stand either by the window or on the balcony of their apartments in the direction of the supposed satellite. However, instead of giving the women their mammogram results later, the 'doctor' rang them back with a rather vivid description of personal sexual desire. I expect the police are looking around neighbouring apartment blocks for a perverted medical conman with a high pitched voice.

POST-MENOPAUSAL MERCILON

February 2008

I have been reading from the memoirs of a market town doctor in the south of England that reflect on a long forty six years of general practice. One observation from his early days was that around Christmas time, there was a sudden and dramatic increase in demand for cotton wool on the National Health Service. It was always the poorer patients who were claiming that supplies in their first aid boxes needed replenishment. In time, the doctor discovered the real reason for the yuletide popularity of cotton wool prescriptions. It was for decoration of Christmas trees and provision of whiskers for domestic Santa Clauses. In my own medical past as a locum general practitioner, I can recall a lady of bus pass vintage asking for a three month supply of *mercilon* (a popular oral contraceptive pill of the day) to be added to her list of medical card requisites. Had I been harried on the day, the request might have passed under the radar, but I did ask what use she had in mind for the contraceptive pill. It transpired that her grand-daughter told her that it was 'a tonic' that she would have to pay privately for, unless Granny asked for it on the medical card! A very early lesson for me in pharmacoeconomics.

PET FALSEHOODS

June 2001

You can call Fido in from the garden. Doctors cocked their legs and piddled on ancient medical dogma last week when a new study suggested that infants who grow up with pets are actually less likely to suffer from allergies and asthma later in life. Dr Zelda of the National Institute of Environmental Health Sciences says that previous conclusions must now be re-evaluated in the light of this new evidence. It's now being suggested that exposure to pets early in life might actually help the body build defences against a number of medical conditions. Soon they could be recommending that you hoover up all the dander and stuff it in the baby's pillow.

A FISHY SMELL
June 1999

Some years ago a lady doctor from Dublin wrote an interesting piece in a medical magazine about the various noxious smells she comes across every day in surgery. The item made it onto the national airwaves, and patients the length and breadth of the country were given a loud and clear message that a little bit of soap wouldn't go amiss when you visit female doctors. But Dr George Preti might not agree. He's an organic chemist working as a body odour specialist in the Monell Chemical Senses Centre in Philadelphia. He approaches his patients like a curious cocker spaniel, sniffing their armpits, snuffling down their necks and taking deep whiffs up and down their bodies. Preti says his greatest diagnostic instrument is his nose. His tour de force involves asking patients to take a deep breath and then to exhale it right over his face. His patients must stop wearing deodorant and perfumes five days before they visit him. They also are told only to shower if at all with unscented ivory soap and to stop shaving their armpits. The night before they visit this doctor, patients fast and stop brushing their teeth. After clinical olfactory examination they undergo lung function and gas tests, spit measurements and microbiological cultures are grown from their armpit scrapings. Much of the centre's work is for the cosmetic and food industry. But Dr Preti sees ordinary patients too. Like a lady with a permanent rotten fish smell. She was diagnosed as suffering from a greatly undiagnosed genetic disorder called trimethylaminuria or as it's known better in the business, fish malodour syndrome. There is more than something in this stinky business of sniffing out illnesses. Dogs don't lie.

METHOD OF DELIVERY
March 2001

It's five years since *The Lancet* published a paper looking at the sort of births that obstetricians might choose for themselves. The question posed was along the following lines:

You or your partner are having an uncomplicated first time pregnancy. Which would you prefer - a vaginal delivery or a caesarean section?

The 17% caesarean preference was not that unusual at the time, but the replies split along very clear gender lines - 31% of female obstetricians wanted the section but just 8% of the men were in the same boat. That was 1996, and we are now in a new century and a different millennium. A new study undertaken at an American obstetrics & gynaecology conference last summer once again asked the question of over a hundred delegates. 46% would now prefer a caesarean section for an average sized first-time delivery and the sex ratio was 57% male and 33% female. Explain that one please.

INSPECTOR OF MENTAL HOSPITALS
March 2011

Dr Dermot Walsh is not a household name, but perhaps he should be. When I worked in psychiatry at St Loman's Hospital in Dublin two decades ago, he was the clinical director. He spotted me at the bus stop one evening and offered me a lift into town in his little red sports car. At the time he was also the state's inspector for mental hospitals and a very respected figure in his speciality. I'm sure my efforts at sensible conversation did little to impress him. Dermot Walsh has done more than any other doctor of his generation to publicise often dire conditions and careless practices in Ireland's mental hospitals. He is retired now, but still writes and agitates for compassionate care of patients in his field. In the current issue of *Irish Psychiatrist*, Dr Walsh has written an excellent article on the stigma that persists in mental illness. He appears underwhelmed by the recent wave of 'mind your mental health' television advertisements that purport to reduce this stigma. He says such measures have had generally negative outcomes in other countries. He suggests more practical measures. He wants the legal profession to abandon use of the word insanity from its lexicon, calling it outmoded and debasing. He repeats his long-standing opposition to stand-alone mental hospitals. He questions the over-prescription of anti-psychotic drugs in dosages 'beyond that required for responsiveness'. He advises fellow psychiatrists against incautious use of the word *schizophrenic*. He decries the lack of attention by carers to appropriate clothing for patients, a measure he says might dispel an appearance of 'oddness'. He writes about denial of full citizenship by the omission of long-stay psychiatric patients from electoral registers. And perhaps most interesting of all is his comment that mental health professionals make a major contribution to negative images for the purposes of promoting their own interests, especially by portraying caring for the mentally ill as dangerous. A learned and interesting and challenging man. He has a lot to say, should anyone care to listen.

MEDICAL MAHLERS
August 2006

There's an obituary in this morning's paper for the late Dr Robert Mahler who passed away recently. He was a direct descendant of uncle Gustav who composed all that eerie music. The Vienna-born endocrinologist worked for most of his life in the United Kingdom, and was once professor of metabolics at the Welsh national school of medicine. He wisely preached that academics should not hold on to their chairs for longer than ten years to allow their juniors to rise in the ranks. And true to his word he relinquished his professorship after a decade to take up a full-time position in Northwick Park Hospital. I read that Dr Robert Mahler's own father was a surgeon who interested his son in medicine by presenting him a chemistry set and a copy of Kreb's *The Microbe Hunters* on his ninth birthday. Beats Harry Potter any day!

THE POSTURE OF SHERPAS
October 2012

There was never a better man in a ministry than Mr Micheál Martin of Fianna Fáil, for setting up a working group and doing precisely nothing that is. Back in 1997, when education was his brief, Micheál set one up a working group to examine the weight of children's schoolbags. It was published a year later with all the usual flannel about raising awareness, teaching youngsters how to lift and talking to educational publishers. And as we came to expect with so many of his reports, nothing actually happened. Many of our nation's children still go to school with the posture of osteoporotic Sherpas. A mother of a boy who has just started in secondary school tells me that she has started to weigh his daily bag. It comes in at average of twenty two pounds, almost ten kilograms. She says this reflects mainly on a ridiculously large subject load on the curriculum for this age. She tells me that many children who would ordinarily get a bus or walk to school, cannot do so on account of bag size. They have to be given a lift by car. Nobody knows what load a child can safely carry, but no more than ten per cent of their body weight has been the traditional recommendation. Meanwhile, at Leinster House, fifteen years after the working group on carrying heavy loads, Mr Martin and his political colleagues are due to take delivery shortly of their new lightweight iPads.

OBLIGATORY MOTHER IN LAW JOKE
May 2005

Apple can't keep doctors away these days. A GP colleague writes to highly recommend that I get one of these new iPod thingies. He tells me it can store 5,000 songs or one telephone message from his mother-in-law.

HUME STREET
June 2006

This week we bid a sad and fond farewell to the City of Dublin Skin and Cancer Hospital on Hume Street. It's a terrible shame that this glorious institution wasn't allowed to reach what would have been a well deserved centenary in 2011. It's a hospital whose interior is very familiar to local general practitioners. We used to visit on a weekly basis to fill up coffee flasks with liquid nitrogen for our wart clinics. My psoriasis patients always had high praise for this hospital, especially those who would be admitted for five day residential treatments on bad flare-ups. I cannot imagine any general hospital volunteering to take on such care today. Access to dermatology services for public patients in the capital, and the regions, remains an absolute disgrace. It does health ministers little credit to be fussing about the danger of sun beds when those who need skin cancer diagnosis can still wait up to two years for appointments in the capital.

Hume Street was named after Mary Hume, daughter of a Fermanagh surgeon and property speculator called Sir Gustavus Hume. Her father was the man who first hired Franco-German designer Richard Cassels to work on his country estate. Cassels subsequently became one of the most prominent architects in Dublin. Mary married Nicholas Loftus, a wealthy neighbour of Castle Hume near Enniskillen, himself a renowned developer with deep pockets. Doubtless the same species will be picking over the bones of a hospital that has been allowed to run down badly in recent years. Hume Street was originally conceived and functioned for many years as a residential area for the well to do. It achieved notoriety in the 1950s for the abortion clinic run by Nurse Mamie Cadden and the subsequent death of a young lady patient of hers whose corpse was dumped across the road from the hospital.

DEATH OF A MINISTER
March 2013

The death of former minister for health Dr John O'Connell passed with very little coverage, except for a nice front page tribute on the *Irish Medical Times*, the newspaper he founded in the 1960s. Dr O'Connell was a most interesting man. I found his 1989 autobiography *Dr John* every bit as enthralling as Dr Noel Browne's *Against the Tide*. I met him only once. My name popped up in the running to be a by-election candidate in his old constituency and he asked me to join him for lunch at his table in the Unicorn restaurant. He was a most genial host, and gave me some background to the constituency, pointing out the various businesses, industries and interests that ruled the roost and made the decisions on party candidates. This information was very helpful and it was an education for me to realise that so many Irish politicians are actually hired guns just like their American counterparts. It also neatly explains how so many governments are little more than fronts for the building and banking industries. I remember leaving the lunch with Dr O'Connell wondering if a career in party politics was really for me. As it turned out, it wasn't.

RUMPOLE'S CREATOR
February 2008

I have been greatly enjoying the newly published biography of John Mortimer, creator of *Rumpole of the Bailey*. Mortimer is a formidable writer, a former barrister himself, who lives up to the phrase 'larger than life' with consummate ease. Those of the punk generation may remember him as the Queen's Counsel who defended Virgin records for their use of a certain 'B' word in the title of the Sex Pistols first album. Like his father, John Mortimer became a divorce specialist at the Royal Courts of Justice. His biographer lets us in on a few secrets many have long suspected about the legal profession. Namely that a way with both words and exaggerations is a prerequisite for a successful legal career. Flinging the toast rack during a matrimonial dispute always becomes a 'charge of cruelty'. Talking too much becomes 'incessant nagging'. Not talking much translates as 'long periods of sullen silence'. Heavens forbid, if you ever had sex it was 'inconsiderate sexual demands'. If you didn't have sex, it was 'wilful refusal to grant conjugal rights'. And of course there was always the mandatory referral to a carefully-chosen doctor to relate in painstaking detail how your health has been affected. I now understand both the divorce and personal injury industries that little bit better.

CANCER SCARE
May 2005

An old medical school pal sent me the following corner shop dialogue. I suspect he made it up!

Customer: Worcester sauce crisps please.
Shopkeeper: Sorry, can't stock them anymore. Cancer scare
Customer: OK then, Chinese chicken wings please.
Shopkeeper: Sorry, same thing.
Customer: OK then, some chicken tikka bites
Shopkeeper: Sorry, cancer scare.
Customer: What? They're all banned for fear of cancer
Shopkeeper: Yep, afraid so. Something to do with the dye and cancer in rats
Customer: (sigh) OK then, just give me a pack of 20 fags
Shopkeeper: Certainly, that will be 6 euro please.

MARTHA'S VINEYARD
August 1999

Any Irish hospitals that are within an ambulance's roar of the beach, need to sit up and take note. Martha's Vineyard Hospital, just south of Cape Cod on the island of the same name, has increased its prices for accident and emergency care to capitalise on the healthy tourist season. The price hike of ten per cent, just for holidaymakers, was decided on this summer and will last until inclement weather sets in during October. The practice has set minds racing and tongues wagging in the hungry world of private healthcare. Officials at the American Hospital Association said they have never heard of seasonal pricing by a hospital. As one official said, 'I can't imagine charging more if you break your leg on the golf course in July than if you're skiing in February'. But it's happening, and could well be a trend that Irish doctors might follow. Call out fees for sunburn could be trebled from April to August, and anyone with symptoms that look or even sound a bit like flu from September to March could incur a £20 winter supplement.

OBESE TITLES
November 2005

I am in the midst of updating the *Irish Medical Directory* for next year. A Geriatric Hospital has written to tell me it no longer wishes to be called a Geriatric Hospital. In future it would like to be known as a Long Stay Care Facility for Older People with Enduring Mental Health Problems. Doctors who wants to refer patients to a specialist in Enduring Mental Health Problems in Older People at the Long Stay Care Facility for Older People with Enduring Mental Health Problems is going to need bigger envelopes and a new inkwell.

USZY, NOS & GARDIO
June 2007

I like to read about good news about chemists in their trade magazines. Costigan's pharmacy in Tipperary town have responded to the arrival of workers from eastern Europe in the county by publishing a Polish -English medical translation service. At first glance, Polish appears to be a most difficult language. My six years of schoolboy German was of very little benefit either in pronunciation or translation. I cannot even begin to try *Powinienes Skontaktowal Sie Zlekarzem*. This is a regular instruction in pharmacies that means 'you should really see a doctor'. *Wymioty* is a slightly easier one, a close approximation to what we call vomiting. *Zatwarzenie* means constipation. And I do like their onomatopoeic description of diarrhoea, which is *Biegunka*. ENT, the acronym for ear nose and throat in English, but in Polish the equivalent is UNG which stands for *Uszy, Nos & Gardio*. I'm ready for bowels and common colds now.

WAITING ROOM MAGAZINES
February 2012

Readers of my Rude Health column in the *Sunday Independent* have been telling me about some of the worst waiting rooms in the land for magazines. I should, but I won't name and shame those family doctors who treat their flock to last year's Argos catalogues. Nor will I expose the eye specialist who always keeps patients waiting two or three hours (especially those with appointments) in a room with abysmal reading matter - old copies of National Geographic, ancient racing journals and torn gossip magazines. My informant well understands that emergencies do crop up in doctors' lives, but having attended twice a year for two decades, the wait has seldom been less than two hours. As I see it, the problem with waiting room material is that a grey area surrounds exactly whose responsibility it is. Some doctors I have spoken to actually believe it's the job of their patients to replenish the supply at intervals. Indeed in my own practice, I had a very pleasant gentleman who would regularly bring me in colourful men's cycling magazines. Before he started to drop them in, the surgery had a definite female bias on the magazine rack. Other doctors and dentists leave it up to their spouses to keep the waiting area spick and span. In truth this job should be firmly stipulated in the contract of the medical secretary or practice manager, who in turn, should insist that the doctor pays a minimum amount into petty cash each month to keep the supply in date. Alas manners aren't what they used to be. One lady told me that when she commented to a medical receptionist about the poor state of a specialist's magazines, she was advised to 'bring a book next time!' Charming.

ISLAND DOCTOR
January 2005

A new position has been advertised for a GP medical officer on the Falkland Islands. It's advertised as a unique environment where 'nature is still in charge'. The successful applicant will work with 3.3 colleagues (seven dwarfs probably) and a small consultant theatre-team that provide total healthcare for 2,700 residents and 2,000 soldiers in a nearby military garrison. English is necessary. Fluency in Spanish, especially Argentinean dialects, is not required. Perks include regular Land Rover jaunts to outlying areas, small aircraft flights when on-call, and attending to sick crew on fishing vessels in your own small launch. I have always fancied a bit of penguin spotting so I wrote to the man in charge of matters medical in the Malvinas. I had a lovely letter back from Mr Norman McGregor Edwards, director of health and social services on the islands, complete with a photograph of the landscape the lucky applicant might expect. It was all very friendly and intimate. A bit like applying for the job as swimming pool attendant at Castel Gandolfo and getting a personal reply from the pope. The salary is negotiable at around £65,000 sterling upwards sort of thing. The tax rate is very low and there is also a cash gratuity on leaving. The rota is one in four which means you could be woken up at an ungodly hour just seven nights a month, and there is a good quality furnished house available at a nominal rent. No wonder Maggie sent the ships in. Norman says it's a great place to live and work, with most doctors extending their planned stay. The vacancy has arisen because one of their docs has been offered a jaunt with the Australian flying doctor service. Now that might be the one for me. If only I could conquer that fear of flying.

CHOOSING A GYNAECOLOGIST
April 2008

Doctors aren't immune to having their practices and clinical peccadilloes dissected on the internet. A contributor to a health forum recently asked fellow users what she should do about a rude gynaecologist whom she felt was 'minimising her period pain'. The first respondent (a bit rashly I would have thought) suggested that she should inform the medical council immediately. But another board user advised that she should have taken more care in choosing her gynaecologist in the first place. 'You can tell a lot about a person from how they handle lost luggage and how they manage tangled Christmas lights' she advised sagely. So let that be a lesson to all gynaecologists out there. If a lady you have never met before is staring at you on the Dublin airport carousel, or peeping through your blinds on the 24th of December, she is probably just a prospective patient, assuring herself of your competence.

NEW SPECIALITY
July 2000

The number of medical specialties continues to grow. I've heard of specialists in stadium medicine who spend their time at sports events at rock concerts. Then there are performing arts specialists who treat ailments of opera singers and comedians. But I never thought I'd see a specialist in nightclub medicine. They have one down in Cork and it sounds like a bit of fun we could import to Dublin. If I can squeeze into my skinny white jeans from 1979, you might see me strutting my stuff some Saturday evening. Coming down with *Night Fever* under a giant disco ball.

MRS MCGAHERN
September 2005

You never quite know where your everyday medical letters and hospital reports are going to end up. Mr John Corcoran was a young general surgeon at Dublin's Mater hospital during the second world war. When he replied to secret letters from Sergeant Francis McGahern at the Garda barracks in Cootehall, Co Roscommon about his wife's precarious breast cancer, Mr Corcoran would never have dreamed that sixty years later, his clinical comments would be available to read in every bookshop in Ireland. Details of her 'highly malignant growth', her 'most radical operative treatment', 'thorough deep x-ray treatment' and her '30% chance of survival' are contained in her son's latest literary offering, *Memoir* The book is a wonderful first work of non-fiction by the author. Described often as 'Ireland's greatest living novelist', I'm sure John McGahern doesn't mind sharing this booth in busy times with Roddy Doyle, John Banville, Joseph O'Connor and whoever else is on the literary prowl. It's always more comforting than being Ireland's greatest dead one.

Post-Script: *John McGahern died in the Mater Private Hospital, Dublin just six months after this piece was written. He was 71. He was interred with his late mother Susan McManus McGahern. She had died in June 1944 at the age of just 42 when John was nine years old. They are buried in St Patrick's churchyard at Aughawillan, County Leitrim where Mrs McGahern taught in the national school.*

ADELAIDE NURSES
May 1998

Navy Dress with white Nightingale spots. Starched White Aprons. Sister Dora caps. Jet Black Stockings. Dark Laced-Up Shoes. No, my brain's temporal lobes aren't firing off again. Any of you who had the good fortune to work in Dublin's Adelaide Hospital will remember its most distinctive and attractive nurse's uniform which made Peter Street ladies the envy of other less fashionable institutions. With the possible exception of the Royal

City of Dublin Hospital on Baggot Street. They matched the Adelaide crew for style with their fetching French berets and pale blue capes as their nursing students trooped up the canal to Sir Patrick Dun's for educational sojourns. Sadly both uniforms are now out of commission. But if you still want to see a traditional Adelaide nurse, albeit one with a waxy complexion, you can venture up to the National Museum at Collins Barracks where the wonderful costume is now on permanent display.

SCOTCH VISITOR
February 2003

Prime Minister Tony Blair was visiting an Edinburgh hospital. He entered a ward full of patients who had no obvious sign of injury or illness. He greeted the first patient who replied 'Fair fa your honest sonsie face, Great chieftain o' the puddin race, Aboon them a you take your place, Painch, tripe or thairm, As langs my airm'. A bit confused, Mr Blair grinned and moved on to say hello to the next patient. The patient responded 'Some hae meat and canna eat, And some wad eat that want it, But we hae meat and we can eat, So let the Lord be thankit'. Even more confused, but trying hard not to show it, Mr Blair moved on to the next patient, who immediately began to chant: 'Wee sleekit, cowerin', timrous beasty, Thou needna start awa sae hastie, Wi bickering brattle'. Now alarmed, Mr Blair turned to the accompanying doctor and asked 'What kind of facility is this? Is this a psychiatric ward?' 'Not at all' replied the doctor. 'This is the serious Burns unit'.

FALSE PROMISES
November 2012

Three cheers for the Advertising Standards Authority of Ireland who are doing their bit to clamp down on misleading health claims. This month, they judged against a television advertisement for 'slimming capsules' that could 'transform your body shape overnight'. They also had harsh words for a 'detox foot patch' advertisement that claimed to 'boost circulation, lose weight, alleviate pain, aid digestion' and much else. There is a part of me which feels that people who buy into miracle cures from seventh sons of seventh sons have more money than sense, and deserve whatever gobbledygook they purchase. But, with the exception of politics, false promises aren't tolerated in any other walk of life, so it's good to see the Advertising Standards Authority on the ball here. But a few more statutory powers for them to do more than slap the odd wrist, wouldn't go amiss.

COLLECTIVE NOUNS
September 2006

A few more suggested titles for collections of medical colleagues have landed on my desk. The gynaecology one was unprintable but I think we can get away with sharing a buttload of proctologists, a supporting cast of orthopaedic surgeons, a hive of allergy specialists, a carvery of surgeons, a growth of oncologists, and my own favourite, a golf-cart of private practice only physicians.

HEALTHY ADVERTISING
April 2008

Despite unconvincing denials, Irish healthcare slavishly follows fashions in the United Kingdom and the United States. Cynics might argue that it takes the worst of private healthcare from one and the worst of public healthcare from the other. I see that Britain's National Health Service is to allow its hospitals to start advertising. Last month they launched a code of practice that will allow public hospitals compete for the affections of hypochondriacs with their private counterparts. Testimonials from film stars, sporting celebrities and medical experts will be allowed, on tow conditions. They must have received treatment at the hospital they promote and no money changes must change hands for the promotion. What a pity Harry Secombe isn't alive. The famous Goon once famously had an operation on his piles and was back on stage the same evening. The British Medical Association has poured some scorn on this latest development, suggesting that quality of care alone should speak for hospitals. Sounds like fun times ahead. Over in the United States, things have got even madder. A paediatric hospital in Columbus, Ohio has just sold naming rights for its casualty department to a teen clothing manufacturer. Thanks to ten million dollars changing hands, all future cases of saucepans on heads will be treated in the Abercrombie & Fitch Emergency and Trauma Centre.

LAVATORIAL PARALYSIS
July 2004

Hospital hygiene is more than a bit of an issue. It stinks. A man told me in surgery last week that he had the misfortune to visit an emergency department in Dublin twice in three days with his sick wife. On his second visit he paid a trip to the gents and was greeted by the exact same disgusting mess of excrement that met him in on his first visit. He examined a notice on the wall recording when the toilets were last cleaned to discover that it had last been signed ten days before. He followed the instructions on the wall and alerted cleaning staff to the problem. Eventually a traffic cone and an out of order sign was placed outside the toilet door. Four hours later he came back to the toilet. The same mess was there, the same traffic cone and the same out of order sign. Any strange groaning sounds you hear are one hundred matrons rotating in their graves.

NURSE CADDEN
January 2005

This was a sad week when patients and staff of the Central Mental Hospital in Dundrum learned that they are all to be re-housed in a prison complex. Centuries of good work in distinguishing those who need hospital treatment from those who receive prison punishment may be about to come to an end.

It's the same week that a book about one of the Dundrum's most famous patients hit the shelves. Some of you may have heard the author Ray Kavanagh on radio as he spun a gripping tale of Dublin's abortion industry in the middle decades of the twentieth century. His book, *Mamie Cadden Backstreet Abortionist*, documents the life and times of Ireland's most notorious midwife. It also opens up a few cans of worms that the Irish medical profession might care to forget. Kavanagh's treatment of Nurse Cadden is unusually sympathetic, but given the harsh attitude of society towards the women she tended to, it is not difficult to see where he is coming from. Few come out of this tale smelling of roses. The text is liberally sprinkled with the names of well known doctors of the era. I was born four years after the death of Mamie Cadden, but she was well known to our family, many of whom resided with her in Dundrum. My late grandfather was the Governor and chief psychiatrist there. Indeed he is mentioned in the book as being singularly unimpressed with the arrival of Nurse Cadden on the wards of the Central Mental Hospital. the book. An anonymous source states that he was unconvinced by the tag of mental illness that led to her transfer to his care. An undertone that courses through this excellent new title is that Nurse Cadden knew a lot more secrets about Dublin's 'respectable society' than she ever divulged. It may well have suited the authorities to keep her personal story behind high walls. Ray Kavanagh makes a good stab at exposing many of the hypocrisies that marked the day.

Post-Script: *Almost ten years later, the Central Mental Hospital remains at Dundrum. Plans to co-locate it with a prison have been shelved and now the talk is of moving it to a new purpose built hospital in the grounds of the old St Ita's, Portrane in north county Dublin.*

RAYNAUDS ON THE BUSES
April 1998

If your hands feel like this then you could have Raynaud's Disease. So reads a poster at many bus stops in Dublin. It depicts a pair of hands in which the nails have been replaced by very cold looking icicles. You could have. But then you could also have nothing wrong at all. Or you could have a condition that has nothing to do with raynaud's. Or you might have forgotten your gloves on a particularly cold day. We should probably cheer the fact that support groups are becoming better funded and more sophisticated in their methods. Many of them do a very valuable job. But we need to consider the dangers of bus stop diagnosis too. Giving a symptom and suggesting a particular disease might be quite an innocent ploy when it comes to raynaud's disease, but do we really want a day when patient support groups take over diagnosis and prognosis to recruit new members. Do we want depression groups asking whether you feel guilty, or cancer groups wondering if your bowels are moving, or aneurysm groups wondering if you've a pulsating pot belly? Many of our patients, and indeed sometimes ourselves, are only half a worry away from a health neurosis. The one feature of health delivery which doctors need to protect as their own is the initial diagnosis of illness. That is what we are trained for. And dare I say, that is perhaps what we are best at. Let bus stops shelter those who are waiting for buses. Let support groups shelter and assist those who have been diagnosed. But we need to debate the pros and cons of casual and directional diagnosis, before there are no hospital appointments left for anyone.

THE RISE OF METROSEXUALISM
March 2004

Whilst perusing the medical press last week, I came across a new adjective that certainly wasn't around during my doctor training days. Apparently these so-called 'metrosexual men' are on the increase and we should all be keeping an eye out for them in our surgeries. Now these bipedal males have the same X and Y chromosomes as the rest of us. They are not a new variety of frotteur who bother fellow passengers on the Harcourt Street Luas line. Metrosexuals are men who indulge in a lot more personal grooming than their fathers and grandfathers did. A new report, doubtless sponsored by a business that sells beautifully re-packaged sea spray or rain water, reveals that the hairier sex are now spending three hours a week preening themselves in front of the mirror. The worrying thing is that this is a full half an hour more than their lady partners. In five years time, men are expected to be spending €25 billion a year moisturising their facial cheeks, smearing fragrant oils on their chests and generally doing things that leave smudges all over the bathroom mirror. Your scribe is not for turning. This is one unisexual who will stick to the toothbrush, razor and soap.

WELLCOME BOOK PRIZE
October 2011

We hear plenty about the Booker prize, the Pullitzer prize and our own Impac Dublin literary award. But how many of you have heard of the Wellcome book prize? In its third year now, this annual award of about €30,000 is given to a work of fact or fiction that celebrates medicine in literature. Two years ago the inaugural award went to *Keeper: Living with Nancy*, the diary of a lady who gave up work to look after her slowly dementing mother-in-law. Last year it was won by *The Immortal Life of Henrietta Lacks*, the true story of an impoverished tobacco worker in Virginia whose tumour was used after her death for some extraordinary medical research. This year's prize is being awarded presently and the short list of books is varied to say the least. There's a lady surgeon with alzheimer's disease who may be a murderer. There are soldiers having pioneering plastic surgery after world war one. Another is about the development of a drug that keeps women fertile forever. And Philip Roth has a book about a 1940s polio epidemic in New York. And these are only the fiction entries. Sounds like a vintage year.

Post-Script: *Turn of Mind by Alice LaPlante won the prize - it's the poignant thriller about the doctor with dementia who is accused of murdering her best friend.*

DOGGY DAYCARE
IN THE BLACKSTAIRS
June 2012

We had a 'do' to attend down the country recently and booked our canine companion into doggy day-care on the foothills of the Blackstairs mountains. He was looked after royally for the day in a brand new premises that's managed by the local vet. I was interested that we had to bring down his immunisation certificate to prove that he had been covered for kennel cough and other dastardly diseases of hairy mutts. This was not for his own safety, but for the wellbeing of all the other animals that are housed at the facility whilst their owners are away. An unvaccinated dog is seen by veterinary surgeons as a threat, not just to himself, but to all other breeds of animal. It set me thinking about whether vets are taking animal health more seriously than doctors take child health? Every day, at perhaps every school in this country, unvaccinated children play with children who have had their shots. The recent serious outbreak of measles in west Cork shows the dangers of lax policies in this area. Most doctors do not agree with mandatory vaccination of all children, but many would be sympathetic to a view that a vaccination certificate should be demanded by all crèches and all schools. Parents have the right to make decisions for their own children. But do they have the right to make decisions that could have catastrophic results for children of other parents? Now that's a debate worth having.

MERCURY AND MRSA
May 2004

I've had a most interesting letter from a surgeon about hospital acquired infections. And it may cause some nurses to think twice before pointing at grubby doctors as the major source of superbug spread. My correspondent attended a meeting some years ago at which a microbiologist referred casually to the increase in nosocomial infections since the introduction of 'new thermometers'. Apparently it's widely accepted in microbial circles that the unwashable, hand held, electronic devices transferred from patient to patient by nurses caused an upsurge in hospital acquired infections when introduced here a decade ago. Interestingly it was the nursing establishment who brought about this change because there was so much hype and exaggeration about the very rare dangers of mercury poisoning. It confirms a long held suspicion of mine that much of the fuss about the dangers of mercury sphygmomanometers and mercury thermometers was simply a ruse by manufacturers of new fangled medical electronic equipment to clear the existing market.

PULLING THE PLUG
February 2000

A second-hand report has landed on my desk from South Africa. As I cannot confirm the veracity of the story, I'll omit the name of the institution in question. For several months, nurses at a hospital were baffled to find a dead patient in the same bed every Friday morning. There was no apparent cause for this series of deaths. Doctors made extensive checks for infections, whilst the hospital engineers took apart the air conditioning system to search for elusive clues. Further enquiries amongst domestic staff eventually revealed the culprit. It seems that early each Friday, the same cleaner entered the ward and removed the plug that powered the life support system so that she could fire up her floor polisher. When finished her chores, she re-inserted the original plug and left. The loud noise of the polisher was enough to muffle any accompanying death rattle of the unfortunate patients. The health authorities apologised for the error. They sent a strong letter to the cleaner in question and arranged for the hospital electrician to fit an extra socket. The local newspaper couldn't resist running the headline - *CLEANER POLISHES OFF PATIENTS!*

STATE CARS
October 2010

That recent image featuring convoys of state cars conveying ministers of our impoverished country to the plush estate at Farmleigh will last long in the minds of Irish voters. Now here's a quiz question. Who was the only government minister in Irish history ever to make a state car available to a doctor in the course of his daily work? Well, the answer is the late Dr Noel Browne, and he did so as minister for health. The doctor who was offered state wheels was the Cork-born surgeon, Mr Maurice Hickey, one of the most respected chest operators Ireland has ever produced. Mr Hickey's work-rate was phenomenal. He operated every week of the year in theatres as far apart as Mallow in Cork, Castlereagh in Roscommon and the old Rialto Hospital (St James's) in Dublin. His skills in the very early days of heart surgery were legendary. Over the course of a long career that began in 1950, he introduced Ireland to heart valve surgery, surgery for children with heart defects, cardiac catheterisation and pacemakers. Many of his skills were honed in the only way they could be at the time, by experimentation and practice on the hearts of animals. When Dr Browne was appointed minister, he wanted to make Maurice Hickey's working week run as smoothly as possible by providing a complimentary state car and driver. But Mr Hickey turned down the offer and continued to drive himself.

BIEN VIERGE
February 1998

Some years ago, yours truly was on Saturday morning duty in a casualty department. Because of the few millilitres of French blood that trickle through my veins, I was volunteered by nurses to tend to a young Parisian lady in cubicle two, who spoke some English, but only of the pidgin dialect. After the *Bonjour, je m'appelle Dr Guéret* and the obligatory *comment allez-vous?*, we got down to the nitty-gritty of continental consultation. Mademoiselle informed me that she had an acute case of alcoholic memory loss for events of the previous night and requested that I check whether or not she was still 'bien vierge'. After checking the dictionaries to make sure that vierge still meant what I thought it meant, and with memorised paragraphs from those cautionary pamphlets which medical insurers delight in sending to young impressionable junior doctors, the only female house medic in the Hospital was summoned to the cubicle for some delicate negotiations. Yours truly was given a tea-break and something to mop my brow by the sympathetic nurses. What brought this episode back to mind was the news last week that Dutch surgeons can now restore the semblance of virginity by reconstructing the hymens of women who wish to turn back their sexual clocks. The technique, known as hymenoplasty, is unlikely to catch on in modern Ireland. But alas there are still countries where brides are expected to be virgins, and men are taught to actually care about such trifling matters.

SALUTING WILSON GREATBATCH
September 2011

It's usually doctors who take all the credit for being the first to transplant this or formulate that. But the full story of invention, inspiration and even chance discovery can be lost in a rush to put one single face on every new innovation. The impressively named New Yorker, Mr Wilson Greatbatch, passed away this month. He was 92 years old and is credited with being the inventor, not of the first cardiac pacemaker, but of the first one that was of real practical benefit to patients. Greatbatch was a telephone repairman who went on to take an engineering degree at Cornell University. His particular skill was in miniaturising electronic devices. It was his idea to switch from short lived zinc-mercury batteries to lithium-iodine ones that would last a decade inside pacemakers. When asked what are the ten greatest medical contributions ever made to mankind, very few doctors include pacemakers. But when engineers are asked the same question, pacemakers are well up their pecking list. Much of Greatbatch's early work was conducted in his garden shed and a lifetime spent 'tinkering' led to him to file more than 300 patents. He once paddled 160 miles in a solar powered canoe in his seventies. But his greatest contribution was to pacemaker design. And the salvation of so many thousands of lives in their fifty years of use.

EXPERT SIGNS
March 2006

You have probably of the rude sign over the door of a gynaecologist's rooms, which says Doctor at your Cervix. Well a colleague has sent me a larger collection of signs from the doors of other trades. One chiropodist has a sign which reads 'Time Wounds All Heels'. And the door of a maternity ward has a sign which says 'Push, Push, Push'. A veterinary surgeon's sign says 'Back in Five Minutes, Sit! Stay!' My friend also has an eye for interesting graffiti. He spotted a septic tank trunk recently on which somebody had scrawled 'Yesterday's Meals on Wheels'. And he knows a plumber whose van says 'Don't sleep with a drip, call your local plumber'. Finally he tells me of a taxidermist who boasted to clients 'We really know our stuff'.

JEREMY BEADLE
February 2008

It's funny what you find out about people after they take up their berth on the Stygian ferry. I've been reading about the life of Jeremy Beadle, whose days were ended by a bout of pneumonia last week. Beadle first came to my attention about twenty five years ago on the popular *Game for a Laugh* television show. Subsequent ventures seem to have attracted ever decreasing circles of viewers. But his story is a remarkable one. Bad enough that his father ran off before his birth, but when he was born, Beadle had a rare congenital deformity. His fingers were webbed and he was missing a pectoral breast muscle on the right side of his chest. The condition was known as Poland syndrome, named posthumously after Alfred Poland, the British surgeon who described it in the

1840s. Poland first spotted the eponymous condition as he was dissecting the corpse of a convict at Guys Hospital in London. Jeremy Beadle was a challenging child, who had difficulty settling at school. Once he dared a pal to climb a tree. His friend did so, but fell to his death. Another chum went tobogganing with him and died when he collided with a tree. It's extraordinary, or maybe it isn't, that Beadle spent his subsequent career daring, challenging and pulling stunts to make others laugh. He raised a staggering £100 million sterling for children's charities, including *Reach*, a charity for young patients with missing hands or arms, of which he was patron.

Alfred Poland was no less interesting a character. A Londoner, he studied medicine on the continent and became an apprentice surgeon at Guys Hospital in 1839. He worked his way up the chain as anatomy demonstrator, assistant and then consultant surgeon. He also dabbled in a bit of nineteenth century eye surgery as an ophthalmologist. Poland was a popular teacher, but shy, and in the words of his colleagues 'careless about his appearance'. The hospital treasurer issued warnings about his personal hygiene and dress code, advice he chose to ignore. Poland timed many of his operations for very early in the morning, or very late at night, as he always preferred to operate unobserved. Private practice held no attraction for him, he preferred to devote his spare time teaching medical students. Alfred Poland retired in his mid forties with poor health and died from pulmonary tuberculosis in his fiftieth year.

ALPINE ARREST
January 2007

Despite the presence of so many medics on the piste, the Alps might not be such a good place to have your first cardiac arrest. A man collapsed there over the winter season and within seconds was receiving urgent assistance from a British lung specialist, two German nurses, a paediatric nurse, a French dentist and a nursing student. Alas, his heart and breathing had stopped, and a defibrillator was nowhere to be found, not even in the nearby first aid room. The nearest village was a cable car ride away and there was an eight minute wait for the electrical shock which eventually came with the emergency helicopter. The treating doctor has written about the experience in the *British Medical Journal* and wants defibrillators at 'all ski resorts'. They might have to steal them from village churches in Ireland. I reckon half the world's defibrillator stock has been installed here already.

DOCTOR TEDDY
March 2002

Tell your children to be careful handling Doctor Teddy on their next visit to the surgery. According to the *British Journal of General Practice*, waiting room toys may not be quite as cuddly as your doctor intended. A team from the Christchurch school of medicine in New Zealand looked at the level of bacterial contamination in toys provided for children in the waiting rooms of general practitioners. Two of the six practices had the time, staff and presence of mind to clean them down every single day. 20% of soft toys showed either moderate or heavy contamination with faecal-type organisms and 90% had either moderate or heavy contamination with general run-of-the-mill bacteria. Hard toys, which are apparently cleaned more often had much lower levels of contamination. I have asked colleagues to scrub down the toy town cash register, all the miniature chairs and the playtime stethoscope. Dr Teddy is in the boil wash.

SADDAM'S LAST ROOM
January 2007

Saddam Hussein received an execution by hanging just after Christmas. The nurse who tended to him in his final days has been speaking about her late patient. It came as a surprise to me that in a country which was starved of basic medical equipment for so long by the west, that Hussein was so well catered for in his final months. His captors went to very great lengths to ensure that their patient didn't perish of natural causes. The late dictator had a personal supply of oxygen and intravenous solutions. He also had his very own defibrillator which was stored in an empty cell next door to him. It was a sad end for a man who was so warmly embraced by mercenaries of Irish medicine in the not so distant past. It was once said that he paid almost as many Irish medical and nursing salaries in Baghdad as health boards did back home. Saddam's ideas on his own personal health were also quite interesting. He told his nurse that the only thing which kept his high blood pressure in check, were copious rations of Cuban cigars and the strongest of coffee.

HOSPITAL PARKING
March 2006

I had to stifle a giggle when reading an obituary to the very first full-time woman consultant at the London Chest Hospital. The good lady passed away recently at the age of eighty after a long and distinguished career in anaesthetics and intensive care. An obituary writer in the *Guardian* noted that she was always immaculately dressed and on this account was known to one and all as 'the Duchess'. She had one failing however. Junior doctors who watched her car being deposited on the hospital grounds each morning would remark that her vehicle always had the look of being abandoned, rather than parked! She took such observations warm-heartedly with her usual good humour. In a show of benevolence a bit rarer in medicine today, the tribute also noted that she had set up a fund into which she paid all her private practice earnings to buy equipment for the intensive care unit. Sounds like a great lady.

GENEROUS DIVORCE
October 2005

Unfaithful Doctor Murphy was up in the divorce courts waiting for the judgement. 'Doctor, I have reviewed this case very carefully,' said Judge Bigwig 'and I've decided to give your long-suffering wife €975 a week, every week for the rest of her life'. 'That's very fair, your honour,' said Doc Murphy, 'and sure every now and then I'll try to send her a few bob myself!'

NO SALE HERE
June 1999

The American Medical Association has narrowly voted to caution doctors against selling health care products. Dietary supplements, bicycle helmets and over the counter medicines should no longer be sold in their clinics. My reading of the ballot is that mugs, baseball caps and t-shirts are still alright. The vote represents a sharp U-turn for the American Medical Association, as it's not long since the organisation offered exclusive endorsement to nine products of the Sunbeam corporation in return for a royalty on each item sold. The Sunbeam deal mortified a dwindling number of doctors who still belonged to the Association. Of late, a newfound self-respect amongst north American medics has led to this new no tied-sales policy being adopted. Dr Robert McAfee, a former association president and retired surgeon from Portland, Oregon said the practice of in-office sales was akin to the 'snake oil peddling' of the 1800s. It's interesting that one of the reasons the American Medical Association was founded in the first place was to tackle such abuses of vulnerable patients. Not all physicians are happy with this recent vote. One orthopaedic surgeon decried the fact that he was no longer able to make a dollar on selling a patient a set of crutches!

STARK RESIGNATION
May 2003

In the running for *Surgeon of the Year* award is orthopaedic specialist Geoffrey Anderson, a 44 year old consultant who has just walked out of his job at a hospital in Plymouth. According National Health Service managers of 'corporate crapness' before resigning, he is now off to mend bones in New Zealand. Last week the London *Times* carried extracts from his resignation letter where he said that 'individual executives are well meaning and hard working but when put together within an NHS trust they do not seem to function. I have christened the phenomenon corporate crapness and I think it's at the root of the problems'.

He claimed that operating theatres he was forced to work in were dirty and inadequate and that managers were manipulating waiting lists to meet government targets. Last year another surgeon in his orthopaedic department left work claiming he had been asked to use a pudding spoon during a hip operation. They'll have their just desserts in the Antipodes.

SHINE ON YOU CRAZY DIAMOND
July 2006

Sad news this week for grey-templed forty-something year olds with word that the original crazy diamond has passed away. Syd Barrett, dubbed the best known recluse in rock circles, has passed on to the dark side of the moon at the age of sixty. A founder member of the Pink Floyd, Barrett had a renowned penchant for psychedelic medication. He was sacked by the band he named in 1968 and replaced by David Gilmour. Whilst Floyd members went on to multi-millionaire status, Barrett lived most of his life boarded up like a hermit in his mother's house. Interestingly, his father was a clinical pathologist from Cambridge who died when Sid was fourteen. Barrett's immersion in music began as a way of coping with this family loss. Reading between the many lines that have been written about Syd Barrett, and considering his many contemporaries who experimented with LSD as lived fairly ordinary lives afterwards, it would appear that schizophrenia may well have on a differential diagnosis list. In later life he suffered from quite severe diabetes. His funeral is to be a musician-free family affair.

NUTRITIONAL THERAPY
April 2013

Patients should know of a very clear distinction between university qualified dieticians, and this new fangled area inhabited by folk who style themselves as nutritional therapists. Putting a brass plate on the door after completion of an overseas correspondence course is becoming quite a fashion. Consumer magazine *Which* carried out a survey last year which found that the advice given by nutritional therapists in the United Kingdom lacked basic understanding of science and was potentially harmful to patient health. Undercover researchers posing as patients had fifteen consultations. One therapist told a lady that her cancer lived off sugar and proposed a diet to cure it, advising against having cancer surgery or radiotherapy. Two therapists 'spotted' problems with the adrenal gland without doing the mandatory blood tests that would suggest a problem in this area. Other 'nutritional therapists' used quack diagnostic methods like mineral testing and examination of iris colour in the eye to reach conclusions. They also failed to latch on to basic symptoms that would alert doctors to consider more serious illnesses. Six of the fifteen consultations were rated as 'dangerous fails' where the advice give could potentially endanger health. Eight other consultations also failed, and just one nutritional therapist received a borderline pass. *Which* has asked the British government to regulate this 'industry' because it is putting patients lives at risk. I think we should ask our own government to do likewise.

INHERITANCE TAX
February 2005

A little boy asked his grandfather if he would make a noise like a frog.

The grandfather asked 'Why, son?'

'Because daddy says the sooner you croak, the quicker we can all go to Eurodisney! '

LLOYD'S BED
June 2004

Doctors can lose touch completely with hospital settings when they set themselves up in family practice. A general practitioner in the north west recently wrote to me with a delicious *mea culpa* he experienced whilst standing in as a locum for a colleague at a district hospital. He was called to see an elderly gentleman who was quite poorly. Anxious to know how he felt, the doctor saw that the names Pearson and Lloyd were printed at the top of the bed and proceeded to ask politely 'Tell me Lloyd, how are you feeling?' With this, the ward sister and staff nurses who were accompanying the doctor on his rounds rolled around the place with mirth. The doctor was suitably red-faced when it transpired that PearsonLloyd was not too poorly at all. He was the manufacturer of the bed!

DOCTORS AT FUNERALS
August 2000

A lot of research has been conducted on the devastating effect that suicide of a loved one has on partners, family and friends. Not so much consideration has been given to the effect it can have on doctors who lose patients in this way. A recent study in the *British Medical Journal* on how psychiatrists cope in the aftermath of suicides of their patients was most informative. Not coping very well seems to be the general conclusion. A large number of psychiatrists consider retirement after such catastrophes. But it's interesting to note that less than 15% of doctors actually attend the funerals of their patients who killed themselves. The authors of the study consider this a reflection of many factors - denial, avoidance and perhaps anxiety about the reaction of relatives. But I think it's a pity. Their absence may well be a loss to themselves and very probably to most bereaved families too.

NURSE'S NIGHT OUT
December 1997

An Irish senator, hotel owner and music impresario was attacked by nurses on radio recently over the 'nurse's night out' theme dance at his establishment in central Dublin. They complained about the stereotyping of nurses and insinuated that nurses might be considered an 'easy item' or 'game for anything' by references to 'nurse's night out' in advertisements. Evidence was given that there might not be anything like a quota of nurses on such nights and an undertaking was given by the good senator to refrain from such references in the future. Now all has changed utterly. The new advertisement tell us that Thursday night in the same hotel is now 'doc's night out'. Doubtless nurses are deserting their wards in droves and flocking to the venue in search of starched white coats and dangling stethoscopes. Sure we doctors are always game for anything!

PAPAL MEDICINE
April 2005

Much has been written in recent weeks about the slow decline and death of Pope John Paul II. It was reported on occasions that the late pope often ignored medical advice, especially that relating to his Parkinson's disease. Compliance with medication was reported to be poor. It was suggested in 2002 that his rapid loss of facial expression had more to do with neglecting his levodopa treatment, than the ordinary course of the disease. A year later his facial muscles appeared to become more mobile, prompting some of the Vatican faithful to claim that Catholic prayers were working. Others said he was back on the pills. One needs of course to be ultra-cautious about armchair commentating. It was once claimed that his condition had improved with natural supplements, I think it was an extract of yam that was given the credit. Vatican aides said they were amazed when the pope 'ran to the lift'. Medics however were more cautious, putting the athletic episode down to a bout of short-stepping festination, a well-recognised characteristic of Parkinson's disease that helps patients maintain an upright posture.

Just eighteen months ago the pope ignored pleas from his doctors and went on a three day trip to Slovakia that culminated in a huge open air mass in Bratislava. A cardiologist travelled with him and it was reported that his hydraulic papal throne was kitted out with a hidden defibrillator and oxygen cylinder.

Other recent popes haven't had it easy either. His predecessor, another John Paul, died from an embolus after just 33 days in office. The only other pope in my memory banks was Paul VI. He was frequently catheterised for urinary retention until his prostate was resected in 1967. It was probably cancerous, but as with many such patients, he may have died with the disease rather than from it. He expired with a massive coronary attack in 1978. The much lauded John XXIII before him succumbed to stomach cancer. But the most fascinating ring wearer of the last century was surely Eugenio Pacelli, known better as Pius XII. He is described as one of the greatest Italian hypochondriacs in history. Nothing entertained Pius more than seeking multiple medical opinions. It wasn't long before the quacks got hold of him. The reign of Pius XII began in 1939. Prior to the second world war, he was regarded as a rather serious man. Pacelli was a canon lawyer, credited with centralising much of church power in the Vatican. He was a far more portentous man than some of his successors. Gardeners at his summer residence were instructed to hide behind sheds or bushes when he was on his walkies. It was even suggested that the faithful had to take his phone calls on their knees. Hardly surprising to learn that his favourite treat was to dine alone.

Pius XII's hang-ups were almost always on matters medical. His hourly needs were met by a German nun who acted as housekeeper for most of his life. She made sure all of his handkerchiefs were dipped in antiseptic. One of the more benign comments made about him was that he was a 'pompous know-all'. He fancied himself as a bit of an expert on scientific matters, reading widely on gynaecology, psychiatry and therapeutics. Indeed he would have felt very much at home in today's coercive health climate. He once refused a sainthood on the grounds that the candidate was a smoker. His biographer was not too saintly either, describing Pius XII as 'a deeply neurotic, narcissistic and arrogant man'. He had a rather irrational hatred of jazz music and spent long hours imbuing irrelevant sexual matters with major importance. Two years before he died, the pope issued an edict on the precise measurements that make a woman's dress decent. There was to be nothing visible above the elbow, elbows, no knees on show, and no cutting deeper than two fingers breadth under the pit of the throat. Just the sort of edict that only a man who dines alone could come up with.

He became even more neurotic as the years advanced. Half a dozen doctors tended to his whims but his favourite was Riccardo Galeazzi-Lisi, a medically qualified quack of the highest order, whose career ended in infamy and disgrace when details of his photos of the pope's body before death and treatment afterwards became public. The side effects of the many toxic home-made remedies prescribed by Galeazzi-Lisi were reckoned to have caused more papal symptoms than they cured. Pius XII died in 1958, some say of 'of a circulatory phenomenon', but popular word in Rome was that he either worked, or worried himself to death.

UROLOGY OUTPATIENTS
June 2007

Murphy had an appointment with the urologist. In the examining room he pleaded with the doctor, 'Please, don't laugh'.

'Of course I won't laugh,' the doctor said. 'I'm a professional.

In more than twenty years I have never once laughed at a patient's complaint'.

'Okay then,' Murphy said, and he proceeded to undo his trousers to reveal the very tiniest organ the doctor had ever seen – no bigger than half the size of the very smallest of small batteries. Unable to control himself, the doctor started giggling before falling to the floor, laughing hysterically. Five minutes later he struggled to his feet and regained his composure. 'I'm so sorry,' he said. 'I don't know what came over me. On my honour as a doctor and as a gentleman, I promise it won't ever happen again. Now, what seems to be the problem?'

'It's swollen'. said Murphy.

CITY GROCERS
January 2007

Sir Victor Horsley was a pioneering brain surgeon who played an active part in the Temperance movement of the early 20th century. He had a number of hobby horses and once described pharmacists of his day as 'a handful of city grocers who have not a particle of medical education'. Things have changed since Horsley slated the society of apothecaries and I don't think you would find too many doctors willing to make such far-flung claims today. But they might make an exception for Dublin chemists who sell sterling silver rings for 50 euro a pop that 'if correctly positioned on one of the meridian lines of the little finger will cure night-time snoring for ever'. Not even a city grocer would fall for that one.

WINDMILLS AND HEALTH
June 2012

I have been following this interesting debate about the ill effects, if there are any, of wind turbines on human health. I know from regular sojourns to the south east that the skylines of many rural communities have been colonised by these slow-turning industrial giants in recent years. There has been very little public debate about their health effects, locals seem to be more concerned about television interference and night-time noise. A recent editorial in the *British Medical Journal* suggested that a 'strong body of evidence' exists that wind turbines disturb sleep and impair health, especially in children. But Professor Simon Chapman, an Australian expert on public health and a sceptic on such matters was not too pleased with this standpoint. He wrote a long reply to the editorial affirming that the two authors of the piece had been objectors to wind farms in the past. He went on to say that there have now been seventeen reviews conducted, all suggesting that evidence for health problems is poor. Professor Chapman compiled a list of 63 symptoms or diseases in humans and animals that have been attributed to wind farms. He says some of them are quite bizarre. It's hard not to agree with him that any actual evidence for harm is just not there. The fact that they spoil the vista of so many idyllic rural landscapes throughout Ireland is perhaps the criticism with the most weight.

LITTLE JERUSALEM
October 2002

Dublin's Little Jerusalem by Nick Harris is a wonderful little memoir from one of our capital city's dwindling Jewish population. As a child, my family had the good fortune to be looked after by one of their number, the late Dr Manne Berber. Harris's book traces all the famous and not so well known names that sprung from a community that never numbered more than about 5,000. It records the fact that Dr Bethel Solomons, former master of the Rotunda was the only Jew ever to represent Ireland at rugby. And only for the talent of Dr Karl Mullen, another member of the community, Louis Jacobson, might have gained the hooker's berth for his country. Other well known names from the medical world that crop up are Eppel, Shillman, Harris, Wigoder, Robinson, Mushatt, Buchalter, Shrago and Abrahamson. There are tales of the hot seaweed baths in Dun Laoghaire used to treat rheumatism, the birth of the first set of Jewish triplets in Ireland, the busy life of the Mohel (cirumciser) and stories of the age-old ritual of a Jewish funeral. A real gem of a book.

BRONCHITIS EPIDEMIC
January 2000

At the height of the recent bronchitis epidemic, waiting times went absolutely crazy at my practice, once a very civilised surgery. A patient with an admirable sense of humour dropped me in a card entitled *Four Ways To Cope With Stress in your Doctor's Waiting Room*. I would have put it straight up on the waiting room wall were it not for the fourth one.

1. Sneeze and then loudly suck the mucous back down your throat.
2. Leaf through *National Geographic* and draw underwear on the natives.
3. Stare at other patients through the tines of a fork and pretend they are all in jail.
4. When your doctor calls you, present him a bill for every minute you've spent waiting on him.

DEAD SAMARITAN
February 2003

A doctor appears before the pearly gates. 'Have you done anything of particular merit outside the medical field?' asks Saint Peter. 'Well, I can think of one thing'. offers the doctor. 'Once I came upon a gang of high-testosterone bikers who were threatening a young woman. I directed them to leave her alone, but they wouldn't listen. So I approached the largest and most heavily tattooed biker. I smacked him on the head, kicked his bike over, ripped out his nose ring and threw it on the ground, and told him to leave her alone or he'd answer to me'. St. Peter was impressed. 'When did this happen?' he asked. 'Oh. About two minutes ago' replied the doctor

SICK CERTS
April 1999

If you ever get sick on a Sunday, or Saturday, for that matter, rest assured, you will find a half dozen members of each medical speciality eating lunch at the National Gallery restaurant. The rest will be having a leisurely promenade through its grand rooms pretending to look knowledgeable about pictorial anatomy. There's no safer place for a heart to stop beating on at the weekend. If some of the staff seem familiar to visiting doctors, it's perhaps because they have recently been dubbed the sickest attendants in the country, averaging almost 30 sick days annually per employee. This is more than twice the civil service average of fourteen days. It apparently accounts for the fact that so many rooms have recently been closed to the public. The chairman of the gallery's board of governors commented on the matter recently. She said that those out ill have sick certificates and suggested that it was not up to the gallery to investigate further. She intimated that provision of illness certification might be a matter for the Department of Health to investigate. My own personal belief is that it's time we took family doctors out of the equation when it comes to certification of short term illness. We have more important things to be doing. Minor illnesses that cause work leave are matters between employees and employer. If there is a problem, let them hire independent experts in occupational medicine for advice. Most general practitioners already refuse to provide parents with notes for school for their ailing children and it's not that great leap to stop providing this worthless service to employees and their employers.

DOCTORS WHO WRITE
September 2012

Fiction & Physicians is a new book from Dublin psychiatrist, Dr Stephen McWilliams. It's well worth a look. Chekhov, Conan Doyle, Crichton, Goldsmith, Gogarty, Guéret - all the literary greats from the world of medicine are there, with the odd work of fiction and delusion tossed in the pot for good measure. Stephen is the son of the late Brendan McWilliams, the much admired meteorologist, broadcaster and science writer. He has been honing his writing talent in the medical press for some years and has also contributed to compilations written by his father. There are chapters on incompetent physicians, psychiatrists in fiction, modern medical writers - all written with a commendable personal and entertaining touch without condescension, sniffiness or fug of academia. Dr McWilliams also includes interesting material on medical students who didn't finish their studies. James Joyce and Charles Darwin, just to name two. So why do so many doctors write? To supplement their income? To exercise vanity? To let off steam? To inform and educate? Well *Fiction* & Physicians won't tell you, but it will lay out all the evidence you require to allow you make up your own mind. And that, in my book, is the hallmark of an exceptionally good medical writer.

DOCTORS IN LOVE
July 2001

At a medical conference, two doctors started to eye each other up and before they knew what was happening, both were are upstairs in a hotel bedroom. Just as things were getting hot and steamy, the female doctor interrupted proceedings to say that she needed to go and wash her hands. She returned and they spent hours making love to each other. Next morning, the lady doctor got up and said she was going to wash her hands again. As she came back the male doctor said 'I bet you are a surgeon'. 'Yes' she confirmed 'how did you guess?'. 'Easy, you're always washing your hands'. 'And I bet you're an anaesthetist' she added. 'Wow, how can you tell that from just making love to me?' asked the man. 'Easy' she said, 'I didn't feel a thing!'

DEATH IN ZURICH
January 2006

Last week, a lady doctor whose speciality had been family planning, booked a one way flight to Zurich. Her three children accompanied her on the trip, but they had return tickets. She wasn't going to do holiday things like visiting James Joyce's grave or circling the lake. Instead, she was planning to go into a little house on an industrial estate, consume a lethal dose of barbiturates and join our aforementioned literary exile on the other side. Dr Anne Turner had progressive supranuclear palsy, the same rare neurological condition that claimed the life of comedian Dudley Moore. Average survival span is about seven years and as a doctor, she perhaps had better idea than most why the adjective progressive is a pertinent part the disease name. Euthanasia proponents have been busy using the case to suggest that an absence of such facilities in the United Kingdom and Ireland is forcing patients to take their lives earlier than they might otherwise choose. The implication being that many of these one-way visitors to Zurich might postpone their decision a lot longer if the option was available at home. Over the years there has been gossip and rumours in medical circles about the deaths of some Irish doctors, with speculation that one or more might have ended their own terminal illnesses prematurely in the comfort of their own homes. Might it be that we have one rule for ourselves, with access to know-how and equipment, and quite another when it comes to our patients?

BARE BONES
June 2006

A story has reached me from the north east of the country. General practitioners in the county of Louth received a memo recently from the County hospital in Dundalk advising that because of a freeze in staff recruitment, they have been unable to replace retiring radiographers. They expressed regret that x-ray requests from Drogheda could no longer be accepted, as they are now at 'skeleton staff level'!

DR RON PAUL
January 2012

Nothing bores me quite as much as a presidential election in the United States. It's always the predictable two candidate race, featuring two party men (always men) who have avoided implosion and have raised the most money from corporate America. Of moderate interest at the moment is the current 'last man standing' routine designed to pick a republican to fight Mr Obama. There is something rather wooden and hollow about Mitt Romney, and for me, the only interesting candidate left is Dr Ron Paul, a 76 year old obstetrician. His finest achievement to date is probably the safe delivery of 4,000 citizens in the state of Texas. What's unusual about Dr Paul, is that his vote is highest amongst voters aged between 18 and 30. The republican party's biggest fear is that he will lose to Mitt Romney and then decide to run as an independent in the race. What marks him out as different is that he is a man of fresh ideas, rather than old dogma. He campaigns, not with rehearsed slogans, but with brainwaves that are teased out on the hustings. He decries American involvement in so many wars. He wonders if drug policy is counter-productive. He opposes torture. A great pity the obstetrician they call Dr No didn't run twenty or thirty years ago when he was at the height of his powers of delivery.

Post-script: *Dr Ron Paul did not get the republican nomination. Nor did he run as an independent. He recently established the 'Ron Paul Channel' which encourages Americans to switch off their televisions.*

CARROTS AND STICKS
July 1998

There is a surgeon in a Dublin hospital who is not just anti-smoking. He is vehemently anti-smoker. As a medical vigilante, he has no equal and draws tears from unsuspecting weed blowers with consummate ease. He treats smokers rather like film star Charles Bronson treats baddies. He blows them away. It's not that he does vascular work or lung cancer surgery or that smoking always enters his surgical equations. I met a lady once who went to him with an abscess above her bottom, known in the trade as a pilonidal sinus. She nearly ended up giving him one of his own, such was her fury at his unprovoked tobacco attack. What brought this episode to mind was a recent publication suggesting that medical arrogance in front of patients who smoke, can be damaging and have the very opposite effect. It may also delay patients from volunteering serious symptoms in the future. At a major conference last month, Professor James McCormick of Trinity College Dublin stated bluntly that fat patients know they are fat, and smoking patients know that cigarettes have a good chance of killing them. He said they need sympathy and comfort, not chastisement. Carrots taste better than sticks.

MULTI-CHANNEL MARKETING
November 2000

Some years ago, family doctors around Dublin were offered a complimentary television for their waiting rooms. Nice gesture you would think, but the catch was that the supplier of the wall-mounted set would choose exactly what patients had to watch. The idea originated in England where doctors' waiting rooms in purpose built surgeries would be a lot bigger than the garage conversions we tend to have here. I didn't get involved. Visions of daily advertisements from local undertakers, no-win no-fee nonsense from solicitors and clinical nonsense from the anti-butter lobby tipped my scales more towards a good radio.

RED FOR DANGER
December 2010

The Christmas edition of the *British Medical Journal* is a national institution across the water. It includes all the research deemed not important enough for serious issues during the year. So this month we found out that the traditional fear which doctors reserve for red heads in operating theatres, has no evidence to back it up.

A long held myth in theatre circles is that red hair spells danger for both surgeons and anaesthetists. In bygone days, they were trained to be on their guard for excessive bleeding when gingers were on the table. The fable had particular relevance in Ireland. Our relatively high red-haired population at 10% ranks us second in the world, only to Scotland. But a team of Welsh surgeons have now reviewed all the scientific literature on the subject. They found no solid evidence for three old clinical fables - that red-heads bleed more, that they are more sensitive to pain and that they are more likely to develop hernias.

ANOTHER OPINION
September 1999

A doctor and his wife were having a big argument at breakfast. 'You aren't so good in bed either!' he shouted at her and stormed off to work. By mid morning, he was racked with guilt and decided to make amends. He phoned home. After many rings, his wife picked up the phone.

'What took you so long to answer?'

'I was in bed'.

'What are you doing in bed this late?'

'I was getting a second opinion!'

A DEATH IN SUMMER
July 2011

There aren't many Booker prize winners who could re-mould their gold nibs to create a series of popular mystery thrillers. Fewer still might centre them around a gruff, heavy-drinking pathologist in 1950s Dublin who was reared in an orphanage. This is the startling achievement of John Banville with his Dr Quirke mysteries. *A Death in Summer* has recently been published, the fourth of these striking books under the Benjamin Black pseudonym. The novels capture that grey uncertain mood of pre-Late Late Show Ireland. Characters with repressed lives tread familiar streets. A class-based social chasm is ever-present as a buttoned-up capital city wallows in religious oppression. Time and again in this series, Banville rattles out a mighty good yarn, paying generous tribute to the hard novels of Georges Simenon that influenced him. Dr Quirke's world revolves around the basement of his hospital pathology department and nocturnal forays above ground. The settings are familiar - the old Hibernian Hotel, Bewley's Cafe and the tram to Howth Head. Between drying-out sessions for alcoholism, liquid dinners in Jammet's restaurant and meetings with Garda friends, Dr Quirke encounters murders, unusual suicides, dodgy adoptions, prostitution, professional jealousies and family secrets. Whether you are looking for a new holiday author in the summer, or simply want a master-class in how to write well, look for Benjamin Black near Banville on the B shelf. Mr Black has raised the bar for an entire genre of whodunnits.

TOTAL ABSTINENCE TWICE A WEEK
January 2012

More 'make-it-up-as-you-go-along' medical advice has been proffered by politicians this new year. Parliamentarians have decreed that everybody should be advised to take at least two alcohol-free days a week. Their new report claims that the public don't understand either alcohol limits or units, and therefore an abstentionist policy is required. I hasten to add that this advice was delivered by the science and technology committee at Westminster, and it was issued some days before the lights in the Dáil bar were turned on again after Christmas. There are one or two ministers in our own funny farm who make honking noises about what you should and shouldn't be drinking. Excessive alcohol consumption seriously impacts on many Irish families. It's no funny business. But taking inconsistent advice from characters who have their own private subsidised bar in their place of occasional work? Well that's just that little bit rich.

A POETIC PHARMACIST
May 2012

The son of an 'old time chemist' has written to tell me of his father's career. His Dad started out in Bell's Pharmacy in Waterford before moving to Dublin where he was employed by Hayes Cunningham and Robinson in Ranelagh. In time he opened his own pharmacy on Morehampton Road in Donnybrook, just before the second world war. The son remembers his father preparing all manner of creams, ointments and even pills in the shop. He recalls how some pills shone when they were coated with silver. As a hobby his father would write poetry and much of it was published in pharmaceutical journals.

In later years the Pharmaceutical Society honoured his father by publishing a book of his poetry. Only about a dozen copies exist. My correspondent sent me a poem that his late father had written during the night whilst a patient in a Dublin hospital more than thirty years ago. The poem made a lasting impression on many. Some years ago the nurses of St Vincent's held a re-union and used the poem on their menu card. Inspired by the legendary nurses of Elm Park, it is simply called *St Vincent's 1980*.

> *White shoes whisper on a polished floor*
> *And now my loneliness is gone once more*
> *Came a soft voice to ease the strain*
> *And gentle hand to soothe the pain*
> *God bless you nurse and may you always be*
> *The angel that once you were to me*

ANGINA
January 2003

Dubliner Jacinta goes to the doctor complaining of chest pains:
'Hello Jacinta, what can I do for you?'
'Well doctor, I has been gettin' dees desperet pains in me chest'.
'Stand up there, hold out your arms and I'll check you out'.
The doctor inspects her chest, takes her pulse and blood pressure, then produces his stethoscope for a good listen.
He narrows it down to either trouble in the heart or an inflammation of her ribcage. To discern which, he has to stand behind her and press his hands firmly on the front of her ribcage to see if there is any tenderness.
Unable to find any tender spots he says 'Angina'.
No reply from Jacinta.
He proceeds to probe her chest again just to be sure.
'Angina, Jacinta'. He says in a slightly louder voice.
'Enjoyin' it, Doctor?...I'm bleedin' lovin' it!'

STOP THE LIGHTS
January 2012

An older gentleman has been in touch about his experience of alternative medicine in a large rural town. He has chronic asthma, and a friend recommended a 'specialist' who tests for allergies and 'cures asthma'. It was a beauty parlour, and a nurse presided over affairs. My correspondent had his hands and feet wired up to a device that in his own words looked like a 'Bunny Carr Stop the Lights Machine'. After a few minutes of flashing disco lights, he was told he had one short of a dozen 'impurities in the blood'. He was given a faded page of a 'What Not To Eat' diet that was photocopied on an ancient Gestetner machine. When he showed it to his wife, her comment was 'I don't think you'll be having any breakfast'. No milk. No bread. No rashers. No sausages. No cheese. No alcohol. No fruit juice. Cornflakes and meat just once a week. No tea. No coffee. Just rice bread and soya milk. After ten days he had lost a stone, the will to live and his breathing was the same as ever. It transpired that the person who had recommended the clinic for its asthma cure, had her own asthma diagnosed at the clinic - she had actually gone in with a bad stomach. You have been warned. Most of this food intolerance jibber jabber deserves a very wide berth. There are a few general practitioners and medical specialists who deal with real food allergies in both adults and children. Waiting lists can be long, but they know what they are talking about. They don't use stop the lights machines or dodgy blood tests. Nor do they photocopy the exact same diet for everybody.

SPARE PARTS
April 1998

Here's something that might get you a point at your next charity pub quiz. What have Albert Einstein, Galileo, Napoleon, George Washington, King Richard II and Percy Bysshe Shelley all got in common? Well the truth is that they all had body parts removed and preserved after their deaths. And for a bonus six points, can you name the parts? Answer: Brain, finger, penis, tooth, jawbone and heart. I double-checked this. It's especially important when compiling lists in medicine, that you get everything in the correct order.

HERO FROM MELBOURNE
October 2011

The death of a Melbourne gynaecologist rarely makes international headlines, unless he's the one with Dame Edna Everage wedged up in the stirrups. An exception to the rule was Professor Carl Wood who has passed away at the age of 82. In 1973, Wood arranged for the world's very first human egg to be fertilised in a test tube and then implanted it in a would-be mother. It was the world's first IVF pregnancy. Alas, it resulted in miscarriage after twelve weeks. However five years later, his

273

pioneering work made possible the birth of the world's first so-called test-tube baby in England. It's hard to believe now how controversial fertility treatments were just over three decades ago. Professor Wood had all the usual suspects protesting at his clinic, abusing women who were desperate for treatment, and accusing the doctor of 'playing God'. He was recognised as a great teacher of his craft to medical students. Recognising how essential it was to train doctors to do vaginal examinations, Professor Wood arranged for professional models to be paid for such assignments. His rather forward thinking was that relaxed women would result in relaxed doctors, and this would help make doctors more confident and sympathetic with all future gynaecology patients. Like many in this field, Wood was an absolute workaholic. Having divorced his second wife, he developed Alzheimer's disease and his first wife, an old nursing colleague, took him back in for the final decade of his life.

HOKEY COKEY
June 1996

A doctor tells me that there was a great loss in the entertainment world recently, when Larry LaPrise, the songwriter who penned that most famous of party anthems, the Hokey Cokey, passed away. The native of Detroit was 83 years old. I hear there was trouble after the wake as they tried to get him into the coffin. Apparently they started by putting the left leg in and things went rapidly downhill from there.

ALL CREATURES GREAT AND SMALL
February 2008

I have collected DVD box sets of the first four series of *All Creatures Great and Small*, and the fifth one is set to be released on a forthcoming birthday. Just the other evening I watched the episode with the legendary Mr Pickersgill, the farmer with a small holding and an even smaller grasp of the English dictionary. He always had a tendency to mangle his words, something that gave endless pleasure to Messrs Herriot and Farnon, the veterinaries of Darrowby. If an animal is ill, Mr Pickersgill trudges off to the telephone *cossack* (kiosk) on top of the hill to phone the veterinary. Once he told Siegfried that his younger brother Tristan had *insemblamated* his cow with *ICI* and gave her the *mastics*, later clarified as a chill in d'udder. The Yorkshire vets delighted in his local patois and took particular pleasure in gathering a crowd around the phone whenever Mr Pickersgill pressed button A in the *cossack*. The farmer once called veterinary assistant Calum Buchanan out for an urgent case of *semolina* (salmonella) in a calf that was bleeding from the *rectrum* (rectum). He suggested that the calf was always a weakling on account of bleeding from the *biblical* cord at birth and pleaded with the young vet to send some samples to the *labrador* (laboratory). Needless to say Mr Pickersgill couldn't quite get his tongue around the eventual diagnosis – a simple case of telescopic bowel blockage known as intussusception.

SUPERVISING EXECUTIONS
October 2000

I was interested in a recent study which looked at the attitude of doctors to executions, and more particularly their role in them. My late grandfather once worked as medical officer in Mountjoy prison at a time when supervision of hangings was part of the job description. A recent survey conducted by the American Medical Association shows that a substantial number of doctors still approve of allowing physicians to participate in executions, though others argue that it violates the Hippocratic oath's pledge to do no harm. When asked about specific duties, 43% said it's alright for doctors to inject condemned inmates with lethal drugs and 74% said it's fine for doctors to pronounce an inmate dead. The latter was all my grandfather had to do. And not only did he hate doing it, it haunted him for the rest of his life.

ON THE PISTE
October 2006

There is growing evidence from the courts that at last, judges are beginning to clamp down on compensation culture. Last week a judge of the Dublin circuit court told a young female plaintiff that 'Falls will inevitably occur on ski slopes'. The lady had the misfortune of toppling over ten minutes into her first lesson on the Kilternan nursery slope. She sustained a Colles fracture of the wrist and looked for a whopping €38,000 compensation because the instructor had not told her how to stop. The ski club argued that you have to be taught the simple art of going forward before you are taught how to stop, and that tuition on the more complicated technique would have come later on in the lesson. As the worst skier in Ireland and with bruises still to show for it, I'd like to commend this judge for the most sober of judgements. He dismissed the case, and is welcome to come on the piste with me anytime.

DANGEROUS NURSES
September 2012

Nurses were reluctant participants in the newspaper headlines this month when some strange goings-on and strike-offs from the register were revealed by their regulating body. There was the bizarre case of an axillary thermometer (meant for the armpit) being used to rupture a patient's tympanic membrane (ear drum) when it was mistaken for thermometer that one places in the ear. Then there was the unfortunate patient who had earwax drops administered to their eyes. Such errors shouldn't cast aspersions on the whole body of nurses in Ireland, but they do raise questions about education attainment, particularly overseas training and the level of competence and language skills that registration bodies demand here before you get to work. I wouldn't dream of practising medicine in a country with a different language unless I had undergone at least six months or even a year's in-house training. Not to mention a serious assessment of ward proficiency by fellow doctors before being let loose on patients. Patients deserve no less and I hope these off the wall cases spark some action in medical and nursing circles, rather than more cases down the road.

CALF AND A HALF
February 2007

If a patient in surgery had one calf that was four inches bigger in diameter than the other one, deep venous thrombosis (a local blood clot) would be foremost on most doctors' minds. All the more so if the patient has just hopped off a long haul flight from Australia. But what if he is a skateboarder? I have been reading about a young graphic designer from Oxford called David Cornthwaite. He has no clot. He has skateboarded three and half thousand miles across Australia, from Perth to Brisbane and that's what caused his calf to swell. Besides his newfound calf-measurements, other vital statistics include thirteen discarded pairs of shoes, five broken skateboards and a very tidy sum raised for charity. Next time I see a patient with a swollen calf, I will make a point to ask if they possess a skateboard.

NEXT PLEASE
August 1997

I enjoyed a piece in this month's *Forum* magazine that was written by a nurse who administers vaccinations on the north side of Dublin. Her immunisation uptake rate of 85% is rather commendable. I was somewhat taken aback by the fact that she detains babies on the premises for a full fifteen minutes after the jab. This is a luxury that nurse-less doctors can ill afford, particularly those practicing from cramped premises. Some doctors would have the surgery door ajar and the pram pushed out on the street before the pierced little mites have even a chance to scream!

SOCIETY OF POOR WRITERS
July 2004

The Writer is the journal of the Society of Medical Writers, a guild which proudly boasts yours truly, as its most inactive member. The Society is open to all doctors who scribble to make ends meet and whilst membership is primarily UK based, it not only tolerates Paddies and other assorted foreigners, it actively encourages us to join in. I've just got around to reading the spring edition of *The Writer* and it's mighty good entertainment as usual. There's a nice listing of poorly translated notices for English speaking tourists. A hotel in a humourless Austrian ski resort implores guests 'not to perambulate the corridors in the hours of repose in the boots of ascension'. A Japanese hotel says that 'guests are invited to take advantage of the chambermaid'. Some of the best ones emanate from the arid air of dry cleaning establishments. In Bangkok tourists are invited to 'drop your trousers here for best results' whilst an Italian laundry corners the female market with 'Ladies leave your clothes here and spend the afternoon having a good time'.

VISIT MEXICO
September 1999

Mexico is becoming a brochure destination that's attracting more and more Irish holidaymakers in recent years. Patients often ask about vaccine requirements, but more important advice to lend them might be about the unwelcome financial attentions of a few Mexican doctors. I recently tended to an older man and his wife who were both unfortunate enough to end up in the same private hospital on their South American vacation. They recovered, but not before the treating doctor relieved them of all of their travellers cheques. He filled out more credit card slips in their name than test forms. Their experience was horrific to say the least. A trawl on the internet tells me that their troubles were not unusual. Comprehensive holiday insurance in Mexico is about as useful as a yellow fever vaccine in Edinburgh. Patients are being detained in hospitals until they can raise huge sums of cash to release themselves. Mexico is going to have to tackle the problem of its rogue doctors if it's ever to figure in my summer plans.

GIVING UP SMOKING
June 2012

I smelled a smoker for the very first time in my life this week. And I found the experience a lot more unpleasant than smelling smoke. We were travelling back to Dublin on the Irish Ferries boat from Holyhead. Two gentlemen sitting in front of me took a break on deck for cigarettes. When they returned, I noticed that stale whiff I had only ever heard about before. You see, I smoked myself for well over thirty years, and only managed to stop last summer. My sense of smell has just returned and I have to say that a smoker's smell really is quite repugnant to the non-smoker. It's not the same odour as pipe, cigar or cigarette smoke, all of which I could still enjoy as a passerby. The chemical reaction between tobacco, skin and clothes is a different kettle of fish, and it's not nice. If you are a hopeless smoker like I was, don't give up hope. What worked for me was doing it half way through holidays, in a place where there were no newsagent shops adjacent. Any weakness for a packet of cigarette meant a journey by car. Grumpy wasn't the word for it, but a glass or two of red wine, some strong cheese after dinner and bed at nine sharp with a good book can pacify any cold turkey for a few weeks. Nicotine replacement regalia has never done anything for me, other than serve as a reminder of the thing I was trying to give up. But it has its successes, so I would never discount it from the armoury. Many chemists will now negotiate their profit margin on this sort of product, so don't be afraid to ask. Stop-smoking courses are only as good as the person who is giving them and success rates tend to be wildly inflated. It's a personal view but I don't think they are good value for money. If I can do it after almost four decades, any smoker can do it for themselves. For an understanding of what it's like to be a smoker who is controlled by their habit, I would always recommend a read of the late Allan Carr's original book on the subject. What also helped me in the early weeks and months was a new exercise-based hobby. Living a short drive from the foothills of the Dublin mountains and with a dog who loves wild terrain, the choice was easy. I got some guidebooks, maps, boots and warm clothing and climbed every peak in sight. They weren't all easy. Some remind you more than others of the damage that cigarettes have already done to your lungs. This summer I'm going back to climb them all again, and more. An evening time hobby is also essential. Preferably something that never ends, like scanning every photograph your family ever took and filing them all in order. That worked for me too.

MOUNTAIN OF TESTS
December 2002

A medical secretary told a family doctor recently that the local laboratory could not test the bloods they had received from him as they were *Himalayas*. He decided there and then to get her a medical dictionary for Christmas as the word from the lab was haemolysed (which means the blood had clotted).

Irish Pharmacist also had a wonderful true story about a man who walked into a Dublin chemist and asked the counter girl for 'a cough bottle for my wife - as a present'. The assistant started laughing at this strange gift request in the run-up to Christmas and asked if he would like it gift-wrapped! The pharmacist was in earshot of the conversation and left his hatch to investigate. Thankfully all was resolved to everyone's satisfaction. What the man had actually requested was 'a cough bottle for my wife - a suppressant'.

DATING GAMES
September 1999

A business magazine caught my eye in the waiting room this week. The cover feature was about the lucrative world of Irish dating agencies. Our supposedly booming economy has left us with a glut of lonely thirty and forty something year olds, too busy killing themselves with work to hunt down a mate. In the last ten years the number of single Irish women in their thirties has increased by 70% whilst the number of single men of the same age has risen by 40%. The Irish dating business is reckoned to be worth about £5 million a year. Reading through the piece, it seems you have to pay about £750 up front to get set up with eight blind lunch dates. Those who use dating agencies were asked what they considered to be the most attractive professions in prospective partners. The favourite male occupations for women looking for dates were as follows: in first place were architects (seriously?), then bankers and stockbrokers, doctors or surgeons are a respectable third, followed by film directors then barristers. Also-rans were media men, artists, company types, computer boffins and teachers. For male daters however, lady doctors are way down the list in ninth place, behind recruitment consultants, designers and marketing personnel. Female lawyers creep into tenth spot. And which female professions do men find most attractive - well journalists come third, and actresses are just second best. In first place, it's the ladies in public relations. There is no accounting for taste!

DENTAL BOOZE
April 2012

Dentists have been asked this week to start screening their patients for alcohol intake. For a brief second I thought the clinical newspapers may have got this story the wrong way around. Numbed and speechless patients on a reclining couch would have all the time in the world to survey their dentist's relationship with alcohol. The logic, if that is what it can be called, is that doctors only see you when you are off the juice and sick, but that our experts in enamel, drills and titanium are in a better position to issue 'tut tut' noises when you lie back and open wide. Dentists up and down the United Kingdom have been advised to be on the lookout for booze-induced tooth decay, a sure sign of alcohol abuse. On that grinding note, I'll close my mouth for another day. Where's my funnel?

WOMANINIUM AND MANEUM
June 2000

Not sure who sent me this one, but I enjoyed it. Geniuses in the chemistry laboratory have come up with two new elements on the periodic table. The first is WOMANinium, chemical symbol Wo. Chemists have been too polite to check for its atomic weight, but they describe its physical properties as round in form, boils at nothing, freezes at any time, melts when treated well but can get very bitter if mishandled for long periods. Chemical properties include a tendency to become highly unstable as well as a strong affinity to gold, silver, and precious stones. There can be a certain volatility when left alone, but Wo has great powers of absorption, and is prone to turning green when placed next to a shinier specimen. Usages are few, Wo is considered highly ornamental, an extremely good catalyst for dispersion of wealth - indeed the most powerful income reducing agent known and highly explosive in inexperienced hands.

Before men laugh too loudly, they should know that the second new element to be discovered is MANeum, whose symbol is XY. Atomic weight is 180 give or take 50. This element is solid at room temperatures, but easily bent out of shape. Physical properties include a profound denseness with a certain flakiness. Because of rust, ageing samples are unable to conduct electricity as easily as young samples. Its chemical properties include attempting to bond with WO any chance it gets. XY also tends to form strong bonds with itself but these attributes can be neutralised by saturating with alcohol. There are no known usages except that XY is a reliable source of methane - good specimens able to produce large quantities on command. Users are cautioned that in the absence of WO, XY rapidly decomposes and begins to smell. Charming.

THE FRENCH SUPPOSITORY
December 2007

My information is that the following story emanated from the late Dr John Fleetwood senior of Blackrock, a delightful man and a wonderful doctor. A patient attended his own general practitioner after a holiday in France. During the vacation, the man had been quite ill and had to attend a clinic. He showed his own doctor the packet of suppositories that the French physician had prescribed for his ailment. The doctor asked him if they were any good. The patient replied that for all the use they were, he might as well have sticking them up his arse!

SCHOOL CONTAGION
September 1999

With children back to school, it's usually only a matter of days before surgeries fill up with fevers, runny noses and tummy upsets. It's hard to explain to mums why some children get sick twice a month whilst other mothers' children never miss a day. But recent research from the United States might be worth quoting when parents express concern. At a large primary school in Virginia, pupils were urged to wash their hands at least four times a day. Researchers found that absenteeism fell substantially. There are plans to extend the practice to other schools, described as the very best preventive medicine for children and adults. Irish parents who waste millions a year on vitamins for their darlings, might be better off packing a bar of soap in the lunchbox.

MEDICINE AT BEWLEY'S CAFE
November 1998

One advantage of attending the city centre medical school of Trinity College Dublin was its close proximity to the Bewley's Oriental cafes on Grafton Street and Westmoreland Street. Professors, particularly those of an endocrinological persuasion, urged us to put our newfound powers of clinical observation and spot diagnosis into practice over coffee and sticky buns. Bewley's obliged with its ageing staff and even more senior customers. I remember one wet day when three students made eleven diagnoses within ten minutes of arrival. Hoarse and bearded hypothyroid ladies were plentiful in the early afternoons, as were the spluttering blue-lipped 'chronny bronny' male smokers. The waitress with orbital xanthelasma (skin growths around the eyes that signify high levels of cholesterol) which nearly obscured her vision was unusual. There were plenty of customers who walked with parkinsonian shuffles. Ladies with acne rosacea whose cheeks shone like beacons after a mug of Bewley's morning tea. Not to be confused with those of menopausal age whose sudden hot and wet flushes often made them rush out for cold air before finishing their bun. One colleague was fortunate enough to assist at a successful resuscitation and received a plate of cakes for his troubles. Alas Bewley's as we knew it is gone. The Grafton street branch has undergone a recent transformation. Though still a treat to dine in, cushingoid Connie and wheezy Winnie are gone, along with the rest of the Bewley's staff too. They have replaced by Ahmed, Katarina, Otto and other young trendy continentals. Far too healthy looking for my liking.

DR BUCK RUXTON
May 1998

All doctors secretly aspire to having some clinical sign, a disease or even an operation named after them. But precious few succeed. Not many are commemorated by having public houses named after them either. The Boar's Head in Lancaster, England is no more as the landlady has decided to rename it Ruxtons. This is in honour of a popular local doctor, Buck Ruxton, who tended to the townsfolk in the early 1930s. She plans to display all sorts of memorabilia concerning the doctor on the walls. Now if you drop by, don't expect to see too many prescription pads or old fashioned bell stethoscopes. Buck Ruxton fame was for something other than his good medicine. In May 1936 the doctor, a native of Bombay who had anglicised his name, was hanged at Manchester's Strangeways prison. He had been found guilty of the murder of his wife Isabella and the family's housemaid. Ruxton had dismembered the bodies in gruesome fashion before driving them to Scotland where he dumped them into a ravine. At his trial he dismissed the prosecution's evidence as 'bunkum with a capital B'. Shortly after the hanging, his confession was published. It was revealed a few years ago that the white enamel bath tub in which he chopped up the remains of the poor women survives as a drinking trough for police horses at Longton near Preston. It even carries a commemorative brass plaque. Better there than in the pub I feel.

MIDLANDS MEDICINE
June 2011

A study of attitudes to alternative medicine in the counties of Laois and Offaly caught my eye. One hundred patients were asked if they had ever availed of such therapies. About 40% nodded in agreement. Most seemed pleased enough with the outcome. Just three said they were no better, and not one patient volunteered any bad outcomes. But when 48 doctors in the same region were surveyed, the results were strangely different. About 40% of them had witnessed adverse outcomes. These events included a ten year old child who had a vertebra fractured by chiropractic treatment, a 70 year old man who had a mini-stroke during manipulation of his neck and a 40 year old who had a full stroke during the same procedure. I detect a certain lack of trust between regulated and the unregulated practitioners.

AN ILLNESS FOR EVERY DAY
October 2012

There is hardly a calendar day left now that some illness, trait or misfortune hasn't claimed as its very own. *National Boil on your Bottom Day* cannot be far away. Too much of all this disease awareness malarkey could end up closing down even the most receptive of ears. Just the other week, courtesy of the United Nations, we had *Global Handwashing Day*. To pump up the public relations for this earth shattering event, microbiologists at the

London school of hygiene & tropical medicine were set the pleasant task of measuring the percentage of banknotes, credit cards and human hands that harboured faecal bacteria - bugs from your bowels. For the boffins amongst you, the percentages were 14% for banknotes, 10% for credit cards and 26% for hands. This survey had the desired effect of providing handy next-day headlines for dozens of newspapers, glad that their own rags weren't subjected to counts of nasty E Coli bacteria too. 'Why are the British so bad at washing their hands?' shrieked the tabloids. But the public had moved on. It was *National Diarrhoea Day* already.

OUT OF OFFICE
January 2007

I pray every night for medical colleagues that work for the Health Service Executive. All doctors sheltering under the HSE umbrella received an email in advance of the Christmas holidays with a very long message entitled 'Out of Office replies must be in Irish and English'. This contained a strict warning to all physicians and surgeons to ensure that all their automatic email replies must be in two languages. The threat of the *Official Languages Act 2003* was hung over their heads and the email included no fewer than seven sample replies that doctors could tag on to their seasonal emails. One wonders how many of the 100,000 staff working for the health service are producing this sort of guff. My favourite sample was 'Beidh mé as láthair ón oifig go dtí 04.09.2007. Déan teagmháil le mo chomhghleacaithe ag (seoladh) le do thoil' which I translate as meaning 'My Christmas lasts until early September so please contact someone else'. There must be many good clinical folk in the HSE who find this sort of nonsense clogging up their inbox each day. In bygone times, they'd simply pack their trunks and run off to join a circus. A different one.

DR TERENCE JACKSON
January 2000

It's not often that a national newspaper will publish a letter from a reader that simply pays tribute to their deceased personal doctor. But an exception was made for the patient of the late Dr Terence Jackson. He pointed out that his favourite physician had that rare disappearing commodity in doctors, appearing to have all the time in the world for the patient in the chair. It never mattered how many were queuing to come in behind him. There was another nice obituary in the medical press to the late Dr Jackson which stated that an ever bustling waiting room didn't allow him the time to actively participate in politics, something that he loved. But the writer did say that Dr Jackson's convivial relationship with patients meant he was always very well informed of current affairs. The obituary went on to say that Dr Jackson could always predict election results with great accuracy following a straw poll of his patients.

ERROR IN TRANSCRIPTION
July 2007

A doctor from Galway wrote to me last week with a tale about a discharge letter he received about one of his patients. It stated that Mrs X was suffering from diabetes and syphilis. He was shocked at the results found on her admission and never thought of her as 'that sort of a lady'. It was then the realisation came to him that the hospital had made a grave error of transcription. What she had was a simple case of diabetes insipidus rather than diabetes and syphilis. Beware of medical typists and consultants who mumble into their Dictaphones!

GRIEVOUS BODILY HARM
November 1998

Grateful patients and their families can be very kind indeed to their doctors. A second-hand story has reached me about a post-operative proposition received by a popular surgeon. The surgeon had performed an operation on a somewhat shady character, and had all gone according to plan. When he asked the man back to the outpatients for the usual post-surgery review, the patient, obviously delighted with the result, asked him if there was anything that he could do for the surgeon in return. A little taken aback, the surgeon asked him what exactly had he in mind. 'Do you need anyone bumped off?' came the unexpected reply. Further details were not reported to me so I'm not sure if the consultation ended with a handshake or a hit-list. But it did bring back memories of an a very similar event in my junior doctor career when I was offered the same sort of favour. In my case, I think it was a vague promise of grievous bodily harm that was on offer. Declining hastily, I said my preferred gifts were a Christmas turkey or a dozen eggs. With all thank-you's, it's really the thought that counts.

PRIVATE CAESAREANS
October 1997

Public concern about maternity services has been raised this week on the island republic of Trinidad & Tobago. A visiting obstetrician made pointed comments about the marked difference in caesarean section rates between private and public hospitals. The nation's medical profession were incensed at the implication, but the figures quoted do suggest that that some sort of clinical review is merited. Caesarean section rates on our own island republic have been steadily rising over the past decade and the trend suggests it will not be long before they reach one in five of all deliveries. It would be an interesting exercise in this new age of openness and transparency if our own maternity hospitals would include a breakdown of public and private figures, in their annual reports. Many public sections in our major maternity centres are carried out by junior doctors in obstetric training who then account for their action before their peers in weekly or monthly conferences. But the delivery methods used on private patients tend to remain hidden from view. They are lumped in together with public deliveries for each institution's annual report. With these changing times, it is only a question of time before each hospital is asked to account. Obstetricians need to release public versus private figures before they are asked to do so.

SHARED SHAVES
March 2000

The correspondence section of the *New England Journal of Medicine* carried an interesting letter recently from a Dr Colleen Kelly, who queried why the rate of viral hepatitis B and C was significantly higher amongst patients in veterans hospitals than amongst the general population. On ward rounds at one such institution in Massachusetts, Dr Kelly noted a practice which she considered a potential source on transmission. She observed a patient shaving with an electric razor which had the ward label on it. When the man had finished grooming himself for the day, another elderly gent picked it up immediately and began to shave. Further enquiries by Dr Kelly revealed that the appliance was not regularly disinfected and that communal use of electric razors is a common practice in hospitals. Viral transmission by electric razor has not been proven, but a few moments thought would lead one to the conclusion that it's by no means an impossibility. I have a vague recall of a similar practice taking place in mental health institutions and geriatric wards in this country. Does anyone know the level of hepatitis infection amongst long term patients at such institutions? There's some research to be done here, perhaps a scientific paper and who knows, perhaps another national scandal.

AUTO-ENUCLEATION
March 2007

I have been catching up on my life's education with a recent edition of the *Journal of Psychological Medicine*. There's always one piece in every psychiatric journal that captures my attention for at least five minutes. This time, it was a case study of oedipism, or auto-enucleation in a 67 year old lady. I'll explain further if you put aside your dinner. The unfortunate lady was found sitting on the floor of a ward, and beside her lay an eyeball with 5cm of optic nerve still attached. I was fascinated by the description of this thankfully rare condition and how it is treated by the combined efforts of neurosurgeons, eye surgeons and psychiatrists. The latter are particularly useful to have around after the event as the risk to the second eye is greatly magnified. The lady had an underlying serious psychiatric condition as this is not something you would see at all regularly in mental illness. But if you did see it, I dare say you would never forget it.

My well stressed copy of the *Oxford Textbook of Psychiatry* makes no mention of the condition, or even of Charles Blondel, the French professor of pathological psychology who first described oedipism a century ago. However popular psychiatrist, Dr Raj Persaud does cover self-mutilation in graphic and gory detail in his book *From the Edge of the Couch*, a journey through mental extremes. One case history describes a twenty year old man from New York who removed virtually his entire face and then blamed the event on three Belgian shepherd dogs which his family kept at home.

Post-Script: *Following my mention of this subject, I had a very nice letter from one of our very best medical historians. The good doctor told me of another case of eye gouging. Some years ago he was taking part in a symposium to celebrate the centenary of Omagh Hospital and came across a case in old hospital records. A very commonly made diagnosis at the time was religious mania, and Omagh had its fair share of these problem cases. A local woman took rather too seriously the biblical injunction to pluck out an eye that had caused sin. On admission, both of her eyes were badly traumatised and inflamed. She then bit off her finger which had failed to do the enucleation properly. It got badly infected and unfortunately she died from a septicaemia five days after admission. The records went on to state that the medical officer firmly laid the blame for this tragedy on the doorstep of an over enthusiastic revivalist preacher. The piece on Omagh Hospital suggested that a diagnosis of religious zeal was also common at the other end of the country. Twenty patients in Cork were once diagnosed with the condition and the phenomenon attracted international attention with a write-up in the Journal of Mental Science. That was in 1860, and long before the moving statues of Ballinspittle.*

HAROLD BROWNE
February 2007

Harold Browne is a formidable figure in Irish surgery and a past-president of the Medical Council. A doctor who had the privilege of working under Mr Browne wrote to me recently to compliment him as a rock of common sense. Commenting on increasing medical specialisation, Harold Browne once said that specialists are learning more and more about less and less. Soon they will know everything about nothing. He added that general practitioners are learning less and less about more and more and soon they will know nothing about everything.

FALSE ALLERGY SYNDROME
April 2002

Some patients have a different take to their doctors on what constitutes an allergy. My first lesson in false allergy syndrome took place in the casualty department of a now defunct Dublin hospital. A workman came in to seek attention for a puncture wound in the sole of his foot. He had stood on a long rusty nail which not only penetrated his heavy boot, but travelled at least an inch into the soft and ill-perfumed flesh of his sole. Following the x-ray, mandatory to ensure we weren't sued, I grabbed a vial of tetanus, only to be told by the shuddering labourer that he was allergic to it. Further questioning revealed the true nature of his allergy. 'Sure the last time I had a tetanus, didn't I have a pain in me arse for days, doctor,' he exclaimed.

Another 'allergy' was presented by a rather luxurious patient who didn't like the idea of 'yellow pack' prescriptions. He would succeed in getting the original premium brand in the market every time by stating that he was allergic to all generic medicines!

There are other novel allergies described by patients. An anaesthetist was once told by an 'allergic' patient that nitrous oxide made her light-headed. Another patient who received novocaine claimed an allergy because he said the anaesthetic made him numb. Another novocaine patient said he was allergic to it because he felt a lot of pain when it wore off. And a lady once told her doctor that she was allergic to morphine, because it made her sleepy. Doctors are always wary of patients who try and wangle their own way into getting one particular narcotic painkiller. 'I'm allergic to all painkillers, except pethidine' would be one such ruse to watch out for.

A doctor in Cork told me of an elderly man who recalled in surgery that he was allergic to penicillin. It transpired that he had previously worked in the British merchant navy. Once they arrived in a port in north Africa and all the crew were given a week's shore-leave. On their return to sea, the ship's doctor gave each and every one of them a prophylactic shot of penicillin. A few days later he noticed pus coming out of his penis. He was absolutely certain it was an allergic reaction and had nothing whatsoever to do with his behaviour on shore.

SCARE MONGERING
July 2000

This war against cholesterol is getting a bit shameless for my liking. As if teenagers hadn't enough to worry about, a campaign has been launched in the United States to identify 'at-risk' adolescents and warn them of the dangers of lipid-induced heart disease. Fourteen year olds in Boston are being rounded up for finger-prick blood testing and a possible lifetime of cardiovascular neurosis. The doctor leading the battle announced last month that 'At-risk young people are like the Titanic. They may be ship-shape now, but the iceberg is out there'. Next thing they'll be testing blood from the umbilical cord and scaring the fat out of babies.

SMOKING CESSATION
July 2012

In celebration of my first year in almost forty off the cigarettes, I have been trying to pass on some learned wisdom to fellow slaves who want to cease the dying habit. A gentleman called Michael wrote to say that he came across the Allen Carr book in his mid fifties, an age when he thought he was beyond quitting. Michael read it in one week and promptly threw his cigarettes in the fire. He missed them for three days, no more, and hasn't smoked since.

Another correspondent, Pat, was a 'lunatic for the Major brand' of cigarettes - nothing else would do but forty of them every day. About thirty years ago he was advised to try a group hypnosis session in an eleventh century Norman castle in Naas. He recalls that the edifice was entirely carpeted in purple. There were sixteen smokers at the gathering, all sitting in a huge room. The hypnotist put them under and told them some home truths about smoking. That all the sporting and mountaineering imagery used by cigarette companies was a myth. That all the mannerisms of smokers could easily be removed from their minds. That the group would have no need for them when they came around. Both Pat and his brother walked out of the session and never smoked again.

Some older readers may know from the description and location of the hypnotist's home who he was. It was none other than Dr Jack Gibson (1909-2005) former county surgeon of Kildare, who counted Nelson Mandela and Mahatma Gandhi as two great influences on his life. From 1960 until 1974, Jack Gibson ran what was then one of the busiest casualty departments in the country - at Naas General Hospital. A native of Ranelagh, who attended school at Wesley College, Dr Gibson trained at the Royal College of Surgeons in Dublin, qualifying in 1933. He spent much of his early working life abroad, in places like Malawi, Yemen, Ethiopia and the Channel Islands. Whilst working in South Africa he watched stage shows and became interested in hypnosis. It is reckoned that during his long career, he performed 4,000 operations under hypnosis (including amputations). Dr Gibson also claimed to have cured himself of a basal cell skin cancer and chronic varicose veins through self hypnosis.

In his book on *Irish Surgeons of the 20th Century*, Professor Barry O'Donnell calls Dr Gibson a 'legend', a 'James Mason lookalike' in his youth, and 'a short balding dynamo who feared no one'. He was described him as a walking contradiction - the bane of many a hospital hierarchy and high court judge. He was alternative yet conventional, rebellious yet still an establishment figure, informal yet intense, self-mocking yet proud.

My correspondent, Pat, became quite friendly with him. The last time he saw Dr Gibson was when he was in his nineties, and he was queuing like everyone else at the casualty department of Naas General Hospital. Pat asked him why he had to wait, seeing as how he had once held such a high position at the hospital? Dr Gibson replied that he could indeed be seen earlier, but would prefer to 'wait his turn like everyone else'. A legend indeed.

Post-Script: *After writing about Jack Gibson, I subsequently received a letter from an old school orthopaedic surgeon who knew him well and described him as charming and very articulate. They often collaborated on accident cases at St David's Castle in Naas and he mentioned that Mr Gibson once reduced a dislocated ankle under hypnosis much to the patient's satisfaction. He also said that Mr Gibson recorded a disc on how to give up smoking. In fact it was this record that knocked the Beatles off the number one slot in the Irish charts in 1969.*

NON-SLIP STOCKINGS
January 2013

The family of a deceased doctor wrote to the *British Medical Journal* recently to tell readers how they might prevent deaths such as his. The retired medic was a hospital inpatient who was fitted with 'anti-thrombosis' stockings to prevent him suffering from a blood clot. The risk of such clots is highest in the days immediately after operative surgery. Unfortunately he slipped on his ward, sustained a nasty bang to the head, and a brain haemorrhage subsequently killed him. The family called for the abolition of anti-clot stockings unless they are fitted with non-slip soles. They quoted another doctor who agreed with their position and had also observed that these stockings can be 'lethal', particularly on shiny and regularly buffed hospital floors. If you are asked to tread corridors wearing anti-thrombosis stockings without non-slip soles, keep them inside your non-slip slippers.

TESTOSTERONE FUEL
May 2004

This month, a new fangled disease arrived on our shores that may be of interest to Irish men and their elected representatives. Officially known as testicular deficiency, those promoting this malady have abbreviated it to TD. Sounds serious, incurable even. Cynics argue that TD is just another case of manufacturing a disease to suit a particular product or niche market. In my medical school days there was little mention of male gonad malfunction, save for the odd genetic condition like Kleinfelter's syndrome where testosterone injections were the mainstay of treatment. Indeed the whole existence of a *male menopause* has long been a subject of derision, often applied to once loved hunter-gatherers who now have permanently paralysis in front of the television.

Twelve years ago, I visited a rather swanky clinic on London's Harley Street to investigate the goings-on at a male menopause centre. It was offering 'the best news for men since the invention of the Ferrari'. They claimed enormous successes - of the testimonial type mainly. They had octogenarians thrusting up the street on their motorbikes and world war two veterans boasting of their magnetic attraction for younger ladies. This treatment certainly wasn't cheap. A few visits, with tests thrown in would set you back a tidy four figure sum in sterling - a couple of grand at least. Whilst the clinic proved a draw for wealthy men from all corners of the world, the idea of fortifying ageing blokes with testosterone remained very much on the fringes of modern medicine. Mai West said it wasn't the men in her life that counted, but the life in her men. But there has been general apathy in boy's town about regular male hormone injections.

Now, more than a decade later, a group of Irish doctors have come together to form the 'testosterone deficiency advisory board', a group with a mission to inform the public about this and other conditions of evolving manhood. The formation of the board coincided with the launch of a prescription rub-in gel product which has a once daily dosage and costs about €1.50 a day, excluding the fees of your pharmacist and doctor. Loss of sex drive and erections, depression, fatigue, sleep disturbance, joint or muscle pain, increased weight gain, mood swings, decreased motivation, lowered drive – these are all the suggested symptoms of TD. But some of these symptoms may have nothing to do with testosterone or the lack of it. They may in fact be due to other diseases. Or they may be just an acceptable part of a normal ageing process. I remain to be convinced.

ADA'S DYING WISH
June 2011

There can't be many doctors who make a special request before dying to be buried with their patients. But this is precisely what one extraordinary lady psychiatrist did in the town of Ballinasloe, at the tail end of the second world war. The current edition of the *Irish Journal of Psychological Medicine* has a fascinating historical article by Professor Brendan Kelly about Dr Ada English, a psychiatrist who spent forty years working at St Brigid's, the town's mental hospital. The Kerry-born daughter of a chemist who then settled in Mullingar, Ada graduated in 1903 from the Cecilia Street school of medicine in Dublin's Temple Bar. A contemporary remembered her as having 'crisp blond hair, remarkable blue eyes and a fascinating lisp'. She is said to have played an active part in the Easter rising as a medical officer and she was jailed in Galway four years later for possession of 'nationalistic literature. In 1921 Ada English was elected as a TD to the Second Dáil but lost her seat soon after. The plight of the poor and the care of mentally ill patients became her twin children. She was a long-time advocate for better housing in working class neighbourhoods, and was a pioneer of occupational therapy for asylum residents. She took a particular interest in allowing long-stay patients out to the local cinema on Sunday afternoons. Her hospital was also at the forefront of the new physical treatments of psychiatry in the late 1930s. It's believed that Ballinasloe was the first town in Ireland to experiment with convulsive treatments, initially with injections of cardiazol in 1939 and later with electro-convulsive therapy. Dr Ada English died in January 1944, in the small Mount Pleasant nursing home of Ballinasloe that pre-dated Portiuncula Hospital. She was granted her dying wish, a resting place with her patients in Creagh cemetery, immediately adjacent to the Asylum. Drop a flower if you are passing.

Post-Script: *In October 2014, Professor Brendan Kelly's biography of this extraordinary lady doctor was launched. Ada English: Patriot and Psychiatrist is published by Irish Academic Press.*

NERVOUS LEGS
September 2002

A consultant surgeon in Surrey is concerned about the 'dumbing down' of medical training, particularly the latest fashion for abandoning books to fast-track medical students through college. He wrote to a London newspaper last week to say that he doesn't want to be cared for in his dotage by 'a doctor who knows less anatomy than the compiler of the *Times* crossword'. Harsh words indeed. The surgeon went on to say that he had recently come across a final year medical student who couldn't name a single nerve in the human leg. Shocking stuff. In my day we all knew the precise course of the femoral, the sciatic, the superior and inferior gluteals, the obturator, the saphenous, the tibial and common, deep and superficial fibulars. And we had barely passed below the knee at that stage.

PARISIAN PROPERTY
August 2007

Instead of issuing guidance for patients, the Irish Medical Organisation are lending investment advice for their own flock again. They have written to impoverished doctors up and down the land encouraging them to invest their fees overseas rather than at home. Medics have being asked to part with a minimum of €50,000 each to go towards the purchase of an exceptionally ugly property on Avenue Paul Doumer in Paris. It's on the market for €30 million - Allied Irish Banks are putting €20 million towards the cost and Irish Medical Organisation members are being asked to empty their night call piggy banks and ear syringing tip boxes to contribute the rest. The IMO property prospectus hypes up the area as the 'Kensington of Paris' and indulges potential clients with trifling facts about neighbouring shops like Frank & Fils which is 'comparable to Brown Thomas in Dublin'. The organisation studiously avoids mentioning the fate of Paul Doumer whose name is on the Avenue. A former governor general of Indo-China and then president of France, Doumer took a bullet in the head from a Russian refugee 75 years ago whilst opening a book fair in Paris. The assassin, Paul Gorgulov, was a mentally ill medical doctor and might have expected the very best of Parisian hospitality. He was not to be disappointed. In September 1932, after a public trial, he underwent a rather extreme form of head and neck surgery, known as the guillotine. His final words were 'Russia, my Fatherland'. I wonder if the hedge funds of Irish doctors will fare any better on Avenue Paul Doumer.

DOCTOR BAM BAM
January 1999

Traditional medicine wasn't curing Murphy's dyspepsia. The amateur opera singer had had his fill of barium meals, breath tests, gastroscopes and duodenal biopsies, each one followed by a course of hugely expensive tablets. Neither his family doctor nor his specialist could effect a cure. His wife encouraged him to visit Doctor Bam Bam, the new herbal healer who had just set up practice on the edge of town. After a brief examination, the shaman cut off a thong of elk hide from his belt and gave it to the man. 'Bite off and chew one inch of this leather each day until it's all gone'. When Mr Murphy returned a month later, the healer asked how he was feeling. And Murphy answered in his best tenor voice 'The thong is gone, but the malady lingers on!'

SUICIDE –
THE LAST MALE REFUGE
October 2003

The recent high profile deaths of weapons expert Dr David Kelly and a television journalist on Sky News, have thrown a spotlight on a taboo subject - men who feel shamed into sacrificing their own lives. The tragic demise of these two men, has served some small purpose, in that it confirms the reality of the 'dutiful suicide' where a person feels shamed into death by their own hand. Other cultures are well aware of this phenomenon, but here we have a tendency to shroud all suicides under a mantle of depressive illness, and fail to acknowledge that a very different set of circumstances pertains to each and every loss.

It also highlights just how little we know and understand about men, and about male suicide. Were the Department of Health's performance on suicide prevention to be studied, it may well give us a taste as to where billions disappear each year into the morass of Irish healthcare. At a time when mental health services are feeling the pinch from chronic under-funding, pet projects of do-gooder politicians such as 'suicide prevention' continue to receive considerable amounts of taxpayer's money. In September each year, one of the many junior ministers in health is wheeled out to welcome the annual report of the national suicide review group. This group outlines the measures being taken by health boards to prevent suicides. Each year a drone in Hawkins House drafts yet another press release for the minister to recite. But careful examination of the text reveals that each year it is exactly the same document – except that the figures are changed. More money is spent on prevention yet more suicides take place. Last year 451 people in the Republic took their own lives. That was 3 more than in 2001 and 38 more than in 2000. A decade before this, long before the obsession with suicide prevention took hold, Ireland recorded just 334 suicides annually. So why is the Department continuing to plough taxpayers money into something that plainly isn't working? And where is all this money going? In the last five years, more than €13 million has been spent here on suicide prevention. Most goes on salaries. Suicide prevention and self-harm resource officers have been employed by health boards up and down the state. Doubtless these are well meaning, perhaps even well qualified personnel, but the fact remains that every week, ten or more people on this island still take their own lives. Suicide prevention policies in Ireland are failing miserably. Male suicide is far more prevalent than female suicide, in some years by a factor of four to one. Whilst pundits bleat on about how men need to start getting in touch with their feminine side, the increasing feminisation of our health services continues apace. A small study I conducted of entries in the *Irish Medical Directory* reveals that doctors and practice nurses in primary care are ten times more likely to say they have a special interest in women's health than men's health. In recent months there have been calls for decentralised midwife-led and mobile maternity services, a nationwide full-time epidural service, more female gynaecologists, compulsory provision of breast screening with county based breast clinics, better access to smear clinics in rural areas, free contraception, more representation of women on health boards, women's refuges in every community care area. All completely worthy aspirations in their own right. But constant pre-occupation with improving the lot of women is in danger of leaving men standing in a very dark corner. The Department of Health's own four year plan for the 1990s, enunciated in *Shaping a Healthier Future*, is fatally blinkered in so far as it makes absolutely no mention of men's health issues. There is a deafening silence about male cancers of the testicle or prostate. No mention of the mental health issues that affect Irish men or the gender divide in suicide rates. Nobody rises in the Dáil to call for improvements in vasectomy services, public sports injury or orthopaedic services, prostate diagnosis, urology waiting times, access to evening clinics by working men. No special interest groups are calling for public centres for treatment of male sexual problems. The health promotion unit of the Department of Health produces ten pieces of literature concerning babies and children and eight leaflets concerning women's issues. Currently it has no publications concerning men. It's interesting that production of the very first waiting room leaflets for Irish men coincided only with the development of new drugs for prostatic disease. We need reminding that the male sex is already the least likely to avail of health services. That Irish men die on average six years before their female counterparts. That men are far more ignorant on health matters, less likely to recognise worrying symptoms, more likely to delay presenting with lumps to their doctors. That mentally distressed men are less likely to seek medical help and more likely to turn to rope, shotguns, car exhausts, rivers and violence for release. The minister might consider halting cheques to those who do badly on suicide prevention, and spend the money on improving front-line access for men and women to get help, quickly, with serious mental health issues. It's the minister who needs to get in touch with his masculine side.

FRIED SCIENCE
March 2012

At last there is some good news for frying fatalists the world over. The *British Medical Journal* published a paper this month on fried foods and the risk of coronary heart disease. It was written by an eminent German professor of preventive medicine and concludes, after reasonable argument, that 'the myth that frying food is bad for your heart is not supported by available evidence'. In summary, it says that we simply don't have enough hard scientific facts to draw conclusions about frying. The authors call for more study of the types of oils used in frying, the type of frying (deep fried or pan fried), the time of cooking, the temperature of cooking and the degree to which oils are re-used. That sounds very reasonable to me. In fact it should be reasonable to anybody who enjoys a full Irish breakfast once a week.

LANGUAGE POLICE
January 2007

Language police are well entrenched in Irish healthcare. In my capacity as editor of the *Irish Medical Directory*, a letter was sent to me recently by a communications person asking that we remove all mention of 'mental handicap' from our publication. Apparently this year's approved nomenclature is intellectual disability. Not even learning disability is kosher any more. I was told in no uncertain terms that the term 'mental handicap' was offensive to people with intellectual disability (I don't think we can say patients anymore either) and to their families. 'Continuing use of the term mental handicap in a highly circulated publication like the IMD may reinforce that it is acceptable to use by medical professionals' were her precise words. If there is any organised resistance out there to this onward march of communications people telling us who we are, what we should be doing and how we should be speaking – please count me in. If we have to use labels at all, I'd much rather a handicap to a disability any day.

SINGAPORE SLING
June 2000

A retired consultant surgeon in Kent wrote to *Hospital Doctor* recently, to describe what happened when a grandchild of his was taken ill in Singapore. Within two hours of the boy's admission, his grandfather back in England had received a fax from a senior consultant at the Mount Elizabeth Medical Centre detailing full results of the clinical examination and his plan of action. Four hours later a second fax arrived detailing the lumbar puncture picture, blood results and confirming the final diagnosis. The pensioner surgeon in Kent contrasted this service with the appalling delays that doctors accept as par for the course in these islands. I know what he means. One of my local radiology departments currently takes a full ten days to send back x-ray results. Where there's a will, there's a way, and having been to Singapore I have to say, there is a lot there to recommend itself.

BEEF-BURGER INJURY
October 1997

Hand wounds sustained at home make up a fair amount of suturing work for general practitioners and casualty doctors. They are sore, bloody and suturing can be tricky too. I was delighted to see a paper in a recent journal devoted to one of my favourite wounds from emergency department days, the beef-burger hand injury. This is caused when a poor unfortunate (male usually) tries to separate stacked frozen food items with a sharp knife. Such manipulations a la cuisine are responsible for numerous nerve injuries, tendon lacerations, and injuries to the ligaments. Frozen beef-burgers are the foodstuff most commonly responsible for these accidents but chops, steaks, sausages and crumpets also feature strongly. The study's authors call upon manufacturers to use non-adherent film between the items of food to help prevent these injuries. They also suggest that packets of frozen foods should carry warnings about the risk of this injury, or at least provide instructions on how best to separate frozen foods. I have devised my own approach. It involves a blunt lump hammer.

DECEPTIVE DOCTOR
July 2003

Whilst holidaying in Britain recently, I read that the nation's most notorious bogus doctor was on his way back to jail. 41 year old Paul Bint, a lady's hairdresser turned serial fraudster, gained notoriety in the early 1980s when he toured the hospitals of northern England as a pretend junior doctor. He stitched beautifully, prescribed liberally and authorised blood transfusions up and down the region, before his bogus credentials were discovered. His most tragic mishap was to tell the parents of a seventeen year old road traffic accident victim that their daughter would be fine. Alas, she died under his care six hours later. It's hard to keep a 'would-be medic' down and now twenty years later he has been found guilty of deceiving and robbing a female hospital consultant who took pity on him. Mr Bint pretended to be a lonely member of the landed gentry class, with nobody on his estate to look after him. After a short hospital stay, the consultant at University College Hospital London took him in to her own house to recuperate. He paid her back by robbing cash and her credit cards. No word of a sentence yet. The papers say that 'courts are awaiting his psychiatric report.' I'm sure he'll write a good one.

ODE TO A MAMMOGRAM
October 1998

As our country prepares to embark on a national breast screening programme, dissenting voices will struggle to be heard. Time perhaps to remind ourselves of a famous medical ode that was not written by Keats. It will not form part of the patient information leaflet.

For years 'n years they told me,
'Be careful of your breasts.
Don't ever squeeze or bruise them,
And give them monthly tests'.
So I heeded all their warnings
And protected them by law.
Guarded them very carefully,
And always wore a bra.
After thirty years of careful care,
The doctor found a lump,
He ordered up a Mammogram
To look inside that clump.
'Stand up very close,' she said,
As she got my breast in line,
'And tell me when it hurts,' she said,
'Ah, yes! There! That's just fine'.
She stepped upon a pedal. . .
I could not believe my eyes!
A plastic plate was pressing down.
My boob was in a vice!!!
My skin was stretched 'n stretched
From way up by my chin,
And my poor tit was being squeezed
To Swedish pancake thin!!!
Excruciating pain I felt,
Within its vice-like grip,
A prisoner in this vicious thing,
My poor defenceless tit!!
'Take a deep breath' she said to me

Who does she think she's kidding?
My chest is smashed in her machine,
I can't breathe and woozy I am getting.
'There, that was good,' I heard her say
As the room was slowly swaying.
'Now let's get the other one'.
'Lord, have mercy,' I was praying.
It squeezed me from the up and down,
It squeezed me from both sides,
I'll bet she's never had this done
To her tender little hide!
If I had no problem when I came in,
I surely have one now. . .
If there had been a cyst in there,
It would have popped, Ker-pow!
This machine was made by a man,
Of this I have no doubt.
I'd like to get his bits in there,
For months, he'd go without!

RELIGIOUS OBSESSIONS
June 2002

This week, an Italian study in *New Scientist* magazine linked Catholicism and excessive piety with severe obsessive-compulsive symptoms. The authors compared the behaviour of nuns, priests and frequent churchgoers with the demeanour of agnostics, atheists and others on the lapsed end of the scale. They acknowledged in the article that many patients with obsessions and compulsions have a genetic disposition to these traits, but also suggest that environmental influences such as a strict upbringing or frequent participation in rituals may have an influence. Any more of that sort of science and there will be calls for an extra decade to be put on rosary beads.

LORENZO'S OIL
February 2007

Dr Hugo Moser passed away last month at the age of 82. Not every doctor has the privilege of being played on the big screen by Peter Ustinov, but this was the accolade Dr Moser, a paediatric neurologist, received in the film *Lorenzo's Oil*. The film dealt with the Odone family and their desperate search for a remedy when their son Lorenzo developed adrenoleukodystrophy. This devastating genetic illness causes rapid brain and neurological deterioration in children who have heretofore developed normally.

The research came up with an oil composed of fat extracts from olive and rapeseed oil. In 2005 Dr Moser published research which showed some benefit in the treatment, provided it is given before symptoms become apparent. There is still no effective cure for this horrendous disease. I saw the condition at first hand during my undergraduate training. For many years Hugo Moser campaigned to have the disease included in routine neonatal screening. Lorenzo Odone is still alive. He will be 29 years old in May and is cared for by his father and a team of nurses in Virginia. He communicates by either wiggling fingers or blinking his eyes and enjoys music and having books read to him.

Post-Script: *Lorenzo Odone died from pneumonia just over one year later, at his home at Fairfax, Virginia. He was one day past his thirtieth birthday.*

A GOOD LIFE
February 2013

Another cigarette smoker who missed life's final hurdles has passed on. The sad death of English stage actor, Richard Briers, has been announced at the age of 74. Those of a certain age will remember him fondly as the earth-loving, tree-hugging, jumper-wearing Tom in the BBC sitcom *The Good Life*. Briers succumbed, as many old smokers do, to emphysema, which by all accounts made ordinary tasks in his last five years very difficult. His last newspaper interview involved climbing just a few steps into another actor's home. It took him thirty minutes to regain his breath. Briers said that he had probably smoked half a million cigarettes in a lifetime which by my calculations is about 35 a day for 40 years. He gave up smoking ten years before he died, but he admitted that this was way too late. He deeply regretted not doing so in his thirties. By all accounts Richard Briers seems to have been a thoroughly nice fellow. A common thread in the tributes being paid to him is that he would always 'speak to the crew', something that is apparently not common in the upper echelons of the entertainment world. Come to think of it, the common touch wasn't always particularly prevalent in the theatre of medicine either. *Upstairs, Downstairs* type behaviour all too often ruled the roost.

MEAN ABOUT VIAGRA
February 2012

No prescription drug in modern times has had the ability to dominate headlines quite like Viagra. Last month, a councillor for the Green party pleased the tabloid press considerably by suggesting that Ireland's six million euro annual spend on these little blue diamonds could no longer be justified. The fact that his name was councillor Meaney did not go unnoticed. He isn't alone. A liberal-leaning barrister of my acquaintance was apoplectic when he discovered the size of the nation's annual impotence bill. When I suggested that he wasn't sounding very liberal, he retorted 'I don't mind them doing it, I just don't want to pay for it!' The truth of the matter is that our spend on erectile dysfunction remedies is not in any way different from international norms. Across the Irish sea, they spend precisely twelve times the amount we spend here, which reflects perfectly the population difference. It should also be noted, and these things assume importance when your country haemorrhages high-tech jobs, that holy Ireland is the country where this drug, sildenafil, is actually manufactured. Nearly fifteen years ago, when the imminent arrival of Viagra was being discussed in the Dáil, the Department of Health had estimated that the cost could be anything as high as twenty million punts per year. Way off the mark, as usual. Family doctors see very little abuse of this product. It's essentially used in the GMS scheme by a cohort of men with prostate disease, diabetes and other illnesses. Those who haven't given up on the love-making. And long may they continue.

LOAVES AND FLUSHES
September 1997

'Give us this day your daily loaf, and forgive us our hot flushes'. Britain's leading bakery has launched a new enriched soya and linseed loaf which it claims can help reduce the symptoms of menopause. Allied Bakeries have begun to promote Burgen Bread or Lady's Loaf, suggesting it can help reduce the symptoms of a million menopausal women. It has been postulated that Asian women experience far fewer menopausal symptoms than their European counterparts, and some believe this could be linked to the high levels of soya in their diet. Test marketing in Australia met with very positive results, where the bread claims to 'put the Waltz Back into Matilda' and has been nicknamed as Sheila's Slice. One wonders what poor old Mr Brennan would make of this.

DEATH IN PARIS
March 2007

What is it about Paris hotel rooms and death beds? We know Oscar Wilde spent his final days cooped up in the Hotel d'Alsace, in the city's Saint-Germain-des-Prés. When he wasn't moaning about French wallpaper design, Oscar was worrying about the financial cost of dying. Wilde's death in a rented Parisian room followed a poetic tradition started in 1870, when French literary giant and hero of the surrealist movement, the poet Comte de Lautréamont passed away at the age of 24 in a tiny Montmartre hotel.. In more recent times, Pamela Churchill Harriman, Winston's favourite daughter-in-law and one-time United States ambassador to France had a cardiac arrest whilst swimming in the Ritz hotel. And what about rock singer Robert Palmer, he of tailored suits and cloned lady guitarists fame. He suffered his final heart attack in the Warwick hotel near the Champs Élysées. As it happens, his demise came about just two weeks after the cardiac health screeners had given him the all clear.

Just the other day another Parisian hotel death, albeit from 1919, came to the notice of the medical community. Sir Mark Sykes, a British diplomat and minor politician of the early twentieth century met his end in a 'well-appointed' hotel room although nobody seems to know exactly which one it was. Sykes was just 39, a victim of that year's great winter initiative, the Spanish flu. What has catapulted the poor man back in to the headlines is that his six grandchildren have given permission to a team of researchers led by virologist Professor John Oxford to exhume his body from an English country churchyard. In the days before we had heard of cryogenics, one of the perks of great family wealth was that you could be laid to rest in a sealed lead coffin that would keep creepy crawlies out until long after you got to meet your maker. Scientists are a much trickier breed to exclude. They made a very good case for digging him up in order that they might retrieve some good viral samples. 'If we can get a well preserved body it will be a huge step forward' read the statement. We shall see. The dear wife of Sir Mark, who passed on a few decades later, straddles his lead tomb, so she too will have to be rudely awoken. Senior church figures have insisted that the scientists confine their meddling to the man who had flu. Now don't get me wrong, I'm all for science. But I'm even more for the concept of a well earned rest. Next thing, somebody will want to measure Oscar's absinthe levels at the Père-Lachaise cemetery.

BOXING BAN
March 2001

Dr Gallagher is an Ulsterman who has tickled my fancy with his recent letter to *Doctor* magazine. On the proposed ban of boxing by nanny-doctors of the British Medical Association, the good doctor from Antrim delivered a knock-out blow for evidence-based medicine when he asked, not unreasonably, 'where does it all end?' Quoting sudden deaths on squash courts, cricket bowlers throwing missiles at 100 miles an hour and golfers being hit by lethal flying clubs and balls - he suggests that the British Medical Association might also like to ban ping pong in case somebody chokes on the ball.

CLINICALLY PROVEN
April 2012

The award for most abused medical terminology this month goes to *clinically proven* followed closely by *boosts your immune system*. If you see either phrase on pain-killing magnets, anti-ageing poly-fillers, yoghurt pots, diet fads, brain food for children or anything else, you have full medical permission to walk on by. The words clinic and clinical derive from the Greek *klinike* which means practice at the bedside of a sick person. I'm afraid much of the nonsense we see labelled today as *clinically proven* has not been tested within an ass's roar of somebody sick in a bed. It's a pity that such important words can be commandeered and trashed for posterity with such ease. But hell, it's only healthcare. Nobody seems to care.

OLDEST DOCTOR IN THE WORLD
February 2002

The *Guinness Book of Records* is claiming that the world has a new oldest man. Following the death of Italian man Signor Antonio Todde at the tender age of 113, a retired Japanese silkworm breeder called Mr Yukichi Chugani now holds the title. The secret to the breadth of his timeline is reckoned to be eternal optimism coupled with moderation in all bad habits. The *Guinness Book of Records* doesn't err very often but I feel that they should have close look at the electoral register for Trinity College Dublin. I am putting my name forward for their Senate election later this year and I note that there is a medical graduate eligible to vote who graduated in 1908. That makes him at least one hundred and eighteen years old in my book. A vote worth digging for.

CLEARLY JINGOISTIC
May 2012

I'm not sure what to make of the new sign in a local optician that shouts 'clearly Irish'. The fact that I can read it probably means a visit is unnecessary, but it really makes no difference to me whether my optometrist is clearly from Cork, clearly from China or clearly from Clondalkin. A barber shop nearby is displaying a sign saying 'classically trained Irish Barber'. Whatever does he mean? I really don't give a flying Figaro where a barber is from but I'd generously tip a baritone of any nationality who sings arias from the Barber of Seville as he trims.

DYING WITH DIGNITAS
November 2012

Terry Pratchett is a prolific and well-read author, who also happens to have an unusual slow-moving form of dementia. It allows him a reasonable life with some assistance, and to date he has been able to continue producing high quality work. Last year, Pratchett made an extraordinary documentary about British people who chose to end their own lives with the Dignitas organisation in Zurich. I had intended to write about it at the time, but the programme had such an effect on me, that I simply didn't know what to say. It was a very difficult film to watch, but a very powerful one. It didn't preach. It simply featured some very pleasant and ordinary people wanting to take control of the final chapters of their lives for themselves. It was hard to pick out which bit was the most poignant. There was the planning, the packing, the journey, the flights, the location of the house in the middle of an industrial estate, the paying of fees, the form-filling, the clinical people at Dignitas and the family members who flew out without hope and then flew home alone with urns. This month, *Choosing to Die* won an international Emmy award for best documentary. I watched it again. I found it easier to watch the second time around and was less shocked, as I knew the precise outcome of each case. If you believe that assisted and planned death should only be reserved for mammalian species that are less evolved than we are, then you are entitled to this view and it should be heard. But if you are less certain, you are not alone. Assisted suicide is an uncomfortable issue for all of us, just as it is, or was, for our neighbours in Europe. Perhaps it's the high precipices and heavy snow they have in Switzerland, for they don't worry about slippery slopes half as much as we do.

ERNST CHAIN
February 2003

The 75th anniversary of the discovery of penicillin by Alexander Fleming at St Mary's Hospital in London is upon us. Plenty of myths have grown up about that momentous time in 1928, when the Scottish bacteriologist, returning from holidays, found an interesting mould lurking on a staphylococcal culture dish. Whilst the Fleming name continues to be associated with penicillin, it must be said that the professor singularly failed to recognise and follow up on the potential of his discovery. It was the Oxford University trio of Australian pathologist Howard Florey, and biochemists Ernst Chain and Norman Heatley that set the world on a path to our antibiotic miracle drug. British accounts of the discovery of penicillin can be somewhat jingoistic. It's important to recognise also that because of an inability to attract home support for improving the yield of penicillin, it was entrepreneurial Americans and their research facility at Peoria, Illinois that provided the catalyst for its mass production. Ernst Chain was perhaps the most interesting link in the Oxford team. A Jewish refugee from 1930s Germany, Chain was an excitable character. It was he who had combed the available literature and found Fleming's forgotten piece of research. After retirement, Chain moved to Ireland and lived at Mulranny near Castlebar.

He died in Mayo General Hospital. A young doctor is reported to have treated him with extreme kindness as a patient there during his final illness, and Chain is supposed to have said before he died that he felt the future of medicine was in safe hands.

PRESCRIPTION FRAUD
July 2004

A friendly druggist tells me that a cultured gentleman with a American accent is doing the rounds of Dublin's pharmacies presenting credible repeat prescriptions for a nocturnal sedative called Stilnoct. Credible, because some of the scripts are genuine and a number of general practitioners have been taken in by his requests for a month or two's supply. There are also reports of some prescription pads going missing in the capital and the Gardaí are on the mysterious case of the Yankee insomniac. It does beg the question - how widespread is prescription fraud in this country? There is very little to stop Joe or Josephine Public getting their own prescription pads printed up and writing scripts for whatever tickles their fancy. Pharmacists are quite careful when presented with any script for what might be loosely termed a psychoactive medication, but surely it's about time that all scripts, private and otherwise, were security coded to prevent something that most pharmacies see on a weekly basis. We also need some sort of alert system so that doctors and pharmacists can warn each other when bogus patients come to town.

BAD BACK AT GREAT MISSENDEN
December 2011

Just before Christmas, we took the boat to Blighty and jostled along the motorways to the village of Great Missenden in the Chiltern hills. It's Roald Dahl country in leafy Buckinghamshire and the delightful little hamlet was home to the children's author for the second half of his life. I often heard a rumour that Dahl didn't like children very much, but whether he did or didn't, he certainly left a wonderful legacy of rude fiction for them to enjoy. The people of Great Missenden have a superb child-friendly museum to honour their most famous resident. He died there in 1990, of a disorder called myelodysplasia where the bone marrow stops producing adequate numbers of blood cells.

One of the many attractions of Great Missenden's literary museum is that you can sit in the very armchair that Dahl wrote his books in. What's fascinating about the armchair is that what looks like a large mouse-hole was cut out of the seat at just the spot where your coccyx (or tail-end) would be parked. Roald Dahl was plagued by medical problems for much of his life, many of them attributed to a nasty air crash he had when serving as a second world war pilot. He suffered from chronic spinal pain and spent much his life desperately searching for remedies. One which did give him relief and allowed him be comfortable enough to write, was the seat with a strategically placed hole.

Also Available by this Author

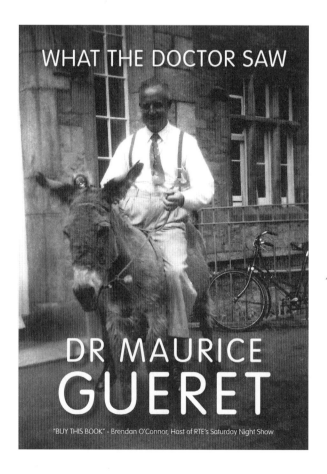

For further details see
www.drmauricegueret.com